Advanced Functions 12

Study Guide and University Handbook

AUTHORS

Antonietta Lenjosek

B.Sc., B.Ed.
Ottawa Catholic School Board

Paula Thiessen

B.Math, B.Ed.
District School Board of Niagara

Laurissa Werhun

B.Sc., B.Ed., M.A.
Toronto District School Board

REVIEWERS

Kirsten Boucher

Durham District School Board

Dr. Steven J. Desjardins

Department of Mathematics and Statistics
University of Ottawa

Dr. Gilles Lamothe

Department of Mathematics and Statistics
University of Ottawa

Carol Miron

Toronto District School board

NELSON

NELSON

For more information contact Nelson Education Ltd., 1120 Birchmount Road, Toronto, Ontario M1K 5G4. Or you can visit our website at nelson.com.

Advanced Functions 12 Study Guide and University Handbook

ISBN-13: 978-0-07-072455-6
ISBN-10: 0-07-072455-5

4 5 6 7   21 20 19 18

Printed and bound in Canada

The Geometer's Sketchpad®, Key Curriculum Press, 1150 65th Street, Emeryville, CA 94608, 1-800-995-MATH.

Statistics Canada information is used with the permission of Statistics Canada. Users are forbidden to copy the data and redisseminate them, in an original or modified form, for commercial purposes, without permission from Statistics Canada. Information on the availability of the wide range of data from Statistics Canada can be obtained from Statistics Canada's Regional Offices, its World Wide Web site at http://www.statcan.ca, and its toll-free number 1-800-263-1136.

PUBLISHER: Linda Allison
ASSOCIATE PUBLISHER: Kristi Clark
PROJECT MANAGER: Janice Dyer
DEVELOPMENTAL EDITORS: Carol Fordyce, Paul McNulty
COPYEDITOR: Dianne Brassolotto
ANSWER PREPARER: Daniela Spiroska, Ken Stewart
ANSWER CHECKER: Maria Stewart
MANAGER, EDITORIAL SERVICES: Crystal Shortt
SUPERVISING EDITOR: Jaime Smith
EDITORIAL ASSISTANT: Erin Hartley
MANAGER, PRODUCTION SERVICES: Yolanda Pigden
PRODUCTION COORDINATOR: Madeleine Harrington
COVER DESIGN: Valid Design/Michelle Losier
ELECTRONIC PAGE MAKE-UP: Aptara
COVER IMAGE: Courtesy of Masterfile

Contents

Chapter 3 Rational Functions

Chapter 4 Trigonometry

Chapter 5 Trigonometric Functions

Chapter 6 Exponential and Logarithmic Functions

Chapter 7 Tools and Strategies for Solving Exponential and Logarithmic Equations

Chapter 8 Combining Functions

University Preparation

Overview

Advanced Functions play an important role in many activities, from business and economics to the social, medical, and physical sciences. *McGraw-Hill Ryerson Advanced Functions 12 Study Guide and University Handbook* is designed for students planning to qualify for college or university. The study guide is designed to either complement the *McGraw-Hill Ryerson Advanced Functions 12* student book, or to stand alone as a thorough review of the course.

Study Guide Organization

- Chapter 1 introduces polynomial functions and the process of using secants and tangents to analyse average and instantaneous rates of change. Characteristics of polynomial functions are explored, including key features of their graphs and the relationship between finite differences and equations of polynomial functions. The chapter also examines the connection between equations and graphs of polynomial functions, along with transformations.

- In Chapter 2 equation-solving skills and graphing skills are combined to solve polynomial equations and inequalities. The relationship between the Remainder Theorem and the Factor Theorem is identified. Techniques for factoring polynomial functions of degree greater than two are examined and also applied to determine the roots of polynomial equations. Families of polynomial functions are analysed, including representing families of functions algebraically and exploring quartic functions. Finally, inequalities are solved graphically using technology, and algebraic methods for solving factorable polynomial inequalities are demonstrated.

- Chapter 3 focuses on anlysing properties of those rational functions created by taking the reciprocal of linear functions and quadratic functions. The equations and key features of the graphs of these rational functions are analysed, including finding their vertical and horizontal asymptotes. Different forms of rational functions are explored and, rational equations and inequalities are solved using a variety of methods (e.g., algebraically, using technology). Connections between real-world situations and rational functions are explored in the last section of the chapter through problem solving.

- Chapter 4 extends concepts of trigonometry by defining trigonometric ratios (both primary and reciprocal ratios) of any angle using radians for angle measures. Methods to convert between radian measure and degree measure are defined. The connection between trigonometric ratios and special angles is identified, along with equivalent trigonometric expressions. Compound angle formulas, including addition and subtraction formulas for cosine and sine, are examined and finally, the chapter ends with proofs of trigonometric identities.

- Chapter 5 applies the concepts from chapter 4 to analyse trigonometric functions. The graphs of the sine, cosine, and tangent functions, along with graphs of the reciprocal trigonometric functions are analysed and their key features are identified. Transformations of the graphs of the cosine and sine functions are examined. Trigonometric equations are solved by combining factoring techniques with knowledge of trigonometric ratios of special angles. The chapter ends with applications of instantaneous rates of change to problems involving trigonometry.

- Chapter 6 introduces two new functions, the exponential and logarithmic functions. The chapter begins by studying the exponential function and its inverse, including writing equations to fit data and graphing inverse functions. Then, logarithms and transformations of logarithmic functions are explored. The power law of logarithms is examined, including solving problems, evaluating logarithms, and graphing logarithmic functions. Finally, problems and applications connecting logarithms and the physical sciences, are solved.

- Chapter 7 builds on the concepts related to exponents and logarithms from chapter 6. Equivalent forms of exponential equations are identified, and techniques to solve exponential equations are investigated and applied. The Product and Quotient Laws of logarithms are developed and techniques to solve logarithmic equations are demonstrated. The final section of this chapter examines mathematical modelling with exponential and logarithmic equations, including solving problems using these equations.

- Chapter 8 integrates concepts from the seven preceding chapters to examine combined functions. The key features of the graphs and equations of the sum, difference, product, and quotient of different functions are examined. Composite functions are evaluated, and solutions to inequalities of combined functions are found. The chapter ends with an exploration of modelling with combined functions, including solving problems and developing models.
- In the University Preparation section, a collection of important Advanced Functions topics are explored. The section examines conics, including the ellipse and hyperbola. The connection between the graphs and equations of the ellipse and hyperbola are identified, as well as the development of the equations based on given information. Another topic is solving absolute value equations and inequalities. Matrices are also introduced and the operations of addition, subtraction, scalar multiplication and matrix multiplication are studied. The final topic of this section deals with extending important algebraic skills, including factoring and solving complex equations.

Study Guide Features
- Each section begins with a page of Key Concepts that summarize the concepts needed to complete the exercises.
- Exercises are organized into three sections: A (practice), B (connect and apply), and C (extend and challenge).
- Each chapter includes additional challenge questions that cover the concepts in the chapter, as well as extend your thinking and combine concepts from previous chapters.
- Selected questions in each section are marked by a star that indicates that full worked solutions are provided at the back of the book. Answers to all other questions are also provided.
- Each chapter ends with a checklist of concepts that specify what you should be able to do by the end of the chapter.
- A practice exam at the end of the study guide gives you the opportunity to determine if you are ready for the final examination.

Formulas

SYMBOLS

$\mathbb{R}$	real numbers	**Greek Lower Case Letters**	
$\mathbb{N}$	natural numbers	α	alpha (a)
$\mathbb{Z}$	integers	β	beta (b)
∞	infinity	γ	gamma (g)
$\in$	belongs to	δ	delta (d) lower case
$[a,b]$	$a \leq x \leq b$ (closed interval)	Δ	delta (d) upper case
(a,b)	$a < x < b$ (open interval)	λ	lamda (l)
$\overrightarrow{AB}, \vec{u}$	vector	ρ	rho (r)
$|\vec{v}|$	magnitude of a vector	θ	theta (th)
$\vec{u} \cdot \vec{v}$	dot product of vectors	τ	tau (t)
$\vec{u} \times \vec{v}$	cross product of vectors	π	pi (p)
$\frac{d}{dx}$	derivative operator	ω	omega (o)

ALGEBRA

Factoring Special Polynomials	$x^2 \pm 2xy + y^2 = (x \pm y)^2$ $\qquad$ $x^2 - y^2 = (x - y)(x + y)$ $x^3 \pm y^3 = (x \pm y)(x^2 \mp xy + y^2)$
Factor Theorem	$(x - a)$ is a factor of the polynomial $f(x)$ if and only if $f(a) = 0$
Quadratic Formula	If $ax^2 + bx + c = 0$, then $x = \dfrac{-b \pm \sqrt{b^2 - 4ac}}{2a}$

Rules for Exponents

Product	$(x^a)(x^b) = x^{a+b}$	Power of a Product	$(xy)^a = x^a y^a$
Quotient	$\dfrac{x^a}{x^b} = x^{a-b}$	Rational Exponent	$x^{\frac{1}{a}} = \sqrt[a]{x}$
Power	$(x^a)^b = x^{ab}$	Negative Exponent	$x^{-a} = \dfrac{1}{x^a}$

Logarithms	Logarithm Laws
$y = \log_a x \Leftrightarrow a^y = x$ $\log_{10} x$ is usually written as $\log x$. $\log_a a = 1 \qquad \log_a a^x = x \qquad a^{\log_a x} = x$ $\log_e x$ is written as $\ln x$. $\ln e = 1 \qquad \ln e^x = x \qquad e^{\ln x} = x$ Change of base: $\log_b x = \dfrac{\log_a x}{\log_a b}$	$\log_a (xy) = \log_a x + \log_a y$ $\log_a \left(\dfrac{x}{y}\right) = \log_a x - \log_a y$ $\log_a x^n = n \log_a x$

ANALYTIC GEOMETRY

Distance between Two Points Distance between two points $P_1(x_1, y_1)$ and $P_2(x_2, y_2)$	$P_1 P_2 = \sqrt{(x_2 - x_1)^2 + (y_2 - y_1)^2}$
Linear Function For a line through the points $P_1(x_1, y_1)$ and $P_2(x_2, y_2)$	Slope: $m = \dfrac{y_2 - y_1}{x_2 - x_1}$ Slope y-intercept form of equation: $y = mx + b$, where b is the y-intercept Point-slope form of equation: $y - y_1 = m(x - x_1)$
Quadratic Function Equation for a parabola with vertex (p, q)	$y = a(x - p)^2 + q$
Circle Equation for a circle centre (h, k) and radius r	$(x - h)^2 + (y - k)^2 = r^2$

MEASUREMENT

In the following, P represents perimeter, C the circumference, A the area, V the volume, and SA the surface area.

Triangle

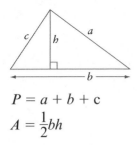

$P = a + b + c$

$A = \frac{1}{2}bh$

Trapezoid

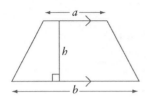

$A = \frac{1}{2}(a + b)h$

Circle

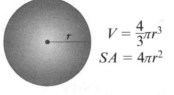

$C = 2\pi r$

$A = \pi r^2$

Cylinder

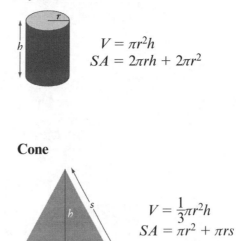

$V = \pi r^2 h$

$SA = 2\pi rh + 2\pi r^2$

Cone

$V = \frac{1}{3}\pi r^2 h$

$SA = \pi r^2 + \pi rs$

Sphere

$V = \frac{4}{3}\pi r^3$

$SA = 4\pi r^2$

TRIGONOMETRY

Angle Measure	π rad $= 180°$	$1° = \frac{\pi}{180}$ rad	1 rad $= \frac{180°}{\pi}$
Primary Trigonometric Ratios	$\sin \theta = \dfrac{\text{opposite}}{\text{hypotenuse}}$	$\cos \theta = \dfrac{\text{adjacent}}{\text{hypotenuse}}$	$\tan \theta = \dfrac{\text{opposite}}{\text{adjacent}}$
	$\sin \theta = \dfrac{y}{r}$	$\cos \theta = \dfrac{x}{r}$	$\tan \theta = \dfrac{y}{x}$

Sine Law	$\dfrac{\sin A}{a} = \dfrac{\sin B}{b} = \dfrac{\sin C}{c}$ $\dfrac{a}{\sin A} = \dfrac{b}{\sin B} = \dfrac{c}{\sin C}$
Cosine Law	$a^2 = b^2 + c^2 - 2bc \cos A$ $b^2 = a^2 + c^2 - 2ac \cos B$ $c^2 = a^2 + b^2 - 2ab \cos C$
Fundamental Identities	$\sin^2 \theta + \cos^2 \theta = 1$ $1 + \cot^2 \theta = \csc^2 \theta$ $\tan^2 \theta + 1 = \sec^2 \theta$ $\tan \theta = \dfrac{\sin \theta}{\cos \theta}$ $\cot \theta = \dfrac{\cos \theta}{\sin \theta}$
Reciprocal Identities	$\csc \theta = \dfrac{1}{\sin \theta}$ $\cot \theta = \dfrac{1}{\tan \theta}$ $\cos \theta = \dfrac{1}{\sec \theta}$ $\sec \theta = \dfrac{1}{\cos \theta}$ $\sin \theta = \dfrac{1}{\csc \theta}$ $\tan \theta = \dfrac{1}{\cot \theta}$
Sum and Difference Identities	$\sin (A + B) = \sin A \cos B + \cos A \sin B$ $\cos (A + B) = \cos A \cos B - \sin A \sin B$ $\tan (A + B) = \dfrac{\tan A + \tan B}{1 - \tan A \tan B}$ $\sin (A - B) = \sin A \cos B - \cos A \sin B$ $\cos (A - B) = \cos A \cos B + \sin A \sin B$ $\tan (A - B) = \dfrac{\tan A - \tan B}{1 + \tan A \tan B}$ $\sin (A \pm B) = \sin A \cos B \pm \cos A \sin B$ $\cos (A \pm B) = \cos A \cos B \pm \sin A \sin B$ $\tan (A \pm B) = \dfrac{\tan A \pm \tan B}{1 \pm \tan A \tan B}$
Co-function Identities	$\cos \left(\dfrac{\pi}{2} - x\right) = \sin x$ $\sin \left(\dfrac{\pi}{2} - x\right) = \cos x$
Double-Angle Formulas	$\sin 2A = 2 \sin A \cos A$ $\tan 2A = \dfrac{2 \tan A}{1 - \tan^2 A}$ $\cos 2A = \cos^2 A - \sin^2 A$ $\qquad = 2 \cos^2 A - 1$ $\qquad = 1 - 2\sin^2 A$

Chapter 1 Polynomial Functions

1.1 Power Functions

- A polynomial function has the form
$f(x) = a_n x^n + a_{n-1} x^{n-1} + a_{n-2} x^{n-2} + \ldots + a_3 x^3 + a_2 x^2 + a_1 x + a_0$, or where n is a whole number

Examples

$f(x) = 7x^3 + 5x^2 + 10x + 2$

$g(x) = 9x^5 - 8x^2 + x - 15$

- A power function is a polynomial of the form $y = ax^n$, where n is a whole number.

Examples

$f(x) = -6x^3$

$A(r) = \pi r^2$

- Power functions have similar characteristics depending on whether their degree is even or odd.

- Even-degree power functions have line symmetry in the y-axis, $x = 0$.

- Odd-degree power functions have point symmetry about the origin, $(0, 0)$.

Power Functions Summary

Function	$y = a$	$y = ax$	$y = ax^2$	$y = ax^3$	$y = ax^4$
Degree	0	1	2	3	4
Name	Constant	Linear	Quadratic	Cubic	Quartic
Type		Odd-degreed	Even-degreed	Odd-degreed	Even-degreed
Domain	$x \in \mathbb{R}$	$x \in \mathbb{R}$	$x \in \mathbb{R}$	$x \in \mathbb{R}$	$x \in \mathbb{R}$
Range	$y = a$	$y \in \mathbb{R}$	$y \geq 0, y \in \mathbb{R}$	$y \in \mathbb{R}$	$y \geq 0, y \in \mathbb{R}$
End Behaviour (for $a > 0$)	Extends from quadrant 2 to quadrant 1	Extends from quadrant 3 to quadrant 1	Extends from quadrant 2 to quadrant 1	Extends from quadrant 3 to quadrant 1	Extends from quadrant 2 to quadrant 1
Symmetry	Line	Point	Line	Point	Line
Graph	a	b	c	d	e

(a)

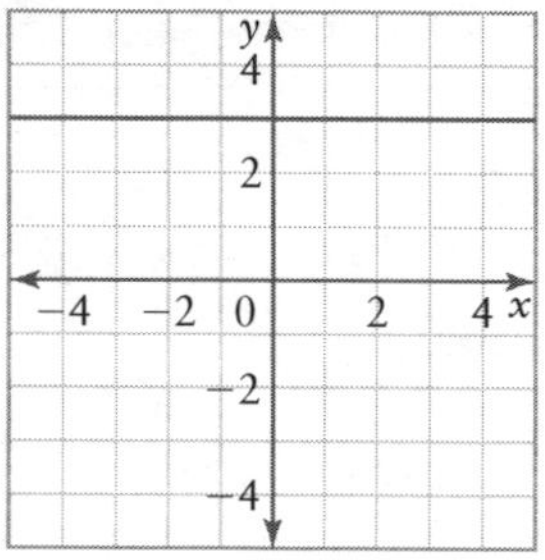

(b)

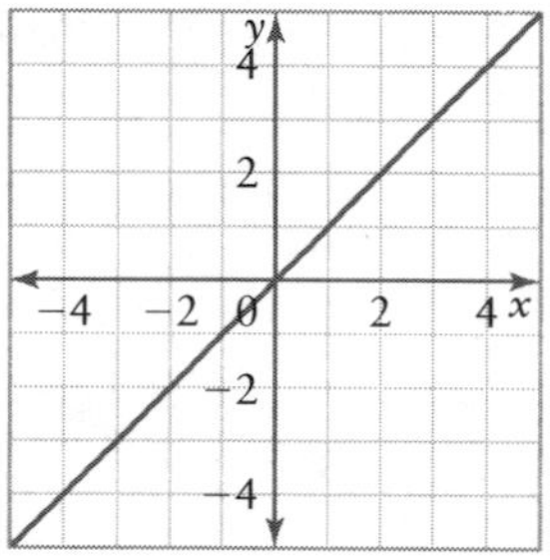

(c)

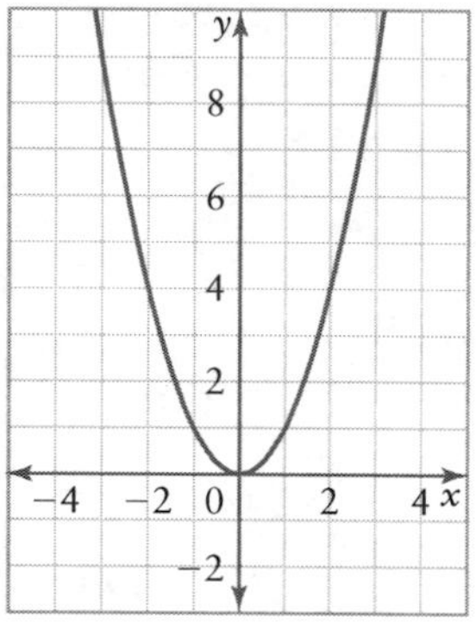

(d)

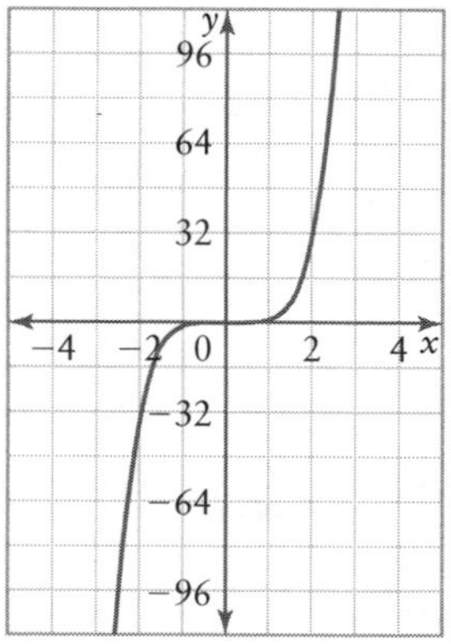

(e)

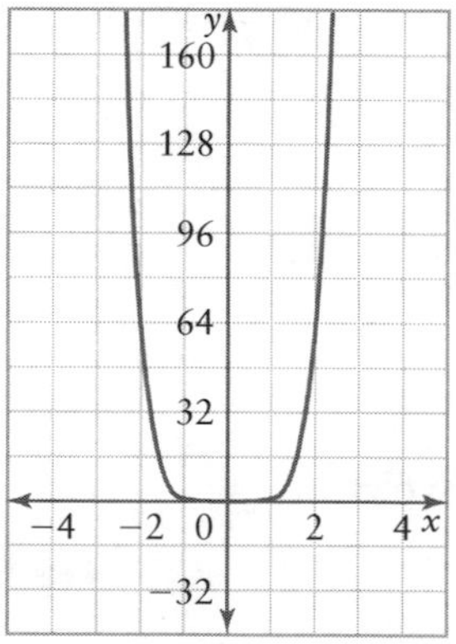

Bracket Interval	Inequality	Number Line	In Words
			The set of all real numbers x such that
(a, b)	$a < x < b$		x is greater than a and less than b
$(a, b]$	$a < x \leq b$		x is greater than a and less than or equal to b
$[a, b)$	$a \leq x < b$		x is greater than or equal to a and less than b
$[a, b]$	$a \leq x \leq b$		x is greater than or equal to a and less than or equal to b
$[a, \infty)$	$x \geq a$		x is greater than or equal to a
$(-\infty, a]$	$x \leq a$		x is less than or equal to a
(a, ∞)	$x > a$		x is greater than a
$(-\infty, a)$	$x < a$		x is less than a
$(-\infty, \infty)$	$-\infty < x < \infty$		x is an element of the real numbers

A

1. Identify the degree of each of the following power functions.

   a) $y = 8x^2$

   b) $y = -3x^3$

   c) $y = 0.25x^{10}$

   d) $y = -2x$

   e) $y = 3x^3$

   f) $y = x^4$

   g) $y = -\frac{1}{3}x^6$

   h) $y = 5x$

2. Which of the functions in question 1 have line symmetry? Which have point symmetry? Justify your choices.

3. Describe the end behaviour of each of the functions in question 1. For example, the graph of $y = 3x$ is an odd-degree function with a positive leading coefficient. The end behaviour is from quadrant 3 to quadrant 1.

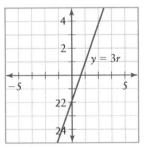

4. Identify whether each of the following is a polynomial function. Justify each answer.

   a) $y = 0.6x^4 - 3x^2 + 2$

   b) $y = 3 \cos x$

   c) $y = \dfrac{1}{x^3 - 4}$

   d) $y = 3^{x-1} - 11$

   e) $y = 3x - 2$

   f) $y = -7$

   g) $y = \sqrt{3x^2 - 5x}$

B

5. Determine a possible equation for a power function for each of the following:

   a) the function has point symmetry at (0, 0)

   b) a positive function

   c) an odd negative function

   d) a function that begins in quadrant 3 and ends in quadrant 4

6. Determine which graphs below represent polynomial functions. Justify your choices.

   a)

   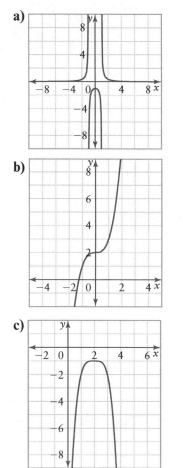

   b)

   c)

   d)

   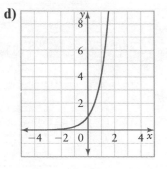

★**7.** A stone is dropped into a pond and its ripple increases in a circular pattern. The area of the circle, in square centimetres, and the ripple's distance from the centre, as represented by the radius of the circle, r, can be modelled by the function $A(r) = \pi r^2$.

   a) Graph the function for $0 \le r \le 30$.

   b) Determine the domain and range of the function.

   c) Describe the similarities and differences between the graph of $A(r)$ and the graph of a quadratic function.

8. The circumference, in centimetres, of the ripple in question 7 can be modelled by the function $C(r) = 2\pi r$.

   a) Graph the function for $0 \le r \le 30$.

   b) Determine the domain and range of the function.

   c) Describe the similarities and differences between the graph of $C(r)$ and the graph of a linear function.

9. **a)** Graph the functions $f(x) = x^5$, $g(x) = (x + 2)^5$, and $h(x) = (x - 2)^5$ on the same axes. Compare the graphs. Describe how they are related.

   b) Repeat part a) for the functions $f(x) = x^4$, $g(x) = (x + 2)^4$, and $h(x) = (x - 2)^4$.

   c) Make a conjecture for the relationship between $y = x^n$ and $y = (x + b)^n$, where $b \in \mathbb{R}$ and n is a whole number.

   d) Test the accuracy of your conjecture for different values of n and b.

⭐**10. a)** Sketch graphs of the functions $f(x) = 3x^3$, $g(x) = 3x^3 - x$, and $h(x) = 3x^3 + x$ on the same axes.

b) Compare and describe the key features of the graphs of these functions.

11. a) Use Technology Graph the following functions on the same set of axes.

   i) $y = 3x^4$

   ii) $y = 3(x - 2)^4$

   iii) $y = 3(x - 2)^4 - 1$

   iv) $y = -3(x - 2)^4 - 1$

b) Compare and describe the key features of the graphs of these functions. Discuss domain and range, symmetry, and end behaviour.

12. The surface area of a spherical snowball is given by the function $S(r) = 4\pi r^2$, where r is the radius of the snowball, in centimetres, and $r \in [0, 12]$.

a) Graph $S(r)$.

b) State the domain and the range.

c) Describe the similarities and differences between the graphs of $S(r)$ and $y = x^2$.

13. a) Describe the relationship between the graph of $y = x^3$ and the graph of $y = -\frac{1}{2}(x + 1)^3 - 4$.

b) Predict the relationship between the graph of $y = x^5$ and the graph of $y = -\frac{1}{2}(x + 1)^5 - 4$.

c) Verify the accuracy of your prediction by graphing the functions in part b).

14. a) Graph $y = x^5$, $y = (x + 3)^5$, and $y = (x - 3)^5$ on the same set of axes.

b) Describe the similarities and differences among the graphs in part a).

c) Make a conjecture about the relationship between the graphs of $y = x^n$ and $y = (x - h)^n$, where $h \in \mathbb{R}$ and n is an odd whole number.

C

⭐**15.** A conical reservoir is filling with water at a constant rate. The reservoir is 5 m deep and has a maximum diameter of 10 m.

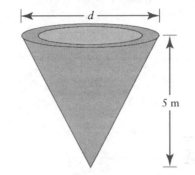

a) Determine a function $V(r)$ that describes the volume of the reservoir.

b) Graph $V(r)$.

c) What are the domain and range of this function?

16. Use Technology Graph each pair of functions below, using graphing technology. What is the degree of each function? Describe any similarities and differences in each pair.

a) $f(x) = x^2$, $g(x) = x^2 - 2x$

b) $f(x) = x^3$, $g(x) = x^3 - 5x^2 - x - 10$

c) $f(x) = x^4$, $g(x) = x^4 - 8x^2 + 15$

d) $f(x) = x^5$, $g(x) = (x - 3)^2 (x + 2)^3$

17. Draw the graph of a function that is not a polynomial function, and explain why it is not.

⟪ KEY CONCEPTS ⟫

Odd-Degree Polynomial Functions

Positive Leading Coefficient
- The graph extends from quadrant 3 to quadrant 1 (similar to the graph of $y = x$).

Negative Leading Coefficient
- The graph extends from quadrant 2 to quadrant 4 (similar to the graph of $y = -x$).

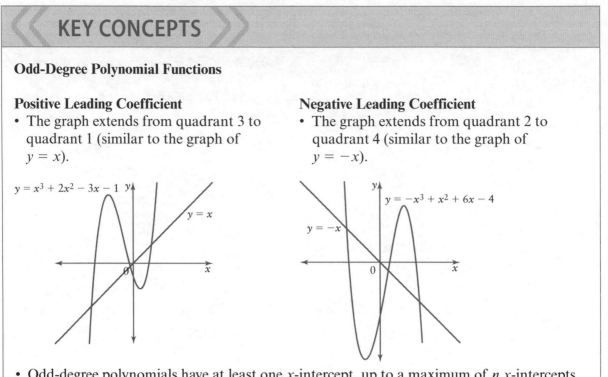

- Odd-degree polynomials have at least one x-intercept, up to a maximum of n x-intercepts, where n is the degree of the function.

- The domain of all odd-degree polynomials is $\{x \in \mathbb{R}\}$ and the range is $\{y \in \mathbb{R}\}$. Odd-degree functions have no maximum point and no minimum point.

- Odd-degree polynomials may have point symmetry.

Even-Degree Polynomial Functions

Positive Leading Coefficient
- The graph extends from quadrant 2 to quadrant 1 (similar to the graph of $y = x^2$).

- The range is $\{y \in \mathbb{R}, y \geq a\}$, where a is the minimum value of the function.

- An even-degree polynomial with a positive leading coefficient will have at least one minimum point.

Negative Leading Coefficient
- The graph extends from quadrant 3 to quadrant 4 (similar to the graph of $y = -x^2$).

- The range is $\{y \in \mathbb{R}, y \leq a\}$, where a is the maximum value of the function.

- An even-degree polynomial with a negative leading coefficient will have at least one maximum point.

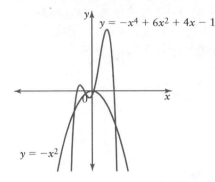

- Even-degree polynomials may have from zero to a maximum of n x-intercepts, where n is the degree of the function.

- The domain of all even-degree polynomials is $\{x \in \mathbb{R}\}$.

- Even-degree polynomials may have line symmetry.

Key Features of Graphs of Polynomial Functions

- A polynomial function of degree n, where n is a whole number greater than 1, may have at most $n - 1$ local minimum and local maximum points.

- For any polynomial function of degree n, the nth differences
  - are equal (or constant)
  - have the same sign as the leading coefficient
  - are equal to $a[n \times (n - 1) \ldots \times 2 \times 1]$, where a is the leading coefficient
    $$= a(n!)$$

A

1. State the degree of the polynomial function that corresponds to each constant finite difference. Determine the value of the leading coefficient for each polynomial function.

   a) first difference $= -3$

   b) second difference $= 2$

   c) fifth difference $= -240$

   d) fourth difference $= 144$

   e) third difference $= 31.5$

2. Each graph represents a polynomial function of degree 3, 4, 5, or 6. Determine the least possible degree of the function corresponding to the graph. Give reasons for your choice.

   a)

   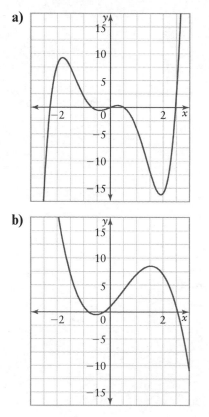

   b)

c)

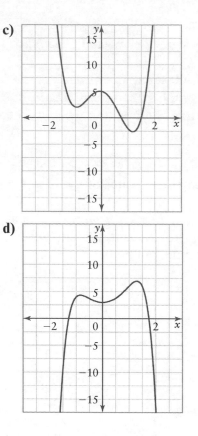

d)

3. Refer to question 2. For each graph, do the following.

   a) State the sign of the leading coefficient. Justify your answer.

   b) Describe the end behaviour.

   c) Identify any symmetry.

   d) State the number of minimum and maximum points and local minimum and local maximum points. How are these related to the degree of the function?

4. Use the degree and the sign of the leading coefficient in each of the following functions to

   i) describe the end behaviour of each polynomial function

   ii) state which finite differences will be constant

   iii) determine the value of the constant finite differences

a) $y = x^4 - 3x^2 + 2$

b) $f(x) = 9 - 7x$

c) $y = -3x^7 + 5x^2$

d) $g(x) = 8x - 6x^2$

e) $y = -0.5x^4 - 8x^3 + 4x^2 - 3x + 1$

f) $h(x) = 27x^3 - 81x$

B

5. Match each polynomial function below to the appropriate graph. Justify your choice.

a) $y = x^4 + 2x^3 - x^2 - 6$

b) $y = x^5 - 3x^3 + 5x + 1$

c) $y = -x^3 + 2x^2 + 5x + 6$

d) $y = -x^4 - 3x^3$

i)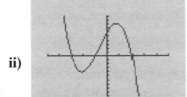

ii)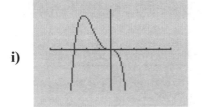

iii)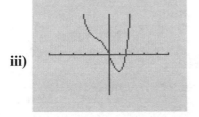

iv)

★6. Use finite differences to determine

i) the degree of each polynomial function

ii) the sign of the leading coefficient

iii) the value of the leading coefficient

a)

x	y
-3	140
-2	37
-1	8
0	5
1	4
2	5
3	21

b)

x	y
-3	0
-2	-4
-1	0
0	6
1	8
2	0
3	-24

c)

x	y
-3	36
-2	16
-1	4
0	0
1	4
2	16
3	36

★7. Flipus Discus manufactures flying discs for a recreational sports league. The company determines that its profit, P, in thousands of dollars, can be modelled by the function, $P(x) = 0.65x^4 - 3.5x^2 - 12$, where x represents the number, in hundreds, of flying discs sold.

a) What type of function is $P(x)$?

b) Without calculating, determine which finite differences are constant for this polynomial function. What is the value of the constant finite difference? Explain how you know.

c) Describe the end behaviour of this function, assuming that there are no restrictions on the domain.

d) State the restrictions on the domain in this situation.

e) What do the x-intercepts of the graph represent for this situation?

f) If the Disc Golf League wants to buy 500 flying discs to distribute to its members, what is Flipus Discus's profit from the sale?

8. Consider the function $f(x) = -x^4 + 3x^3 + 2x^2 - x + 2$.

a) How do the degree and the sign of the leading coefficient correspond to the end behaviour of the polynomial function?

b) Sketch a graph of the polynomial function.

c) What can you tell about the value of the fourth differences for this function?

9. Explain why odd-degree polynomials have unrestricted domain and range. What does this tell you about the number of maximums or minimums? What does this tell you about the number of x-intercepts?

★10. Use Technology The data below show the stopping distance required for various speeds. The stopping distance is a function of speed, reaction time, and braking time.

Speed (km/h)	Total Stopping Distance (m)
30	18
50	35
70	57
100	98
110	114

SOURCE: http://www.mpi.mb.ca/PDFs/WatchYourSpeed.pdf

a) Graph the data in the table using a graphing calculator.

b) Use the regression feature of the graphing calculator to determine an equation for the function that models this situation. What type of polynomial function appears to be the best fit? Justify your choice.

C

11. Sketch a graph of a quintic (degree 5) polynomial function

a) with point symmetry

b) without point symmetry

c) with the maximum number of zeros

d) with the minimum number of zeros

12. Describe how to determine the number of x-intercepts as well as the number of maximum and minimum points from the degree of a polynomial function.

★13. A farmer wants to construct a cylindrical grain silo where the ratio of radius to height is 1:6.

a) Write a polynomial function to represent the surface area of the silo (not including the top and bottom) in terms of the radius, r.

b) Write a polynomial function to represent the volume of the silo, in terms of the radius, r.

c) Describe the key features of the graph that correspond to each of the above functions.

KEY CONCEPTS

- The graph of a polynomial function can be sketched using the x-intercepts, the degree of the function, and the sign of the leading coefficient.

- When a polynomial function is in factored form, the zeros can be easily determined from the factors. When a factor is repeated n times, the corresponding zero has order n.

- The graph of a polynomial function changes sign only at x-intercepts that correspond to zeros of odd order. At x-intercepts that correspond to zeros of even order, the graph touches but does not cross the x-axis.

Analysis of Graphs of Polynomial Functions

$f(x) = -x(x-1)^2(x+3)^3$

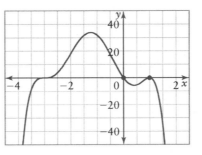

Degree	The product of all factors will give a multiple of x^6. The function is degree 6.
Leading Coefficient	The product of all the x-coefficients is $-1 \times 1 \times 1 = -1$.
End Behaviour	An even-degree polynomial with a negative leading coefficient extends from quadrant 3 to quadrant 4.
Zeros and x-intercepts	The zeros are 3 (order 3), 0, and 1 (order 2).
y-intercepts	The y-intercept is $0(0-1)^2(0+3)^3 = 0$

An even-degree polynomial function is an **even function** if the exponent of each term of the equation is even. An even function satisfies the property $f(-x) = f(x)$ for all x in the domain of $f(x)$. An even function is symmetric about the y-axis.

An odd-degree polynomial function is an **odd function** if each term of the equation has an odd exponent. An odd function satisfies the property $f(-x) = -f(x)$ for all x in the domain of $f(x)$. An odd function is rotationally symmetric about the origin.

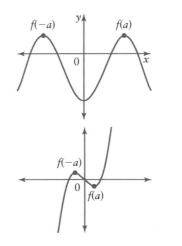

A

1. For each polynomial function below

   i) state the degree and the sign of the leading coefficient

   ii) describe the end behaviour of the graph of the function

   iii) determine the x-intercepts

   a) $f(x) = 3x(x - 2)(x + 3)$

   b) $g(x) = -(x - 2)(x - 4)^2 (x - 6)$

   c) $h(x) = (2x - 1)(x + 3)^3$

   d) $p(x) = (4 - x)(x + 1)^2 (x - 2)$

2. For each graph, do the following:

   i) state the x-intercepts

   ii) state the intervals where the function is positive and the intervals where it is negative

   iii) explain whether the graph might represent a polynomial function that has zeros of order 2 or of order 3

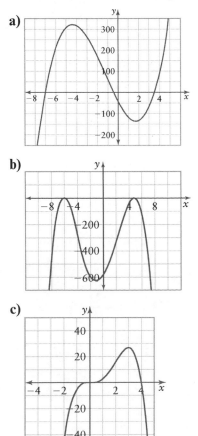

a)

b)

c)

3. **a)** Determine the zeros of each polynomial function below. Indicate whether each is of order 1, 2, or 3.

   i) $f(x) = -x(x - 3)^3$

   ii) $g(x) = (5x - 1)(x + 2)(x - 1)$

   iii) $h(x) = -(x + 4)^2 (4x - 3)^2$

   b) Determine algebraically whether each function is even or odd.

   c) Draw a sketch of each function.

★ 4. **i)** Determine whether each function is even, odd, or neither. Explain.

   ii) Without graphing, determine whether each polynomial function has line symmetry about the y-axis, point symmetry about the origin, or neither. Explain.

   a) $y = -x^4 + 3x^2$

   b) $y = -6x + 5x^3$

   c) $y = x^4 - x^2 + 4x + 2$

B

5. Determine an equation for each polynomial function described here. State whether the function is even, odd, or neither. Sketch a graph of each.

   a) degree 3, a root at 4 (order 2), a root at -3

   b) degree 4, a root at 2 (order 3), a root at 5

   c) degree 3, roots at $\frac{1}{2}, \frac{3}{4}, -1$

   d) degree 3, starting in quadrant 2, ending in quadrant 4, root at -2, and root at 1 (order 2)

6. **Use Technology** Without graphing, determine whether each polynomial function below has line symmetry, point symmetry, or neither. Verify your response using technology.

   a) $f(x) = -x^4 + 6x^2 + 8$

   b) $g(x) = 8x^5 - 3x^2$

7. Determine an equation for the polynomial function that corresponds to each graph.

a)

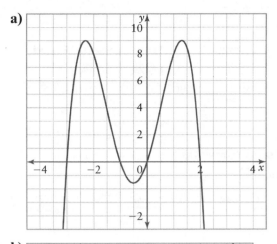

b)

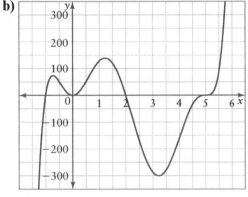

8. Each of the following polynomial functions has x-intercepts at -6, 5, and 0. Determine an appropriate equation for each. Then, sketch a graph of the function.

a) a cubic function with a positive leading coefficient and y-intercept at $(0, 0)$

b) a quartic function that extends from quadrant 3 to quadrant 4

c) a degree 6 function with a negative leading coefficient

d) a cubic function that extends from quadrant 2 to quadrant 4

★**9. Use Technology** Determine the zeros of each of the following functions. Use graphing technology to verify your answers.

a) $f(x) = (30 - 13x - x^2)$
$(x^2 - 10x + 25)$

b) $g(x) = (x^3 - 4x^2 + 4x)(2x^2 - 7x + 3)$

c) $h(x) = (x^2 - 8x + 15)(27 - 3x^2)$

C

10. Determine the equation of an even quartic function with a negative leading coefficient that has no zeros. Draw a sketch of your function.

11. Determine an equation for each polynomial function described below. State whether the function is even, odd, or neither. Sketch a graph of each.

a) a quintic function with zeros at -2 (order 3) and 3 (order 2), and that has a y-intercept at 70

b) a quartic function with x-intercepts at -2 (order 2) and 1 (order 2) that passes through the point $(0, -12)$

c) a quintic function with zeros -3, -2 (order 2), 2 (order 2), that passes through the point $(1, -18)$

12. The Lazy River Ride at a local amusement park is shown below. Determine a polynomial function that will model the path of the river. Let x be the horizontal distance and y the vertical distance from the starting platform. The starting and ending platforms are at the same level. The starting and ending platforms are 300 m apart.

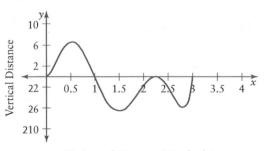

Horizontal Distance (Hundreds)

KEY CONCEPTS

- The graph of a polynomial function of the form $y = a[k(x - d)]^n + c$ can be sketched by applying transformations to the graph of $y = x^n$, where $n \in \mathbb{N}$. The transformations represented by a and k must be applied before the transformations represented by c and d.

- The parameters a, k, d, and c in polynomial functions of the form $y = a[k(x - d)]^n + c$, where n is a non-negative integer, correspond to the following transformations:
  - a corresponds to a vertical stretch or compression and, if $a < 0$, a reflection in the x-axis
  - k corresponds to a horizontal stretch or compression and, if $k < 0$, a reflection in the y-axis
  - d corresponds to a horizontal translation to the left or right
  - c corresponds to a vertical translation up or down

Example

Sketch a graph of the function $y = -\dfrac{1}{2}(4(x - 2))^3 + 1$.

The function $y = x^3$ is

- compressed vertically by a factor of $\dfrac{1}{2}$ and reflected in the x-axis

- compressed horizontally by a factor of $\dfrac{1}{4}$

- translated 2 units to the right
- translated 1 unit up

Another way to describe the transformation is to apply a mapping notation to each coordinate: $(x, y) \rightarrow \left(\dfrac{1}{4}x + 2, -\dfrac{1}{2}y + 1\right)$. This shows that the stretches and compressions should be applied before the translations.

This is a cubic function with a negative leading coefficient. Therefore, it extends from quadrant 2 to quadrant 4.

The function has point symmetry at (2, 1).

The domain is $x \in \mathbb{R}$. The range is $x \in \mathbb{R}$.

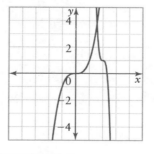

Apply the above transformations to the graph of $y = x^4$. Describe the features of the function that are affected by the transformation.

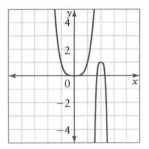

This is a quartic function with a negative leading coefficient. Therefore, it extends from quadrant 3 to quadrant 4.

The function has line symmetry in the line $x = 2$.

The domain is $x \in \mathbb{R}$. The range is $y \leq 1$.

When n is even, the graphs of polynomial functions of the form $y = a[k(x - d)]^n + c$ are even functions and have a vertex at (d, c). The axis of symmetry is $x = d$.

For $a > 0$, the graph opens upward. The vertex is the minimum point on the graph, and c is the minimum value. The range of the function is $\{y \in \mathbb{R}, y \geq c\}$.

For $a < 0$, the graph opens downward. The vertex is the maximum point on the graph, and c is the maximum value. The range of the function is $\{y \in \mathbb{R}, y \leq c\}$.

A

1. Compare each polynomial function below with the equation $y = a[k(x - d)]^n + c$. State the values of the parameters a, k, d, c, and the degree n, assuming that the base function is a power function. Describe the transformation that corresponds to each parameter.

   a) $y = -5(x - 1)^3$

   b) $y = 3x^2 + 5$

   c) $y = -(3x - 2)^4$

   d) $y = \frac{1}{3}(x - 2)^4$

   e) $y = \frac{3}{5}[6(x - 1)]^3 - 4$

   f) $y = 7(-x)^3 + 1$

2. Determine the domain and range of each function in question 1.

3. Sketch a graph of the following function under the transformation defined by $y = f(x + 2) - 4$.

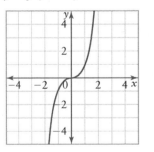

4. Match each graph with the corresponding function. Justify your choices.

  i) $y = -3x^4$

  ii) $y = \frac{2}{3}x^3 + 4$

  iii) $y = -2(x - 1)^5$

  iv) $y = x^4 + 2$

a)

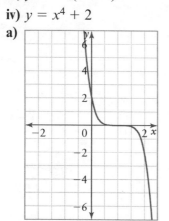

b)

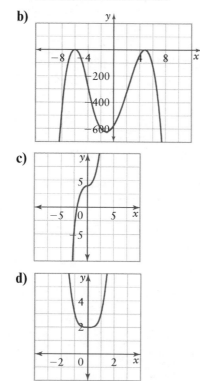

c)

d)

B

5. Describe the transformations that must be applied to the graph of each power function, $f(x)$, to obtain the transformed function below. Write the full equation of the transformed function.

  a) $f(x) = x^4$, $y = 5f(-x)$

  b) $g(x) = x^3$, $y = -2g(x + 1)$

  c) $h(x) = 5(x - 1)^4$, $y = h(-x) + 3$

6. a) For each pair of polynomial functions in question 5, sketch the original and transformed functions on the same set of axes.

  b) State the domain and range of the functions in each pair. For even functions, give the vertex and the equation of the axis of symmetry.

7. a) Use your knowledge of transformations to sketch graphs of the following groups of polynomial functions.

  i) $f(x) = x^3$, $g(x) = -x^3$, $h(x) = (-x)^3$

  ii) $f(x) = (x + 1)^3$, $g(x) = 2(x + 1)^3 - 1$, $h(x) = -\frac{1}{2}(x + 1)^3 - 3$

  iii) $f(x) = x^4$, $g(x) = -x^4$, $h(x) = (-x)^4$

  iv) $f(x) = (1 - x)^4$, $g(x) = [2(x + 3)]^4$, $h(x) = -\frac{1}{4}x^4 + 8$

  b) For $f(x) = a[k(x - d)]^3 + c$ and $g(x) = a[k(x - d)]^4 + c$, summarize the effects of changing a, k, d, and c in terms of transformations.

8. a) Given a base function of $y = x^4$, list the parameters of the polynomial function $y = \frac{1}{3}[-2(x + 4)]^4 - 10$.

   b) Describe how each parameter in part a) transforms the graph of the function $y = x^4$.

   c) Determine the domain, range, vertex, and equation of the axis of symmetry for the transformed function.

   d) Describe two possible orders in which the transformations can be applied to the graph of $y = x^4$ in order to sketch the graph of $y = \frac{1}{3}[-2(x + 4)]^4 - 10$.

9. For each of the transformations described below:

   i) Write an equation for the resulting function.

   ii) State the domain and range. For even functions, give the vertex and the equation of the axis of symmetry.

   a) The function $f(x) = x^3$ is translated 4 units up and 2 units right.

   b) The function $f(x) = x^4$ is compressed horizontally by a factor of 5 and translated 3 units to the right.

   c) The function $f(x) = x^5$ is stretched vertically by a factor of 2, reflected in the y-axis, and translated 2 units down and 4 units to the left.

   d) The function $f(x) = x^6$ is reflected in the x-axis, stretched horizontally by a factor of 3, reflected in the y-axis, and translated 3 units up and 1 unit to the left.

10. i) Describe the transformation that must be applied to the graph of each power function, $f(x)$, to obtain the transformed function.

   a) $f(x) = x^2$, $y = -3f(x - 2) - 4$
   b) $f(x) = x^4$, $y = 2f(2x + 6)$
   c) $f(x) = x^3$, $y = -\frac{1}{2}f\left(\frac{1}{2}(x - 1)\right) - 5$

   ii) Write the full equation of each transformed function in part i).

   iii) Sketch each base function from part i) and its transformed function from part ii) on the same set of axes.

   iv) State the domain and range of each pair of functions in part iii).

11. a) Predict the relationship between the graph of $y = x^4 + x^3$ and the graph of $y = [(x + 3)^4 + (x + 3)^3] - 1$.

   b) Use Technology Graph each function in part a) to verify the accuracy of your prediction.

   c) Determine the x-intercepts of each function in part a). Round your answers to 1 decimal place.

   d) Give the approximate domain and range of each function in part a). Round your answers to one decimal place.

C

12. a) The function $f(x) = -3(x - 2)(x + 3)(x + 5)^2$ is translated 2 units to the right and 1 unit up. Write an equation for the transformed function.

   b) Suppose the transformed function is then reflected in the y-axis and vertically compressed by a factor of $\frac{1}{3}$. Write an equation for the new transformed function.

13. Use Technology

   a) Describe the transformations that must be applied to the graph of $y = -x^5 - x^3 + x$ to obtain the graph of $y = (2x)^5 + (2x)^3 - (2x)$.

   b) Sketch each graph using technology.

14. Use Technology

   a) Graph the function $y = 2(x - 1)^3 + 2(x - 1)^2 - 2(x - 1) + 4$.

   b) What transformations may have been applied to the original function? What was the function before the transformations were applied?

KEY CONCEPTS

- A rate of change is a measure of how quickly one quantity (the dependent variable) changes with respect to another quantity (the independent variable).

- Average rates of change
  - represent the rate of change over a specified interval
  - correspond to the slope of a secant between two points $P_1(x_1, y_1)$ and $P_2(x_2, y_2)$ on a curve

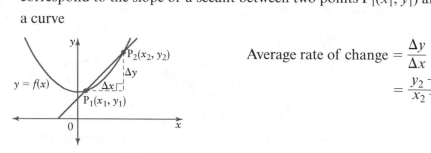

$$\text{Average rate of change} = \frac{\Delta y}{\Delta x}$$
$$= \frac{y_2 - y_1}{x_2 - x_1}$$

- An average rate of change can be determined by calculating the slope between two points given in a table of values or by using an equation.

Calculating Average Rate of Change

Average Rate of Change from a Graph	The points that correspond to month 0 and month 5 are (0, 500) and (5, 1000).
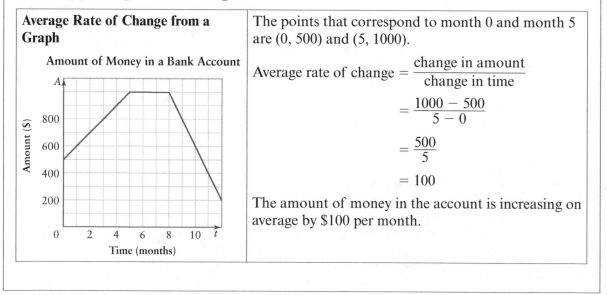	$$\text{Average rate of change} = \frac{\text{change in amount}}{\text{change in time}}$$ $$= \frac{1000 - 500}{5 - 0}$$ $$= \frac{500}{5}$$ $$= 100$$ The amount of money in the account is increasing on average by \$100 per month.

Average Rate of Change from a Table of Values	From the table, the points are (0, 800) and (7, 37).	

A new antibacterial spray is tested on a bacterial culture. The table shows the population, P, of the bacterial culture t minutes after the spray is applied.

t (min)	P
0	800
1	799
2	782
3	737
4	652
5	515
6	314
7	37

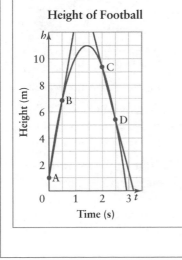

Average rate of change $= \dfrac{\Delta P}{\Delta t}$

$$= \dfrac{37 - 800}{7 - 0}$$

$$= \dfrac{-763}{7}$$

$$= -109$$

During the entire 7 min, the number of bacteria decreases on average by 109 bacteria per minute.

Average Rate of Change from an Equation

A football is kicked into the air such that its height, h, in metres, after t seconds can be modelled by the function $h(t) = -4.9t^2 + 14t + 1$.

Height of Football

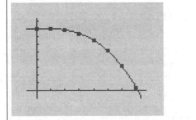

Use the equation to determine the endpoints corresponding to each interval.
For [0, 0.5]:
Substitute $t = 0$ to find the height at 0 s.
$h(0) = -4.9(0)^2 + 14(0) + 1$
$\quad = 1$
Substitute $t = 0.5$ to find the height at 0.5 s.
$h(0.5) = -4.9(0.5)^2 + 14(0.5) + 1$
$\quad\quad = 6.775$
The points that correspond to 0 s and 0.5 s are (0, 1) and (0.5, 6.775).

Average rate of change $= \dfrac{\Delta h}{\Delta t}$

$$= \dfrac{6.775 - 1}{0.5 - 0}$$

$$= 11.55$$

The average rate of change of the height of the football from 0 s to 0.5 s is 11.55 m/s.

A

1. Which of the following are examples of average rates of change?

   a) The average height of the players on a baseball team is 2.1 m.

   b) The class average on the last math test was 75%.

   c) The value of the Canadian dollar increased from $0.81 US to $1.04 U.S. in 8 months.

   d) The track athlete crossed the 100-m finish line at 12 km/h.

   e) The temperature of water in the pool increased by 8°C over a period of 12 h.

   f) Last February, approximately 100 cm of snow fell over a 48-h period.

2. Identify whether or not the average rate of change for pairs of points along each graph is constant and positive, constant and negative, zero, or non-constant. Justify your responses.

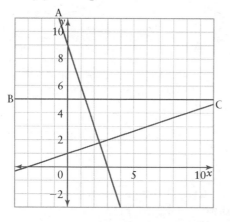

3. Determine the average rate of change for two points on each line segment in question 2.

4. Find the average rate of change of the function f over the given interval.

   a) $f(x) = 4 - x^2$, $[0, 2]$

   b) $f(x) = 0.2x^4 - 3x^2 - 5x + 6$, $[-1, 4]$

   c) $f(x) = x^3 - 3x^2 - 5x + 1$, $[-1, 3]$

   d) $f(x) = -\sqrt{3x^3 - 5x}$, $[0, 3]$

5. The new-housing price index in the St. Catharines-Niagara area rose from 120.5 in 2003 to 150.1 in 2007. Determine the average rate of change of the new-housing price index over this time period.

B

★6. The table below shows the new-housing price index in the St. Catharines-Niagara area for each year from 2003 to 2007.

Year	Index
2003	120.5
2004	128.8
2005	137.8
2006	144.2
2007	150.1

Source: Statistics Canada, CANSIM Table 327-0005

   a) Determine the average rate of change of the new-housing price index for each pair of consecutive years from 2003 to 2007.

   b) Compare the values found in part a). Which value is the greatest? Which is the least? What is the significance of these values?

   c) Compare the values found in part a) with your calculation in question 5. Explain any similarities or differences.

★7. Water is draining from a large tank. After t min, there are $150\ 000 - 7500t + t^2$ litres of water in the tank.

   a) Determine the average rate at which the water empties from the tank in the interval between 5 and 10 min.

   b) Determine the average rate at which the water empties from the tank in the interval between 9 and 10 min.

   c) Estimate the rate at which the water runs out after exactly 10 min.

8. a) Find the average rate of change of the area of a circle with radius r as r changes from

   i) 2 to 2.5

   ii) 2 to 2.3

   iii) 2 to 2.25

   iv) 2 to 2.1

   v) 2 to 2.01

b) Estimate the rate of change at the instant when radius is 2.

c) How is your answer in part b) related to the circumference of a circle of radius 2?

9. The following graph shows the value of a stock over a two year period.

   a) What does the graph tell you about the average rate of change over

   i) the first year

   ii) the second year

   iii) the third year

   b) Determine the average rate of change over the intervals described in part a).

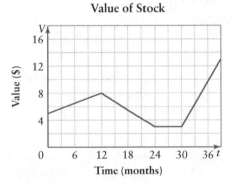

Value of Stock

10. Marshall and Teagan raced their bikes on a straight road, beginning from a dead stop. The distance (in metres) each bike has covered in each time during the first 20 s is shown in the graph.

   a) What is the average speed of each bike during this 20-s interval?

   b) Prove that Marshall travelled at a higher average speed than Teagan from $t = 4$ to $t = 10$.

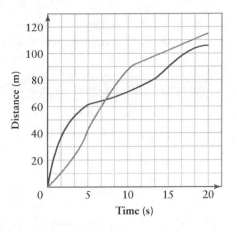

11. The cost, C, of making one unit of a product at any time x, in years, can be modelled by the function $C(x) = 4500 + 1530x - 0.04x^3$, $x \in [0, 200]$.

   a) Determine algebraically the average rate of change of the cost from

   i) year 0 to year 4

   ii) year 4 to year 7

   iii) year 7 to year 9

   b) Interpret your answers from part a).

12. If a ball is dropped from the top of a 120-m cliff, its height, h, in metres, after t seconds can be modelled by $h(t) = 120 - 4.9t^2$.

   a) Find the average rate of change of the height of the ball with respect to time over the intervals

   i) 1 s to 4 s

   ii) 4 s to 6 s

   iii) 6 s to 7 s

   b) What does the average rate of change represent in this situation?

   c) Interpret the significance of your answers in part a).

13. A census is taken of the permanent population, P, of Collingwood, Ontario every five years.

Year	Population
1991	13 500
1996	15 596
2001	16 039
2006	17 290

a) Determine the average rate of change of the population for

i) 1991 to 1996

ii) 1996 to 2001

iii) 2001 to 2006

iv) the entire fifteen-year period

b) What factors do you think might have led to the varied results?

C

14. Suppose you have the flu. The data below show your temperature during the first day of the flu. As you might guess, the faster your temperature rises, the worse you will feel.

a) At what average rate does your temperature rise during the entire day?

b) During what 2-h period do you expect to feel the worst?

c) Find two time intervals during which you feel about the same (that is, during which your temperature is rising at the same average rate).

Hours (t)	Temperature (°C)
0	98.1
2	98.1
4	98.5
6	98.9
8	99.25
10	100

Hours (t)	Temperature (°C)
12	100.7
14	101.8
16	102
18	102.2
20	102.4
22	102.45
24	102.5

★15. The distance, d, in metres, that it takes a vehicle to stop from a speed, s, in km/h can be modelled by the function $d(s) = 0.01s^2 - 0.25s + 10$.

a) What does the average rate of change represent for this situation?

b) Determine the average rate of change in the speed of the vehicle for each time interval.

i) 20 to 30 km/h

ii) 40 to 50 km/h

iii) 60 to 70 km/h

iv) 80 to 90 km/h

c) Describe how the average rate of change changes as the speed increases.

d) Graph the data modelled by the function. Add secant lines to your graph that show the average rates of change you calculated in part b).

16. Describe the average rate of change of each of the following functions. Sketch a graph of the average rate of change.

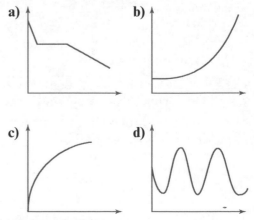

a)

b)

c)

d)

KEY CONCEPTS

- An instantaneous rate of change corresponds to the slope of a tangent to a point on a curve.

- An approximate value for an instantaneous rate of change at a point may be determined using
  - a graph, either by estimating the slope of a secant passing through that point or by sketching the tangent and estimating the slope between the tangent point and a second point on the approximate tangent line
  - a table of values, by estimating the slope between the point and a nearby point in the table
  - an equation, by estimating the slope using a very short interval between the tangent point and a second point found using the equation

Example—Determine the instantaneous rate of change of $y = -x^2 + 6x$ at $x = 5$.

Graph and Two Points

Estimate instantaneous rate of change from the graph by finding the slope of a secant passing through the given point and another point close to (5, 5) on the curve.

$$m_{PQ} = \frac{8 - 5}{4 - 5} = -3$$

Points on the Tangent Line

Estimate the slope of a tangent at a point, P, on a graph by sketching an approximate tangent line through that point and then selecting a second point on that line. Select the point (6, 1). Label it S.

$$m_{PS} = \frac{1 - 5}{6 - 5} = -4$$

x	y
3	9
3.5	8.75
4	8
4.5	6.75
5	5
5.5	2.75
6	0

Table of Values

To estimate an instantaneous rate of change from a table, calculate the average rate of change over a short interval by using points in the table that are closest to the tangent point.

$$\text{Average rate of change} = \frac{\Delta y}{\Delta x}$$

$$= \frac{5 - 6.75}{5 - 4.5}$$

$$= -3.5$$

$$y = -x^2 + 6x$$

Equation

Determine the average rate of change over shorter and shorter intervals.

Interval	Δy	Δx	$\dfrac{\Delta y}{\Delta x}$
$4.5 \leq x \leq 5$	$y(5) - y(4.5)$ $= -(5)^2 + 6(5)$ $\quad - [-(4.5)^2 + 6(4.5)]$ $= -25 + 30 + 20.25 - 27$ $= -1.75$	0.5	$\dfrac{-1.75}{0.5}$ $= -3.5$
$4.9 \leq x \leq 5$	$y(5) - y(4.9)$ $= -(5)^2 + 6(5)$ $\quad - [-(4.9)^2 + 6(4.9)]$ $= -25 + 30 + 24.01$ $\quad - 29.4$ $= -0.39$	0.1	$\dfrac{-0.39}{0.1}$ $= -3.9$
$4.99 \leq x \leq 5$	$y(5) - y(4)$ $= -(5)^2 + 6(5)$ $\quad -[-(4.99)^2 + 6(4.99)]$ $= -25 + 30 + 24.9001$ $\quad - 29.94$ $= -0.0399$	0.01	$\dfrac{-0.0399}{0.01}$ $= -3.99$

As the time intervals decrease, the average rate of change (which corresponds to the slope of a secant line) becomes closer to (or approaches) -4.

A

1. On each graph, a tangent has been drawn at the point where $x = 5$.

   i) At each of the indicated points on the graph, is the instantaneous rate of change positive, negative, or zero? Explain.

   ii) Determine the instantaneous rate of change of y with respect to x, at $x = 5$.

   a)

   b)

   c)

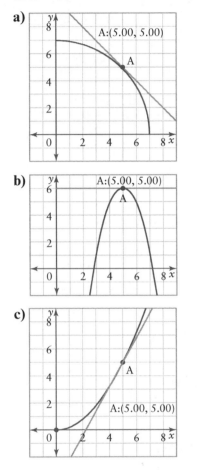

2. For each data set below, calculate the average rate of change of y between each consecutive pair of values for x.

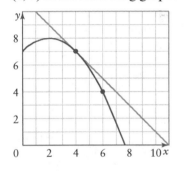

a) x	y
0	1
1	3
2	9
3	27
4	81
5	243
6	729

b) x	y
50	7
100	6
150	4.6
200	2.9
250	0.9
300	−1.3
350	−3.8

B

☆ 3. Use two different methods to estimate the instantaneous rate of change at the point $(4, 7)$ in the following graph.

4. For water draining from a container, the height, in millimetres, of the water as a function of time, in seconds, is $h = 0.00185(250 - t)^2$.

   a) Calculate the average rate of change from $t = 50$ s to $t = 100$ s.

   b) Estimate the instantaneous rate of decrease in height for each time:

   i) 0 s

   ii) 60 s

   iii) 120 s

   iv) 180 s

   c) **Use Technology** Graph the function. How does the graph support your answers in parts a) and b)?

★5. A population increased over the past 50 years and is modelled by the function $P(t) = 0.2t^2 + 500$.

a) Copy and complete the table.

Interval	ΔP	Δt	$\dfrac{\Delta P}{\Delta t}$
$9 \leq t \leq 10$			
$9.9 \leq x \leq 10$			
$9.99 \leq x \leq 10$			
$10 \leq t \leq 10.1$			
$10 \leq t \leq 10.01$			
$10 \leq t \leq 10.001$			

b) What do you notice about the intervals before 10 years and the intervals after 10 years?

c) Estimate the instantaneous rate of change at 10 years. What does this value represent?

6. The data below represent the number of births in Canada from 2000 to 2006.

Year	Births
2000	336 912
2001	327 107
2002	328 155
2003	330 523
2004	337 762
2005	338 894
2006	343 517

Source: Statistics Canada, CANSIM
Table 051-0013

a) Determine the average rate of change of births annually between 2000 and 2006.

b) Estimate the birth rate change in 2001 and in 2005.

c) How do your answers in part b) compare with your answer in part a)?

7. The function $T(d) = -0.1d^3 + 1.2d^2 - 5.4d + 12$ models the thickness, T, of the ice on a lake over a period of d days. The graph of the function is provided below.

a) Use the graph to determine the warmest day. Justify your answer.

b) Use the graph to determine the rate of change between days 1 and 2.

c) Use the equation to determine the instantaneous rate of change at day 1.

d) Write an expression for the average rate of change between $t = 1$ and $t = 1 + h$.

e) Use the expression in part d) to determine the average rate of change of the population when

i) $h = 0.1$

ii) $h = 0.01$

iii) $h = 0.001$

f) Estimate the instantaneous rate of change of the thickness after one day.

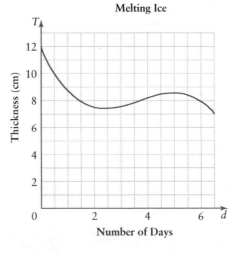

Melting Ice

8. Determine the instantaneous rate of change of $f(x) = -4x^2 + 16x + 12$ at $x = 3$ and use it to find the equation of the tangent line. Graph $f(x)$ and the tangent line on the same graph.

9. The profit, in dollars, of a manufacturer selling video-game systems is given by the equation
$P(x) = -0.05x^2 + 350x - 45000$, where x is the number of systems sold.

a) Find the instantaneous rate of change at $x = 1000$.

b) What are the units of the rate of change?

c) What does the instantaneous rate of change at $x = 1000$ tell you about the manufacturer's profit?

10. The displacement, s, in metres, of a particle moving back and forth in a straight line can be modelled by the function $s(t) = 4t^2 - 10t + 13$ where t is measured in seconds.

a) Find the average rate of change of the distance with respect to time from 1 s to 4 s.

b) Estimate the instantaneous rate of change of the displacement of the particle after 1 s.

c) Sketch the curve and the tangent at $t = 1$.

d) Interpret the average rate of change and the instantaneous rate of change for this situation.

11. The population, P, of a small town is modelled by the function
$P(t) = -2t^3 + 55t^2 + 15t + 22\,000$, where $t = 0$ represents the beginning of this year.

a) Write an expression for the average rate of change of population from $t = 10$ to $t = 10 + h$.

b) Use the expression in part a) to determine the average rate of change of the population when

i) $h = 3$

ii) $h = 5$

c) Use the expression in part a) to estimate the instantaneous rate of change of the population after 10 years.

d) **Use Technology** Graph $P(t)$.

e) Using the graph from part d), would it be justified for a large department store to open 10 years from now in this town? Explain.

f) If the store was not opened 10 years from now, would it be justified to open it 30 years from now? Explain.

C
12. Rachael is a short-distance runner. Her position on the track is given by $s = 10.5t - 0.75t^2$ for $t \in [0, 14]$, where s is in metres and t is in seconds.

a) Sketch the position-time graph of the runner. Why do you think her direction changes?

b) Find Rachael's velocity at five points over the course of the race. Use these points to draw a velocity-time graph.

c) Describe Rachael's motion. Indicate position, direction of motion, and velocity.

★13. A fish dives underwater and follows a path modelled by the function $d(t) = -(t - 1)^3 - 3(t - 1)^2 + 0.5(t - 1) - 2$, where d is the depth in metres after t seconds.

a) Draw a sketch of the graph and describe the path of the fish.

b) Copy and complete the table.

Interval	Δd	Δt	$\dfrac{\Delta d}{\Delta t}$
$3 \leq t \leq 4$			
$3.5 \leq t \leq 4$			
$3.9 \leq t \leq 4$			
$3.99 \leq t \leq 4$			

c) Use the table to determine the fish's velocity at $t = 4$ s. Where is the fish at this moment?

C1. If $f(x) = x^2 + 1$ and $g(x) = x - 2$, find the average rate of change of $f[g(x)]$ as x changes from -1 to 1.

C2. Doctors can measure cardiac output in potential heart-attack patients by monitoring the concentration of dye after the known amount is injected in a vein near the heart. In a normal heart, the concentration of the dye is given by $f(x) = -0.006x^4 + 0.140x^3 - 0.053x^2 + 1.79x$, where x is the time in seconds.

  a) Graph $f(x)$.

  b) Find all the zeros of this function. Explain the meaning of the zeros in the context of the problem.

  c) Determine the rate of change of the concentration of the dye for the first 10 s after injection.

C3. At liftoff, a space shuttle has a constant acceleration, a, of approximately 5 metres per second squared. The function $d(t) = \frac{1}{2}at^2$ can be used to determine the distance from Earth for each time interval, t, in seconds after liftoff.

  a) Find its distance from Earth after 10 s, 30 s, and 1 min.

  b) Study the pattern of answers to part a). If the time the space shuttle is in flight triples, how does the distance from Earth change? Explain.

C4. Instantaneous rate of change is the rate of change at a particular instant. Find the instantaneous rate of change of $f(t) = -3t^2 + 12t + 9$ at $t = 3$ and use it to determine the equation of the tangent line. Graph $f(t)$ and the tangent line on the same graph.

C5. A rectangular pool measures 6 m by 8 m. The pool is increased on all sides by the same amount. If the area is increased by 40 m^2, find the new dimensions of the pool.

C6. The profit, in dollars, a company makes selling a new line of MP3 Players is given by the equation $P(x) = -0.03x^2 + 225x - 24000$, where x is the number of players sold.

  a) Find the instantaneous rate of change of the profit at $x = 1000$ players sold.

  b) What are the units of the rate of change?

  c) What does this tell you about the company's profit?

C7. Two soccer players start at opposite sides of an 80-m field. One runs at 4 m/s and the other runs at 5 m/s. If they run back and forth for 15 min, how many times will they pass each other?

C8. Find the point of intersection of $f(x) = 5 + \sqrt{x + 1}$ and $g(x) = 2x + 1$ by solving a quadratic equation.

C9. A function that represents the volume of a cardboard box is $V(x) = -0.65x^3 + 4x^2 + 3x$, where x is the width of the box. Determine the width that will maximize the volume. What are the restrictions on the width?

By the end of this chapter, I will be able to:

- Identify polynomial expressions and polynomial functions

- Represent polynomial functions numerically, graphically, and algebraically

- Describe key features of the graphs of polynomial functions

- Distinguish polynomial functions from exponential and sinusoidal functions

- Identify the connection between the factored form of a polynomial function and the x-intercepts of the corresponding graph

- Sketch the graph of a polynomial function using the key features given the factored form of the equation

- Describe the transformation associated with the roles of the parameters a, k, c, and d in polynomial functions of the form $y = a[k(x - d)]^n + c$

- Determine an equation of a polynomial given a set of conditions

- Identify and distinguish properties of even and odd polynomial functions

- Understand the connection between average rate of change and the slope of a secant, and instantaneous rate of change and the slope of a tangent

- Apply numerical and graphical methods to calculate and interpret average and instantaneous rate of change in real-world applications that involve polynomial functions

Chapter 2 Polynomial Equations and Inequalities

2.1 The Remainder Theorem

> ### ❮❮ KEY CONCEPTS ❯❯
>
> - Long division can be used to divide a polynomial by a binomial.
>
> - The result of the division of a polynomial function $P(x)$ by a binomial of the form $x - b$ can be written as $P(x) = (x - b)Q(x) + R$ or $\dfrac{P(x)}{x - b} = Q(x) + \dfrac{R}{x - b}$, where $Q(x)$ is the quotient and R is the remainder.
>
> - To check the result of a division, use divisor $\times$ quotient + remainder = dividend.
>
> - The Remainder Theorem states that, when a polynomial function $P(x)$ is divided by $x - b$, the remainder is $P(b)$, and when it is divided by $ax - b$, the remainder is $P\left(\dfrac{b}{a}\right)$, where a and b are integers and $a \neq 0$.
>
> **Example**
>
> Use polynomial division (long division) to determine whether the polynomial below is divisible by the given binomial. Verify the result.
>
> **a)** $P(x) = x^3 - 4x^2 + 2x + 3;\ x - 3$
>
> **Solution**
>
> **a)** $(x^3 - 4x^2 + 2x + 3) \div (x - 3)$
>
> $$\begin{array}{r} x^2 - x - 1 \\ x - 3 \overline{)\ x^3 - 4x^2 + 2x + 3} \\ \underline{x^3 - 3x^2} \\ -x^2 + 2x \\ \underline{-x^2 + 3x} \\ -x + 3 \\ \underline{-x + 3} \\ 0 \end{array}$$
>
> Divide x^3 by x to get x^2. Write x^2 in the appropriate column in the quotient. Multiply $x - 3$ by x^2.
>
> Subtract. Bring down the next term, $2x$. Divide $-x^2$ by x to get $-x$. Multiply $x - 3$ by $-x$.
>
> Subtract. Bring down the next term, 3. Divide $-x$ by x to get -1. Multiply $x - 3$ by -1.
>
> Subtract.
> The remainder is 0.
>
> Therefore, $x^3 - 4x^2 + 2x + 3 = (x - 3)(x^2 - x - 1)$.
>
> Verify that $P(x)$ is divisible by $x - 3$ using the Remainder Theorem.
>
> Since $x - 3 = x - (+3)$, the remainder is $P(3)$.
>
> $P(3) = 3^3 - 4(3)^2 + 2(3) + 3$
> $ = 27 - 36 + 6 + 3$
> $ = 0$
>
> Therefore, $x - 3$ is a factor, since $P(3) = 0$.

b) $S(x) = 6x^3 - 4x^2 + 3x - 2; 2x + 1$

Solution

b) $(6x^3 - 4x^2 + 3x - 2) \div (2x + 1)$

$$2x + 1 \overline{)\begin{array}{c} 3x^2 - 3.5x + 3.25 \\ 6x^3 - 4x^2 + 3x - 2 \end{array}}$$

Divide $6x^3$ by $2x$ to get $3x^2$. Write $3x^2$ in the appropriate column. Multiply $2x + 1$ by $3x^2$.

$\underline{6x^3 + 3x^2}$

$-7x^2 + 3x$

Subtract. Bring down $3x$. Divide $-7x^2$ by $2x$ to get $-3.5x$. Multiply $2x + 1$ by $-3.5x$.

$\underline{-7x^2 - 3.5x}$

$6.5x - 2$

Subtract. Bring down -2. Divide $6.5x$ by $2x$ to get 3.25. Multiply $2x + 1$ by 3.25.

$\underline{6.5x + 3.25}$

-5.25

Subtract.

The remainder is -5.25.

Then, $(2x + 1)(3x^2 - 3.5x + 3.25) - 5.25 = 6x^3 - 4x^2 + 3x - 2$

Verify the result using the Remainder Theorem.

Comparing $2x + 1$ to $ax - b$, gives $a = 2$ and $b = -1$.

The remainder $S\left(\frac{b}{a}\right)$ is $S\left(-\frac{1}{2}\right)$.

$$S\left(-\frac{1}{2}\right) = 6\left(-\frac{1}{2}\right)^3 - 4\left(-\frac{1}{2}\right)^2 + 3\left(-\frac{1}{2}\right) - 2$$

$$= 6\left(-\frac{1}{8}\right) - 4\left(\frac{1}{4}\right) + 3\left(-\frac{1}{2}\right) - 2$$

$$= -\frac{3}{4} - 1 - \frac{3}{2} - 2$$

$$= -\frac{21}{4}$$

When $S(x) = 6x^3 - 4x^2 + 3x - 2$ is divided by $2x + 1$, the remainder is $-\frac{21}{4}$.

A

1. **a)** Divide $3x^3 - 2x^2 - 8$ by $x + 5$. Express the result in quotient form.

   b) Identify any restrictions on the variable.

   c) Write the corresponding statement that can be used to check the division.

   d) Verify your answer.

2. **a)** Divide $3x^4 + 2x^2 - 6x + 1$ by $x + 1$. Express the result in quotient form.

   b) Identify any restrictions on the variable.

   c) Write the corresponding statement that can be used to check the division.

   d) Verify your answer.

3. Perform each division below. Express the result in quotient form. Identify any restrictions on the variable.

  a) $2x^2 - x + 5$ divided by $x + 3$

  b) $x^3 - x - 10$ divided by $x + 4$

  c) $x^3 + x^2 - 4x + 4$ divided by $x - 2$

  d) $3x^4 + 2x^2 - 6x + 1$ divided by x

  e) $4x^3 - 10x^2 + 6x - 18$ divided by $2x - 5$

  f) $2x^3 - x^2 + 8x + 4$ divided by $2x - 1$

  g) $x^5 - 10x^4 + 20x^3 - 5x - 95$ divided by $x + 10$

4. Determine the remainder, R, so that each statement below is true.

  a) $(x^2 - 3x - 7)(x - 2) + R$
    $= x^3 - 5x^2 - x - 10$

  b) $(x^2 - 4x - 12)(x + 4) + R$
    $= x^3 - 28x - 41$

  c) $(-3x^2 + 13x + 10)(2x - 1) + R$
    $= -6x^3 + 29x^2 + 7x - 13$

  d) $(x^2 - 3)(x + 4) + R$
    $= x^3 + 4x^2 - 3x - 12$

5. The volume, in cubic centimetres, of a rectangular box can be modelled by the polynomial expression $2y^3 + y^2 - 27y - 36$. Determine possible dimensions of the box if the height, in centimetres, is given by $y + 3$.

6. Use the Remainder Theorem to determine the remainder when $2x^3 - 3x^2 - 8x - 3$ is divided by each of the following binomials. Verify your answers using long division.

  a) $x - 3$

  b) $x + 2$

  c) $2x + 1$

  d) $x - 2$

7. Determine the remainder when each of the following polynomials is divided by $x - 2$.

  a) $x^2 - 4x + 13$

  b) $x^3 + 3x^2 - 4x - 12$

  c) $2x^3 + 3x^2 - 17x - 30$

  d) $x^3 + x^2 - 4x + 4$

8. Use the Remainder Theorem to determine the remainder for each division below.

  a) $(x^2 + 2x + 4) \div (x - 2)$

  b) $(2x^3 + 3x^2 - 5x + 2) \div (x + 3)$

  c) $(2x^2 + 5x + 7) \div (2x - 3)$

  d) $(9x^3 - 6x^2 + 3x + 2) \div (3x - 1)$

B

☆9. a) When $P(x) = x^3 + kx^2 - 4x + 2$ is divided by $x + 2$, the remainder is 26; find k.

  b) Determine the remainders when the $P(x)$ is divided by $x + 1$ and $x - 1$.

10. a) Use the Remainder Theorem to determine the remainder when $(3x^3 + 7x^2 - 2x - 11)$ is divided by $(x - 2)$.

  b) Verify your result with long division.

11. a) When $P(x) = kx^4 - 8x^2 - 6$ is divided by $x + 1$, the remainder is -11; find k.

  b) Determine the remainders when $P(x)$ is divided by $x - 1$ and by $x - 3$.

12. Which of the following values for b give a remainder of zero when the given polynomial is divided by $x - b$?

  a) $f(x) = x^4 + 6x^3 - x^2 + 30x$;
    $b = 2, 3, 0, 1$

  b) $g(x) = 6x^2 + x - 1$;
    $b = 1, \frac{1}{2}, 2, -\frac{1}{2}, 3$

  c) $h(x) = x^3 + x^2 - 8x - 8$;
    $b = 2\sqrt{2}, \sqrt{2}, -\sqrt{2}, 1, -1$

⭐**13.** When a polynomial $p(x)$ is divided by $x + 3$, the quotient is $x^2 - 3x + 5$ and the remainder is 6. What is the polynomial?

14. When a polynomial $k(x)$ is divided by $x - 2$, the quotient is $x^2 + 4x - 7$ and the remainder is -4. What is the polynomial?

15. At the Niagara Ice Dogs Ticket Office, game tickets have just gone on sale. Sayid is the ticket sales manager and he collects sales results that show the number of tickets sold over the first 12 h of sales. Using the data, and a quadratic regression, the total number of tickets, N, sold over t hours is $N(t) = 0.45t^2 + 2.4t$, where t is measured in hours and $t \in [0, 12]$.

a) Divide $N(t)$ by $t - 2$. State the quotient, $Q(t)$, and the remainder, R. Explain the meaning of $Q(t)$ and R.

b) Does the formula for $N(t)$ seem realistic? Explain.

16. a) Determine the remainder when $2x^3 + 3x^2 - 17x - 30$ is divided by $x - 3$.

b) What information does the remainder provide about $x - 3$?

c) Express $2x^3 + 3x^2 - 17x - 30$ in factored form.

17. Dividing $(2x^3 + 4x^2 - kx + 5) \div (x + 3)$ and $(6y^3 - 3y^2 + 2y + 7) \div (2y - 1)$ leads to the same remainder. Find the value of k.

18. Find the values of a and b such that $ax^3 + bx^2 + 3x - 4$ has a remainder of -2 when divided by $(x - 1)$, and a remainder of 2 when divided by $(x - 2)$.

19. a) Determine the value of c such that when $P(x) = 2x^3 - cx^2 + 4x - 7$ is divided by $x - 2$, the remainder is -3.

b) Use Technology Verify your answer in part a) using a computer algebra system.

20. For what value of k will the polynomial $f(x) = x^3 + 2x^2 + kx + 5$ have the same remainder when it is divided by $x + 1$ and $x - 2$?

21. Use the remainder theorem to determine the remainder when $x^4 + x^3 - 3x + 6$ is divided by $3x - 2$.

C

22. The polynomial $mx^3 + 12x^2 - nx + 2$ has a remainder of 14 when divided by $x - 1$ and a remainder of 68 when divided by $x - 2$. What are the values of m and n?

⭐**23.** The polynomial $-x^3 - vx^2 + 2x + w$ has a remainder of 6 when divided by $x + 2$ and a remainder of 119 when divided by $x - 3$. What are the values of v and w?

24. Determine whether the first polynomial in each pair below is divisible by the second.

a) $x^3 + 2x^2 - 5x - 6$, $x^2 + 3x - 1$

b) $x^5 + x^4 - 81x - 81$, $x^2 + 9$

c) $x^4 + 3x^3 - 2x^2 - 3x + 1$, $x^2 + 3x + 1$

25. Determine a and b such that, when $x^4 + x^3 - 7x^2 + ax + b$ is divided by $(x - 1)(x + 2)$, the remainder is 0.

KEY CONCEPTS

- The Factor Theorem states that $x - b$ is a factor of a polynomial $P(x)$ if and only if $P(b) = 0$.

  Similarly, $ax - b$ is a factor of $P(x)$ if and only if $P\left(\frac{b}{a}\right) = 0$.

Example

Is $x - 2$ a factor of $P(x) = x^3 + 2x^2 - 10x + 4$?

Solution

Substitute $x = 2$ into the polynomial expression.

$$P(2) = (2)^3 + 2(2)^2 - 10(2) + 4$$
$$= 8 + 8 - 20 + 4$$
$$= 0$$

Therefore, $x - 2$ is a factor of the polynomial $P(x)$.

- The integral zero theorem states that, if $x - b$ is a factor of a polynomial function $P(x)$ with leading coefficient 1 and remaining coefficients that are integers, then b is a factor of the constant term of $P(x)$.

- The rational zero theorem states that, if $P(x)$ is a polynomial function with integer coefficients and $x = \frac{b}{a}$ is a rational zero of $P(x)$, then
  - b is a factor of the constant term of $P(x)$
  - a is a factor of the leading coefficient of $P(x)$
  - $ax - b$ is a factor of $P(x)$

Example

Is $3x - 2$ a factor of $R(x) = 9x^3 + 2x - 4$?

Solution

For $3x - 2$, substitute $x = \frac{2}{3}$ into the polynomial expression.

$$R\left(\frac{2}{3}\right) = 9\left(\frac{2}{3}\right)^3 + 2\left(\frac{2}{3}\right) - 4$$
$$= 9\left(\frac{8}{27}\right) + \left(\frac{4}{3}\right) - 4$$
$$= \frac{8}{3} + \frac{4}{3} - 4$$
$$= 0$$

Therefore, $3x - 2$ is a factor of the polynomial $R(x)$.

Example

Factor $2x^3 - 3x^2 - 5x + 6$

Find a value for x such that $P(x) = 0$.

Using the Rational Zero Theorem, let b represent values that are factors of the constant term, which are $\pm 1, \pm 2, \pm 3, \pm 6$.

Test the values of b for x to find the zeros.

$$P(1) = 2(1)^3 - 3(1)^2 - 5(1) + 6$$
$$= 2 - 3 - 5 + 6$$
$$= 0 \therefore x - 1 \text{ is a factor.}$$

Synthetic Division of the polynomial $2x^3 - 3x^2 - 5x + 6$ by $x - 1$ gives the other factors.

Write the coefficients from the polynomial in the first row of the division chart. To the left, write the value of 1 from the factor $x - 1$.

Bring down the first coefficient, 2, to the right of the $\times$ sign.
Multiply 1 (top left) by 2 (right of $\times$ sign) to get 2.

$$
\begin{array}{c|cccc}
1 & 2 & -3 & -5 & 6 \\
+ & \downarrow & 2 & -1 & -6 \\
\hline
\times & 2 & -1 & -6 & 0
\end{array}
$$

Write 2 below -3 in the second column.

Add 2 to -3 to get -1.

Multiply 1 by -1 to get -1. Write -1 in the third column below the -5.

Add -5 and -1 to get -6.

Multiply by 1 by -6. Write -6 in the fourth column below the 6.
Add 6 and -6 to give 0.

This gives $2x^3 - 3x^2 - 5x + 6 = (x - 1)(2x^2 - x - 6)$.

Notice that the coefficients in the second factor come from the result of synthetic division.

Factoring further gives $2x^3 - 3x^2 - 5x + 6 = (x - 1)(x - 2)(2x + 3)$.

A

1. Write the binomial factor that corresponds to each polynomial $P(x)$ below.

   a) $P(-4)$

   b) $P(2)$

   c) $P\left(\frac{2}{5}\right)$

   d) $P\left(-\frac{4}{3}\right)$

2. Determine whether $x - 1$ could be a factor of each of the following polynomials.

   a) $x^3 + x^2 - x - 1$

   b) $x^4 - 3x^3 + 2x^2 - x + 1$

   c) $2x^3 - x^2 - 3x - 1$

3. Divide each polynomial below by the given binomial using synthetic division.

   a) $(x^2 + 20x + 91) \div (x + 7)$

   b) $(x^3 - 9x^2 + 27x - 28) \div (x - 3)$

4. List the values that could be zeros of each polynomial below. Then, factor the polynomial.

   a) $x^3 - 3x^2 + 4x - 2$

   b) $x^3 + 2x^2 + 2x + 1$

   c) $x^3 + 7x^2 + 17x + 15$

5. Factor each polynomial below. Start by grouping terms.

   a) $x^3 - x^2 - 4x + 4$

   b) $x^3 - 2x^2 - 4x + 8$

   c) $x^3 + 3x^2 + 3x + 1$

   d) $x^4 + 2x^3 - x - 2$

   e) $3x^4 - 18x^3 + x - 6$

   f) $x^4 - 1$

6. Determine the values of each polynomial below that could be zeros. Then, factor the polynomial.

   a) $2x^3 - 9x^2 + 10x - 3$

   b) $4x^3 - 7x - 3$

   c) $4x^3 - 8x^2 + x + 3$

   d) $3x^3 - x^2 - 3x + 1$

B

7. Complete each of these division exercises using synthetic division.

   a) $(x^2 - x - 56) \div (x + 7)$

   b) $(x^3 - 9x^2 + 27x - 28) \div (x - 3)$

   c) $(2x^3 - 2x - 3) \div (x - 1)$

   d) $(x^4 - 8x^2 + 16) \div (x + 2)$

   e) $(2x^3 - 7x^2 - 10x + 26) \div (2x - 3)$

   f) $(2x - 1 + 9x^3) \div (3x - 1)$

8. **Use Technology** Factor each of these polynomials, if possible.

   a) $2x^3 - x^2 + x - 2$

   b) $2x^3 + 9x^2 + 3x - 4$

   c) $3x^4 - 6x^3 + 2x - 1$

   d) $4x^4 + 4x^3 - 35x^2 - 36x - 9$

   e) $2x^4 - x^3 + 3x - 1$

   f) $6x^3 - 7x^2 + 1$

   g) $2x^4 - 11x^3 + 12x^2 + x - 4$

9. Determine the value of k so that $x^3 + 5x^2 + kx + 6$ has $x + 2$ as a factor.

10. Determine the value of k so that $kx^3 - 10x^2 + 2x + 3$ has $x - 3$ as a factor.

★11. Determine the value of k so that $2x^3 - (k + 1)x^2 + 6kx + 11$ has $x - 1$ as a factor.

12. Factor each polynomial.

   ★a) $x^3 + 2x^2 - 9x - 18$

   b) $4x^3 - 8x^2 + x + 3$

   ★c) $6x^3 + x^2 - 31x + 10$

   d) $4x^3 + 5x + 21$

   ★e) $3x^3 + 2x^2 - 19x + 6$

   f) $x^4 + x^3 - 13x^2 - 25x - 12$

   g) $x^4 + 3x^3 - x^2 - 6x$

13. Factor each sum or difference of the cubes below.

   a) $8x^3 - 1$ b) $512x^3 - 64y^3$

   c) $x^3 - \dfrac{1}{27}$ d) $1 + 125x^3$

   e) $\dfrac{1}{8}x^3 + \dfrac{1}{64}$ f) $135x^3 + 625y^3$

C

14. Divide $3x^4 - 3x^3 - 11x^2 + 6x - 1$ by $x^3 + x^2 - 2$.

15. a) Show that $x - 1$ is a factor of $14x^{99} - 65x^{56} + 51$.

   b) Show that $x - 1$ is not a factor of $x^5 + 1$.

★16. Factor $32x^4 - 128x^3 - 54x^2 + 243x - 108$.

17. Show that $(x - a)$ is a factor of $x^n - a^n$.

18. Use the Factor Theorem to show that $(x - a)$ is a factor of $(a - x)^3 + (x - b)^3 + (b - a)^3$.

KEY CONCEPTS

- The real roots of a polynomial equation $P(x) = 0$ correspond to the x-intercepts of the graph of the polynomial function $P(x)$.

  In factored form, $2x^3 + 3x^2 - 11x - 6$ is $(x - 2)(2x - 1)(x - 3)$.

  The values 2, $-\frac{1}{2}$, and -3 are the roots of the equation $2x^3 + 3x^2 - 11x - 6 = 0$ and are the x-intercepts of the graph of the related function $y = 2x^3 + 3x^2 - 11x - 6$.

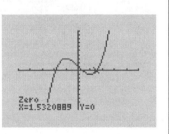

- The x-intercepts of the graph of a polynomial function correspond to the real roots of the related polynomial equation.

  The function $y = (x - 3)(x^2 + 1)$ has only one real zero, so the equation $(x - 3)(x^2 + 1) = 0$ has one real root. The x-intercept of the graph is 3.

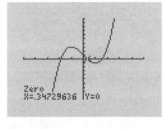

- If a polynomial equation is factorable, the roots are determined by factoring the polynomial, setting its factors equal to zero, and solving each factor.

- If a polynomial equation is not factorable, the roots can be determined from the graph using technology.

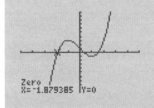
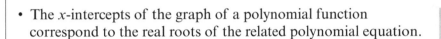

From the graph of $y = x^3 - 3x + 1$, there are three x-intercepts, one near -2, another near 0, and a third near 2. Use the ZERO operation.

The three roots of the equation are -1.9, 0.3, and 1.5, to one decimal place.

A

1. Solve.

   a) $x(x - 1)(x + 3) = 0$

   b) $(x + 2)(x + 5)^2 = 0$

   c) $(2x - 5)(x + 3)(4x - 1) = 0$

   d) $(2x - 7)(3x - 4)(x + 6) = 0$

   e) $(x - 3)(2x + 1)(15x - 2) = 0$

   f) $(x + 8)(x - 9)(3x - 1) = 0$

   g) $4(x - 2)(5x - 4)(5x + 4) = 0$

2. Use each graph below to determine the integral roots of the corresponding polynomial equation.

   a) Window variables: $x \in [-10, 10]$, $y \in [-50, 50]$, Yscl $= 5$

   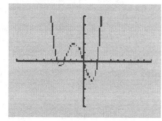

   b) Window variables: $x \in [-2, 2]$, $y \in [-0.5, 1]$, Yscl $= 0.5$

   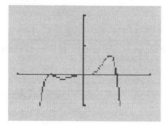

   c) Window variables: $x \in [4, 6]$, $y \in [100, 350]$, Yscl $= 100$

   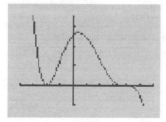

3. Determine the real roots of each polynomial equation.

   a) $(x^2 - 81)(x^2 + 6x + 9) = 0$

   b) $(x^2 - 2x - 15)(x^2 - 4x + 4) = 0$

   c) $(3x^2 - 7x + 2)(x^2 + 10x + 16) = 0$

   d) $(4x^2 - 36)(x^2 - 2x + 1) = 0$

   e) $(4x^2 - 8x - 5)(7x^2 - 28) = 0$

   f) $(x^2 + 4)(x^2 - 100) = 0$

   g) $(3x^2 - x - 4)(6x^2 + x - 1) = 0$

4. Determine the x-intercepts of the graph of each of the following polynomial functions.

   a) $y = 16x^3 - 49x$

   b) $f(x) = x^3 + 12x^2 + 36x$

   c) $g(x) = x^3 - 16x^2 + 63x$

   d) $h(x) = 3x^4 - 363x^2$

   e) $k(x) = x^4 - 27x$

   f) $p(x) = x^4 - 64$

   g) $q(x) = x^4 - 12x^2 + 27$

B

★5. Determine the equation of a cubic function whose graph passes through $(-2, 0)$ and has a local minimum at $(1, 0)$.

6. Determine an equation for a quartic function whose graph passes through $(-4, 0)$, $(2, 0)$, $(1, 0)$, and $(2, 0)$.

7. Solve by factoring.

   a) $x^3 - x^2 - 16x - 20 = 0$

   b) $x^3 - 3x^2 - 4x + 12 = 0$

   c) $x^3 - 3x^2 - 16x + 48 = 0$

   d) $x^3 - 4x^2 + x + 6 = 0$

   e) $x^3 + 8x^2 + 19x + 12 = 0$

   f) $x^4 + x^3 - 13x^2 - 25x - 12 = 0$

   g) $x^4 - x^3 - 11x^2 + 9x + 18 = 0$

8. Compare the zeros of $f(x) = x^3 + 3x^2 - 6x - 8$ and $g(x) = -x^3 - 3x^2 + 6x + 8$.

9. Solve the following by factoring:

   a) $x^2(x + 1) = 12 + 8x$

   b) $x^3(x - 1) = 11x^2 - 9(x + 2)$

   c) $x(x^2 - 4) = -3(x^2 - 4)$

   d) $x^5 + 3x^4 - 5x^3 - 15x^2 + 4x + 12 = 0$

10. **Use Technology** Solve the following by factoring. Round your answers to one decimal place.

   a) $x^2 - 4x + 2 = 0$

   b) $x^3 - 5x + 2 = 0$

   c) $x^3 - 7x^2 + 9x + 2 = 0$

   d) $x^3 + 4x^2 + 7x + 6 = 0$

   e) $x^3 + 8 = 0$

   f) $6x^4 - 10x^3 - 10x^2 - 32x - 8 = 0$

11. **Use Technology** During the first 100 h of an experiment, the growth rate of a bacteria population at time t hours is $p(t) = -0.0041t^3 + 0.02t^2 + 0.5t + 1$ bacteria per hour.

   a) What is the growth rate at 10 h? at 25 h?

   b) At what time is the growth rate 20 bacteria per hour? What does this mean?

   c) At what time is the growth rate 0?

   d) At what time is the growth rate -50 bacteria per hour? What does this mean?

   e) At approximately what time does the highest growth rate occur?

12. A box with a lid is to be made from a 96 cm by 48 cm sheet of metal. It is cut and *folded* as shown in the figure. If the box must be at least 12 cm high, is it possible to cut squares from the corners so that the box has a volume of 9600 cm³? If so, find the size of the squares to be cut. If not, explain why not.

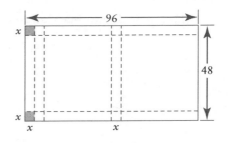

★13. At the turn of the twentieth century, the wolf population north of the Algonquin Park area experienced a rapid increase because hunters had reduced the numbers of natural predators. The food supply was not sufficient to support the increased population, and the population declined. The wolf population for the period from 1905 to 1930 can be modelled by $f(x) = -0.125x^5 + 4.125x^4 + 3500$, where x is the number of years since 1905.

   a) Graph the function.

   b) What value represents the population in 1905?

   c) Use the model to determine the population in 1920.

   d) According to this model, when did the wolf population become zero?

C

★14. Determine the equation of a cubic function whose graph passes through $(1, 0), (0, -1), (-1, -4)$, and $(2, 5)$.

15. Factor $f(x) = x^5 + 4x^4 - 10x^3 - 40x^2 + 9x + 36$.

16. Find all real and complex roots of the given polynomial functions.

   a) $x^3 - x^2 + 5x = 0$

   b) $2x^3 - 9x^2 = 0$

   c) $x^4 - 16x^2 = 0$

   d) $(x^2 + 1)(x^2 + 9) = 0$

   e) $x^4 - 4x^2 + 1 = 0$

   > A complex number is a number that can be written in the form $a + ib$, where a and b are real numbers and $i = \sqrt{-1}$.

KEY CONCEPTS

- A family of functions is a set of functions with the same characteristics.

- Polynomial functions with graphs that have the same x-intercepts belong to the same family.

- A family of polynomial functions with zeros $a_1, a_2, a_3, \ldots, a_n$ can be represented by an equation of the form $y = k(x - a_1)(x - a_2)(x - a_3) \ldots (x - a_n)$, where $k \in \mathbb{R}$, $k \neq 0$.

- An equation for a particular member of a family of polynomial functions can be determined if a point on the graph is known.

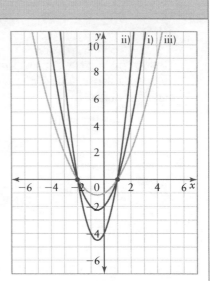

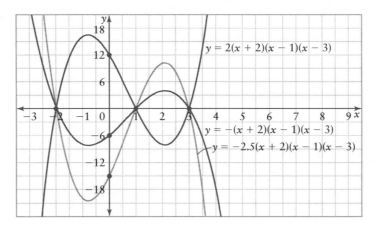

- You can use any point on a function, and the zeros, to determine the equation of a particular function within a family.

- Notice that, if you multiply all the integer values in each equation, the result is the y-intercept.

  Example: Given $y = -2.5(x + 2)(x - 1)(x - 3)$, multiply $-2.5 \times 2 \times -1 \times -3$ to give -15, which is the y-intercept.

- Determine an additional equation that belongs to the same family by changing the multiple in front of the factors.

- Determine an additional equation that belongs to the same family by finding a point on the new function. Substitute the point into the function.

  Example: If the point (2, 16) lies on the graph, then

  $16 = a(2 + 2)(2 - 1)(2 - 3)$

  $\quad = a(4)(1)(-1)$

  $\quad = -4a$

  $a = -4$

  Then, a new equation is $y = -4(x + 2)(x - 1)(x - 3)$.

A

1. The zeros of a quadratic function are 5 and 8.

   a) Determine an equation for the family of quadratic functions with these zeros.

   b) Write equations for two functions that belong to this family.

   c) Determine an equation for the member of the family that passes through the point (7, 6).

2. A cubic function is given by $y = k(x + 2)(x - 3)(x - 8)$.

   a) What are the zeros of this family of cubic functions?

   b) Write equations for two functions that belong to this family.

   c) Determine an equation for the member of the family that has a y-intercept at 192.

3. Examine the following graphs to determine functions that belong to the same family. Write an equation that describes each family of functions.

a)

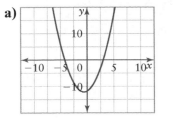

b)

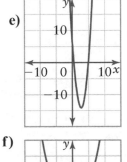

c)

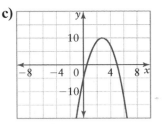

d)

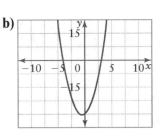

e)

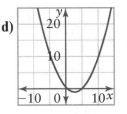

f)

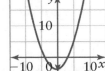

4. Which of the following functions belong to the same families? Explain. Sketch a graph of the functions in each family to verify your answer.

a) $y = 0.3(x - 2)(x + 4)(x + 6)$

b) $y = -2(x - 5)(2x - 1)(1 + 3x)$

c) $y = 4(x - 2)(x + 3)^2$

d) $y = -(3x + 1)(x - 5)(1 - 2x)$

e) $y = -4(x + 6)(x - 2)(x + 4)$

f) $y = 0.5(x + 3)^2 (x - 2)$

g) $y = 4(2x - 1)(1 + 3x)(x - 5)$

h) $y = (5x - 10)(x^2 + 10x + 24)$

5. Write an equation for a family of polynomial functions with the following zeros.

a) $3, -2$

b) $0, 1, 5$

c) $-3, 1, 6$

d) $-\sqrt{3}, 0, \frac{2}{3}, \sqrt{3}$

B

6. The zeros of a cubic function are $-5, -1$, and 2.

a) Determine an equation for the family of cubic functions with these zeros.

b) Write equations for two functions that belong to this family.

c) Determine an equation for the member of the family that passes through (3, 12).

7. **a)** Determine an equation for the family of quartic functions with zeros $-4, -3$, 1, and 6.

b) Write equations for two functions that belong to this family.

c) Determine an equation for the family member whose graph passes through the point$(-1, 21)$.

d) Sketch a graph of the functions in parts b) and c).

★**8. a)** Determine an equation for the family of quartic functions with zeros $-\frac{3}{2}, 0, \frac{1}{2}$, and 2.

b) Write equations for two functions that belong to this family.

c) Determine an equation for the family member whose graph passes through the point $(-1, 4.5)$.

d) Sketch a graph of the functions in parts b) and c).

★**9.** Determine equations for the functions in the graphs below.

a)

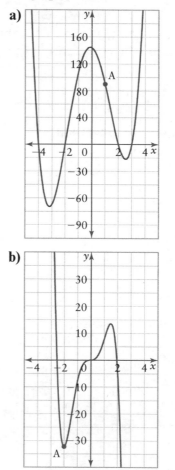

b)

10. a) Determine an equation, in simplified form, for the family of quartic functions with zeros 5 (order 2) and $-1 \pm 2\sqrt{2}$.

b) Determine an equation for the family member whose graph passes through the point (3, 9.6).

11. Determine equations for the families of equations shown in the graph below. Describe the similarities in the graphs and in the equations.

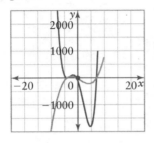

$$f(x) = (x + 4)^2(2x + 1)(x - 7)$$

$$f(x) = (x + 4)(2x + 1)(x - 7)$$

★12. a) Determine an equation for a family of functions with zeros at $1 \pm \sqrt{5}$, -3, and $\frac{1}{3}$.

b) Determine an equation for the family member whose graph passes through the point $(-2, -7)$.

★13. Determine the equation for a family of functions with the same zeros as given in question 12, but with a higher degree. Explain how your equation differs from the equation in question 12.

C

14. a) Write an equation for a family of odd functions with three x-intercepts, two of which are -1.5, and one of which is 7.

b) What is the least degree this family of functions can have?

c) Determine an equation for the member of this family that passes through the point $(-3, 11.25)$.

d) Determine an equation for the member of this family that is a reflection in the y-axis of the function in part c).

e) Determine an equation that is a reflection in the x-axis of the function in part c).

15. Consider the function $f(x) = 4x^4 + (k - 16)x^3 + (17 - 4k)x^2 + 4(k - 1) x + 4$.

a) Use the Factor Theorem to determine an integral root of $f(x)$.

b) Use Technology Investigate how the function changes as k is varied.

c) For what values of k does $f(x)$ have three or more real roots?

d) Choose a value for k that gives the function one real root (order 2). Can you create a family of equations that have the same roots (both real and complex)? Explain why or why not.

16. The graph below represents a section of the track of a roller coaster.

a) Write an equation for the family of functions that models the section of the track.

b) Add an additional section of track to extend the roller coaster to twice its original length.

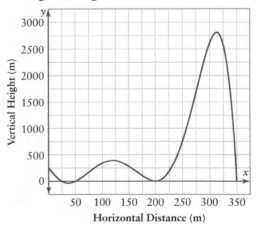

KEY CONCEPTS

- A polynomial inequality results when the equal sign in a polynomial equation is replaced with an inequality symbol.

- The real zeros of a polynomial function, or x-intercepts of the corresponding graph, divide the x-axis into intervals that can be used to solve a polynomial inequality.

Interval	$x < -6$	$-6 < x < 2$	$x > 2$
Sign of Function	+	−	+

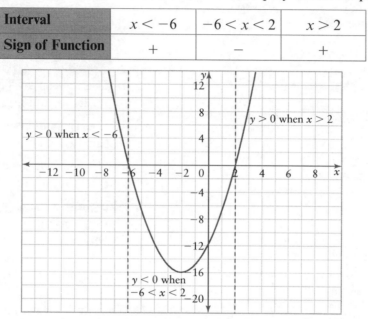

- A CAS may be used to solve a polynomial inequality numerically by determining the roots of the polynomial equation and then testing values in each interval to see if they make the inequality true.

- Polynomial inequalities may be solved graphically by determining the x-intercepts and then using the graph to determine the intervals that satisfy the inequality.

Example

Solving an inequality graphically on the TI-84+:

The zeros of the function
$f(x) = -0.5(x + 3)(x - 1)(x - 4)$
are -3, 1, and 4.

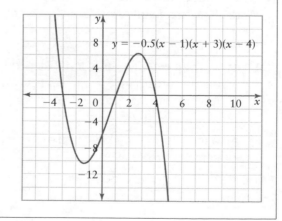

1. Graph the function. Note that the zeros of the function are $x = -3$, $x = 1$, and $x = 4$.

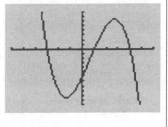

2. • Return to the equation.

   • Press Y =.

   • Position the cursor at the end of the equation and choose the TEST function (2nd MATH).

   • Choose the $\geq$ symbol.

   • Graph the inequality by choosing the ZDecimal operation from the ZOOM Menu.

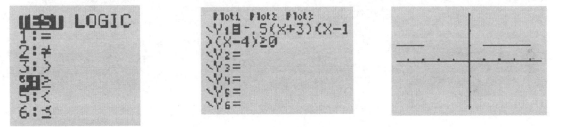

When an inequality is true, the test function plots a point at 1. Otherwise, the plot is set to zero. The intervals where the inequality is true are represented by the horizontal bars at 1.

Use the TRACE key to move the cursor to the end points of each interval.

This test shows that the solution to this inequality is $x \leq -3$, $1 \leq x \leq 4$.

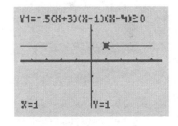

Here is the TI-84+ test for the inequality $-0.5(x + 3)(x - 1)(x - 4) < 0$. The solution is $-3 < x < 1$, $x > 4$. Notice that there are no equal signs in this solution. Also, the solution to this inequality includes the intervals that are NOT in the $\geq$ inequality.

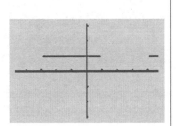

A

1. Write inequalities for the values of x as shown.

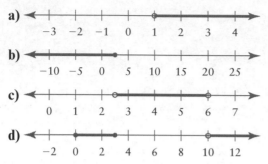

a)
b)
c)
d)

2. Write the intervals into which the x-axis is divided by each set of x-intercepts below.

a) $-2, 0$

b) $-3, 1, 2$

c) $1, 5, 6, 10$

d) $-14, -12, -7.5, 21$

3. For each graph, write

i) the x-intercepts

ii) the intervals of x for which the graph is positive

iii) the intervals of x for which the graph is negative

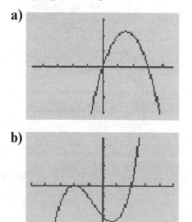

a)
b)

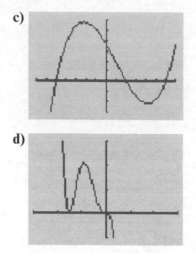

c)
d)

4. a) Sketch the graph of a quadratic polynomial function $y = f(x)$, such that $f(x)$ is negative when $x \in (-\infty, -5)$ or $x \in (10, \infty)$ and $f(x)$ is positive when $x \in [-5, 10]$.

b) Write an inequality statement for the quadratic function described in part a).

★**5. a)** Sketch the graph of a quartic polynomial function $y = f(x)$, such that $f(x) \leq 0$ when $x \in (-\infty, -5)$ or $x \in (2, 3)$ or $x \in (4, \infty)$ and $f(x) > 0$ when $x \in (-5, 2)$ or $x \in (3, 4)$.

b) Write an inequality statement for the quartic function described in part a).

B

6. Solve each polynomial inequality below by graphing the polynomial function.

a) $x^2 - 13x + 30 \leq 0$

b) $x^2 + 20x + 96 > 0$

c) $x^3 - 3x^2 - 4x + 12 \leq 0$

d) $x^3 - 3x^2 - 16x + 48 \geq 0$

e) $x^3 - 4x^2 + x + 6 < 0$

f) $x^3 + 8x^2 + 19x + 12 \geq 0$

g) $x^4 - x^3 - 11x^2 + 9x + 18 < 0$

7. **Use Technology** Solve each polynomial inequality. Use a CAS or a TI-84+ graphing calculator if available.

   a) $2x^3 - 3x^2 - 5x + 6 \geq 0$

   b) $3x^3 - x^2 - 6x + 2 < 0$

   c) $2x^3 - 5x^2 + 1 \geq 0$

   d) $4x^3 - 8x^2 + x + 3 \leq 0$

   e) $2x^3 - x^2 - 15x + 18 > 0$

   f) $4x^3 + 16x^2 + 9x - 9 \geq 0$

   g) $6x^3 + x^2 - 31x + 10 < 0$

8. Solve each polynomial inequality by first finding the approximate zeros of the related polynomial function. Round answers to two decimal places.

   a) $x^2 - 6x - 2 > 0$

   b) $-2x^2 - 17x + 3 > 0$

   c) $x^3 + 4x^2 - 3x - 16 \geq 0$

   d) $4x^2 - 12x + 13 < 0$

   e) $-x^3 + 5x^2 + 10x + 2 > 0$

   f) $x^3 - 2x^2 + 5 > 0$

   g) $x^4 - 3x^2 + 2x - 2 < 0$

9. a) Sketch the graph of a cubic polynomial function $y = f(x)$ such that $f(x) > 0$ when $x < -4.5$ and $f(x) \leq 0$ when $x \geq -4.5$.

   b) Explain what the above information tells you about the cubic function. Why is it possible to determine more than one function that satisfies this criterion?

10. Solve.

   ★a) $-x^3 - 3x - 17 < 0$

   b) $x^3 - 7x^2 + 9x + 2 \geq 0$

   ★c) $x^3 - x^2 - 16x - 20 > 0$

   d) $-4x^3 - 6x^2 + x \leq 0$

   ★e) $x^4 + x^3 - 13x^2 - 25x - 12 \leq 0$

   f) $5x^4 - 3x - 10 < 0$

11. Holly and Matt play in an Ultimate Disc Golf League. On a windy day, and throwing against the wind, the height, in metres, of the flying disc, t seconds after it leaves Matt's hand, is determined by the function $h(t) = 0.69t^2 - 3.26t^2 + 3.33t + 1.2$. How many seconds after it is thrown must Holly catch the flying disc to ensure that it does not hit the ground?

★12. A rectangular prism has dimensions $(2x - 1)$, $(x - 3)$, and $(3x - 4)$.

   a) What are the restrictions on x?

   b) Determine the range of values that x has in order for the volume of the prism to be at least four cubic units.

13. A square-based pyramid has a height that is twice its base length.

   a) Determine an equation to represent the volume of the pyramid, in terms of the base length.

   b) What are the domain and range of the function if the base must be at least 1 cm² and the volume cannot exceed 60 cm³?

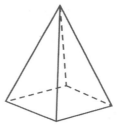

14. The solutions below correspond to inequalities involving a cubic function. For each solution, write two possible cubic polynomial inequalities, one with the less-than symbol ($<$) and the other with the greater-than symbol ($>$).

   a) $-2.5 < x < 3.5$ or $x > 5$

   b) $x < -2\sqrt{2}$ or $-\sqrt{2} < x < \sqrt{2}$

15. Describe the solution to the inequalities as shown in the following graphs. Assume that the *x*-axis scale = 1, and give estimates of the solutions where appropriate.

a)

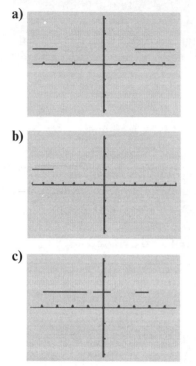

b)

c)

16. Create two polynomial inequalities (of different degrees) that would lead to the solutions shown in question 15.

17. a) Describe the solution to an inequality (either $>$ or $<$) whose polynomial function has

    i) a double root

    ii) no real roots

    iii) complex roots

b) Give an example of each polynomial inequality.

18. Use Technology

Solve each polynomial inequality by first finding the approximate zeros of the related polynomial function. Round answers to two decimal places.

    a) $2x^2 - 5x + 1 \geq 0$

    b) $2x^3 + x^2 - 3x - 1 < 0$

    c) $-4x^3 - 2x + 5 > 0$

    d) $x^3 + 2x^2 - 4x - 6 \leq 0$

    e) $3x^4 - 5x^2 - 4x + 5 < 0$

19. Solve. Round answers to one decimal place.

    a) $3x^3 - 2x^2 - 12x - 12 > 0$

    b) $2x^3 + x^2 + 3x - 2 < 0$

    c) $-x^3 + 10x - 5 \leq 0$

    d) $-2x^4 + 6x^3 - x^2 + 3x - 10 \geq 0$

20. The solutions given below correspond to an inequality involving a quartic function. Write a possible quartic polynomial inequality.

$$x < -\frac{5}{2} \text{ or } \frac{3}{2} < x < \frac{5}{2} \text{ or } x > 7$$

C

★**21.** Solve the inequality
$-x^8 - 3x^7 + 4x^6 - 8x^2 + 24x - 32 < 0.$

22. Solve $2x^3 - 6x^2 + x - 1 \leq 2x - 3$.

23. A bungee jumper models her descent and subsequent bounces according to the function $h(x) = 2.3x^4 - 14.1x^3 + 29.6x^2 - 24.9x + 9.1$. What adjustments could she make to this model so that she does not hit the rocks or water below? Are there any other considerations that might improve the model?

<< **KEY CONCEPTS** >>

- Factorable inequalities can be solved algebraically by
  - considering all cases
  - using intervals and then testing values in each interval

- Tables and number lines can help organize intervals to provide a visual clue to solutions.

> Inequalities that include the end points of intervals are denoted by a filled-in circle. Inequalities that do not include the end points are denoted by an open circle.

Linear Inequalities

a) Solve $2x \le -8$.	**b)** Solve $-3x + 3 < 0$.
$x \le -4$ Divide both sides by 2.	$-3x < -3$ $x > 1$ Divide both sides by -3. Reverse the inequality.
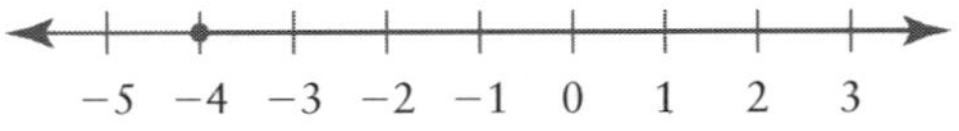	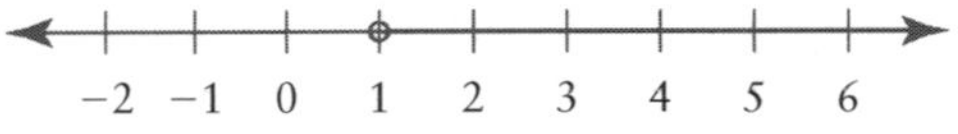

Polynomial Inequalities

Solve $(x - 3)(2x + 1)(x + 2) > 0$.

Method 1: Using a Graph

The factors of the polynomial are $-\dfrac{1}{2}$, -2, 3.

Plot the zeros and sketch a graph of the function.

Locate the intervals where the function is positive, using the zeros as end points for the intervals.

From the graph, the solution to the inequality is $-2 < x < -\dfrac{1}{2}$ or $x > 3$.

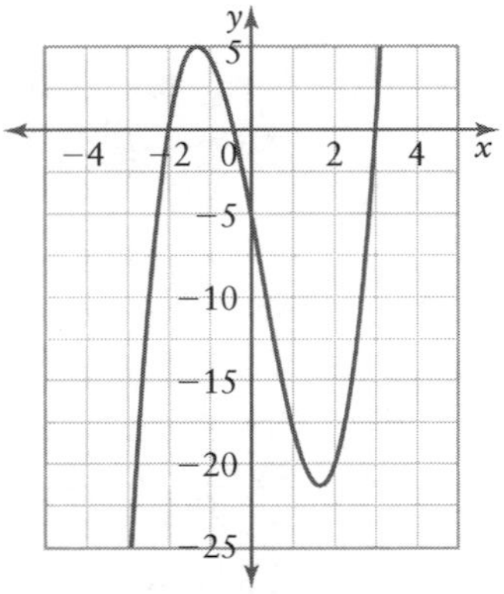

Method 2: Using Intervals

The factors of the polynomial are $-\dfrac{1}{2}$, -2, 3.

Then, the intervals of the polynomial are $(-\infty, -2)$, $\left(-2, -\dfrac{1}{2}\right)$, $\left(-\dfrac{1}{2}, 3\right)$, and $(3, \infty)$.

Choose a test value in each interval to substitute into each factor of the polynomial function. The product of the three factors that produce positive results will satisfy the inequality.

	Interval	$(-\infty, -2)$	$\left(-2, -\frac{1}{2}\right)$	$\left(-\frac{1}{2}, 3\right)$	$(3, \infty)$
	Test Value	-3	-1	1	4
Factors	$(x - 3)$	$-$	$-$	$-$	$+$
	$(2x + 1)$	$-$	$-$	$+$	$+$
	$(x + 2)$	$-$	$+$	$+$	$+$
	$(x - 3)(2x + 1)(x + 2)$	$-$	$+$	$-$	$+$

Therefore, $-2 < x < -\dfrac{1}{2}$ or $x > 3$. This can be shown on a number line.

A

1. Solve each inequality below. Show each solution on a number line.

a) $x - 4 \leq 9$

b) $2x + 1 \leq 13$

c) $-5x + 3 > 18$

d) $3x + 2 \geq 2x - 9$

e) $4(x + 2) < 3 - x$

f) $1 - 4x \geq 8x$

2. Solve the following by considering all cases. Show each solution on a number line.

a) $(x + 4)(x - 2) \leq 0$

b) $(x + 3)(2 - x) \geq 0$

c) $(3x + 2)(4x - 3) > 0$

d) $(2x - 1)(6x - 5) < 0$

3. Solve the following.

a) $(x + 4)(x - 1)(x + 2) > 0$

b) $(x + 4)(x - 1)(x + 2) \leq 0$

c) $(2x - 1)(x + 3)(5x - 3) \leq 0$

d) $(4x - 1)(2 - 3x)(3x - 2) \geq 0$

B

4. Solve the following by considering all cases. Show each solution on a number line.

a) $x^2 - 2x - 24 \geq 0$

b) $x^2 - 10x \leq 21$

c) $6x^2 + 7x - 3 < 0$

d) $2x^2 + 5x - 9 \leq 0$

e) $x^3 + 2x^2 - 16x - 32 > 0$

f) $x^3 + 4x^2 - x - 4 \leq 0$

5. Solve the following, using intervals.

a) $4 - 3x - x^2 \geq 0$

b) $x^3 + x^2 - 20x \leq 0$

c) $x^4 - 2x^3 + x - 2 > 0$

d) $x^3 - x^2 \geq 2x + 12$

e) $3x^3 + 13x^2 < 16$

f) $x^4 - 5x^2 + 9 \leq 0$

6. Solve the following. Describe the differences that you see in the solutions.

a) $x^3 - 3x - 2 \geq 0$

b) $x^3 - 3x - 2 \geq -2$

c) $x^3 - 3x - 2 \geq -10$

★7. The length of a rectangle is 6 m longer than its width. What are the possible widths if the area of the rectangle is at least 630 cm²?

8. Solve the following.

⋆a) $x^3 - x^2 - 34x - 56 \geq 0$

b) $3x^3 + 7x^2 - 2x - 8 < 0$

⋆c) $3x^3 + 4x^2 - 5x - 2 > 0$

d) $x^4 + 4x^3 + 3x^2 - 4x - 4 \geq 0$

⋆e) $x^4 - 13x^2 + 36 \leq 0$

f) $x^4 - 2x^3 + 2x^2 - 2x + 1 = 0$

9. A rocket is fired straight up from ground level with an initial velocity of 32 m/s. Its height above the ground at time t seconds is given by $h = -8t^2 + 32t$. During what time interval will it be at least 19.5 m above the ground?

⋆10. A small rectangular reflecting pool has dimensions 12 m by 6 m by 2 m. A landscaper wishes to increase the size of the reflecting pool, but the budget will allow only 400 m² of liner. The landscaper's design increases the length, width, and height of the smaller pool by the same length, so that the surface area is, at most, 440 m². What are the maximum dimensions of the larger reflecting pool?

11. Ten-year-old Kayla's lemonade stand has experienced rises and falls in sales caused by temperature changes over the last few summers. Her sales over the first two weeks of summer were tracked according to the model $S(x) = x^3 - 12x^2 + 36x$,

where x is the number of days and $S(x)$ is the number of sales.

a) Kayla makes a profit if she sells at least 10 glasses of lemonade. Use the model to determine the number of days that she made a profit.

b) What are the domain and range? Interpret each.

c) Describe the weather for the summer in terms of her lemonade-sales model. Predict the number of sales on her last sales day (August 31). Does this seem reasonable?

12. Marcus and Omar are entering a sandcastle-building contest. Their design assumes that the sand they will use will come in a box with dimensions 36 cm by 48 cm by 60 cm. Later they learn that the box will be smaller; a certain amount will be taken off each of the length, width, and height.

a) Write a polynomial function to model this situation.

b) Graph the function.

c) The amount of sand in the box will be $\frac{3}{5}$ of the amount their design allowed. Write an equation to model this situation.

d) How much was taken off each dimension?

C

13. Solve $x^6 - 9x^4 + 24x^2 - 16 > 0$. How would your answer change if the inequality was greater than or equal to (≥)?

14. For what values of s and t will the equation $\sqrt{2x - 7} \geq s + t$ have no real solution?

15. Find solutions that satisfy both $x^3 + x^2 - 20x \leq 0$ and $x^3 + 4x^2 - 11x + 30 < 0$.

16. Solve $(x^2 + 2x)^2 - 4(x^2 + 2x) + 3 \leq 0$.

C1. Is $x + b$ a factor of each of the polynomials given below? Explain.

a) $x^4 + b^4$

b) $x^5 + b^3x^2$

c) $x^9 - 3b^2x^7 + 5bx^8 - b^9$

d) $x^{12} - 10b^4x^8 - 6b^7x^5 + 5b^{10}x^2$

C2. Show that $x^4 + a^4 = (x^2 - \sqrt{2}ax + a^2)(x^2 + \sqrt{2}ax + a^2)$, and find all roots of $x^2 + 16 = 0$.

C3. A rectangle is inscribed inside the semicircle $y = \sqrt{100 - x^2}$. What are the dimensions of the rectangle with maximum area?

C4. Suppose the cubic polynomial $p(x) = ax^3 + bx^2 + cx + d$, where $a, b, c, d \in \mathbb{R}$ and $a \neq 0$, has zeros r_1, r_2, and r_3.

a) Show that
$$p(x) = a(x - r_1)(x - r_2)(x - r_3),$$
$x \in \mathbb{R}$.

b) Show that $r_1 + r_2 + r_3 = -\dfrac{b}{a}$ and $r_1 r_2 r_3 = -\dfrac{d}{a}$.

c) What other expression involving the roots can you evaluate?

C5. Find an equation (of greater or equal degree) whose roots are double the roots of each of the following:

a) $x^2 - 4x - 6 = 0$

b) $x^3 - 6x^2 + 9x = 0$

C6. The zeros of $ax^2 + 57x + 14 = 0$ are reciprocals of the roots to $x^2 + bx + 2 = 0$. Find a and b.

C7. Descartes Rule of Signs says that the number of positive real zeros of a polynomial function is the same as the number of changes in sign of the coefficients of the terms, or is less than this by an even number. The number of negative real zeros of $P(x)$ is equal to the number of changes in sign of the coefficient of $P(-x)$, or less than this by an even number.
Use Descartes Rule to determine the number of positive real zeros for each function below. Then, find the real roots.

a) $f(x) = 8x^3 - 6x^2 - 23x + 6$

b) $g(x) = 2x^3 + 3x^2 - 8x + 3$

C8. Solve $\dfrac{2x^2 + 6x - 8}{2x^2 + 5x - 3} < 1$.
What are the restrictions on x?

C9. Solve $-3x + 4 < 5x + 9 \leq 2x - 3$. Express the solution on a number line.

C10. Solve by considering all cases. Show each solution on a number line.

a) $(x + 2)(x - 3) \geq 0$

b) $(2x + 1)(x - 2) < 0$

C11. Solve using intervals. Show each solution on a number line.

a) $(x + 4)(3x - 5) > 0$

b) $(3x + 2)(x - 1) \leq 0$

By the end of this chapter, I will be able to:

- Apply the Remainder Theorem to determine the remainder when a polynomial is divided by a binomial

- Apply the Factor Theorem to factor polynomials in one variable of degree greater than two

- Determine the equation of a family of polynomial functions that satisfy given conditions

- Solve polynomial equations using a variety of strategies

- Describe the connection between the real roots of a polynomial equation and the x-intercepts of the graph of the corresponding function

- Solve linear and factorable polynomial inequalities and represent the solutions on a number line

- Explain the difference between the solution to a polynomial equation and a polynomial inequality

- Solve polynomial inequalities algebraically and using technology

Chapter 3 Rational Functions

3.1 Reciprocal of a Linear Function

Rational functions take the form $f(x) = \dfrac{P(x)}{Q(x)}$, where $P(x)$ and $Q(x)$ are both polynomial functions and $Q(x) \neq 0$.

Four Critical Properties of a Rational Function

Property	Example $f(x) = -\dfrac{3}{x-2}$
X-intercepts	Let $f(x) = 0$ and solve for x. $0 = -\dfrac{3}{x-2}$ gives $0 = -3$, which is not true. $\therefore$ there are no x-intercepts for reciprocal linear functions (where the numerator is a constant).
Y-intercepts	$f(0)$ gives the y-intercept. $f(0) = -\dfrac{3}{0-2} = \dfrac{3}{2}$ $\therefore$ the y-intercept is -1.5.
Vertical Asymptotes	Let the denominator be 0 and solve for x. $x - 2 = 0$ $\quad x = 2$ $\therefore$ the graph's vertical asymptote is $x = 2$. Also, note that the domain of the function is $x \neq 2$, $x \in \mathbb{R}$.
Horizontal Asymptotes	When the numerator is a constant, the rational function approaches the x-axis.

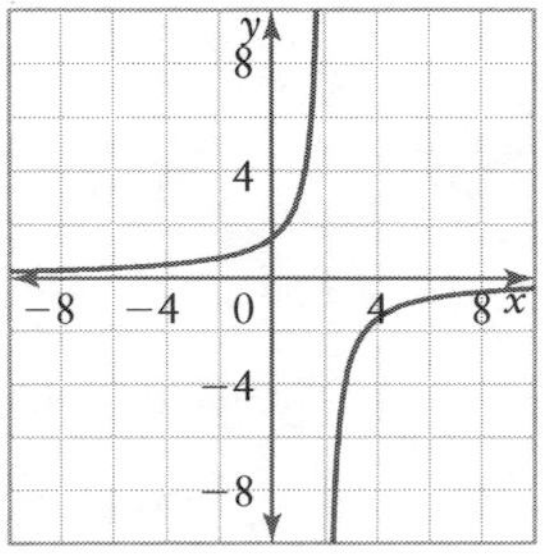

Horizontal Asymptote $y = 0$

No x-intercept

y-intercept
(0, 1.5)

$f(x) = -\dfrac{3}{x-2}$

Vertical Asymptote
$x = 2$

The horizontal asymptote of a reciprocal linear function has equation $y = 0$.

If $k > 0$, the left branch of a reciprocal linear function has a negative, decreasing slope, and the right branch has a negative, increasing slope.

If $k < 0$, the left branch of a reciprocal function has a positive, increasing slope, and the right branch has a positive, decreasing slope.

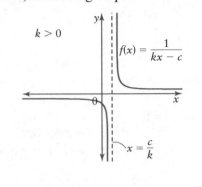

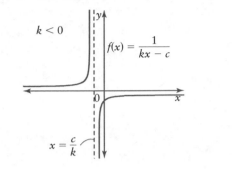

A

1. State an equation representing the vertical and horizontal asymptote of each function.

   a) $f(x) = \dfrac{1}{x - 2}$

   b) $g(x) = \dfrac{3}{x + 7}$

   c) $h(x) = -\dfrac{4}{x - 5}$

   d) $k(x) = \dfrac{2}{9 - x}$

   e) $p(x) = -\dfrac{1}{3x - 4}$

   f) $q(x) = \dfrac{5}{7x + 1}$

2. Find the y-intercepts of each function in question 1.

3. Determine a possible equation to represent each function.

   a)

   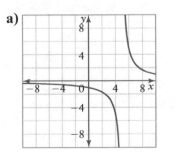

b)

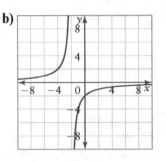

c)

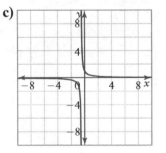

d)

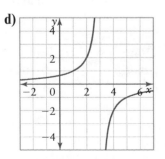

4. Sketch a graph of each function. State the domain, range, and equations of the asymptotes.

a) $f(x) = \dfrac{5}{x - 3}$

b) $g(x) = -\dfrac{1}{x - 4}$

c) $h(x) = -\dfrac{1}{x + 2}$

d) $k(x) = \dfrac{3}{x + 1}$

e) $p(x) = -\dfrac{3}{2x - 1}$

f) $q(x) = \dfrac{2}{x - 1}$

B

5. Copy and complete the table. Describe the intervals where the slope is increasing and the intervals where it is decreasing in the two branches of the rational function $p(x) = -\dfrac{3}{2x - 1}$.

Vertical Asymptote	Comparison of Two Pairs of Points to the Left of Vertical Asymptote	Comparison of Two Pairs of Points to the Right of Vertical Asymptote
	Points:	Points:
	Rate of change:	Rate of change:
	Points (closer to asymptote):	Points (closer to asymptote):
	Rate of change:	Rate of change:
Conclusion (Is rate of change increasing or decreasing?)		

★**6.** Sketch a graph of each function. Label the *y*-intercept. State the domain, range, and equations of the asymptotes.

a) $f(x) = \dfrac{4}{2x - 1}$

b) $g(x) = -\dfrac{2}{5x + 4}$

c) $h(x) = \dfrac{1}{3x + 5}$

d) $k(x) = -\dfrac{3}{1 - 4x}$

★**7.** Describe the intervals where the slope is increasing and the intervals where it is decreasing for the functions in question 6.

8. Describe the behaviour of each function in question 6 as *x* approaches

a) vertical asymptotes

b) $\pm\infty$

★**9.** a) Determine an equation of a linear reciprocal function with a vertical asymptote at -4, and a *y*-intercept at $\dfrac{1}{2}$.

b) Determine an equation of a linear reciprocal function with a vertical asymptote at $\dfrac{1}{3}$, and a *y*-intercept at -6.

10. The Jones family is travelling to the beach. The youngest child, Samantha, determines that the distance from their home is 110 km.

a) How long will the trip take if Mr. Jones averages 75 km/h? 88 km/h? 105 km/h?

b) Write a function that describes the time it takes to make this trip as a function of the speed of the vehicle. Identify the meaning of the variables.

c) Graph the function determined in part b). Show asymptotes.

d) What does this graph tell you about the time it will take to travel, depending on the speed of the car?

11. a) Sketch a graph that satisfies each of the following characteristics.

   i) as $x \to \frac{1}{2}$, $y \to \infty$

   ii) as $x \to -\frac{1}{2}$, $y \to -\infty$

   iii) as $x \to \pm\infty$, $y \to 0$

   b) Determine a possible equation for the graph in part a).

12. The pressure inside a cylinder is inversely proportional to the volume of the gas inside it. When the volume of gas is 50 cm^3, the pressure is 400 kPa.

   a) Write a function to represent the pressure as a function of the volume.

   b) Sketch a graph of this function.

   c) Calculate the pressure for a volume of 75 cm^3.

   d) As the volume increases, what happens to the rate of change of pressure?

13. Investigate a variety of functions of the form $f(x) = \frac{b}{x} + 2$, where $b > 0$.

   a) What is the effect on the graph as the value of b is varied?

   b) Use the results from your investigation to sketch a graph of each function.

   i) $f(x) = \frac{1}{x} + 2$

   ii) $f(x) = \frac{3}{x} + 2$

   iii) $f(x) = \frac{5}{x} + 2$

14. Analyse the key features (domain, range, vertical asymptotes, and horizontal asymptotes) of $f(x) = \frac{1}{\sin x}$, and then sketch the function.

C

15. Analyse the key features (domain, range, vertical asymptotes, and horizontal asymptotes) of each function, and then sketch the graph of each function.

   a) $f(x) = \frac{1}{x + 1} + 2$

   b) $g(x) = \frac{2x}{x + 1}$

   c) $h(x) = \frac{4}{|3x + 1|}$

16. Use Technology Use graphing technology to verify the graphs for the functions in question 15.

17. Find a positive number such that the sum of the number and its reciprocal is minimized.

18. How is a linear function related to its reciprocal?

19. Describe the similarities and differences of the functions $f(x) = \frac{1}{1 - x}$ and $g(x) = \frac{1}{x - 1}$.

20. Describe the similarities and differences of the functions $f(x) = \frac{1}{x + 2}$ and $g(x) = \frac{1}{(x - 2)(x + 2)}$.

21. Determine a possible equation to represent the following function. Give reasons for your choice. Why do you think there are more parts to this function? Why has the number of asymptotes increased?

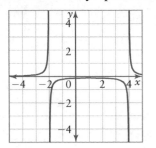

≪ KEY CONCEPTS ≫

- Reciprocal functions can be analysed using key features: asymptotes, intercepts, slope (positive or negative, increasing or decreasing), domain, range, and positive and negative intervals.

- Reciprocals of quadratic functions with two zeros have three parts, with the middle one reaching a maximum or minimum point. This point is equidistant from the two vertical asymptotes.

- The behaviour near asymptotes is similar to that of reciprocal linear functions.

- All of the behaviours listed above can be predicted by analysing the roots of the quadratic relation in the denominator.

Key Features of the Rational Function

Property	Example $f(x) = \dfrac{1}{2x^2 - 9x - 5}$
X-intercepts	Let $f(x) = 0$ and solve for x. $$\frac{1}{2x^2 - 9x - 5} = 0$$ $1 = 0(2x^2 - 9x - 5)$ $1 \neq 0$ $\therefore$ there are no x-intercepts. For a rational function, only the numerator determines x-intercepts.
Y-intercepts	The y-intercept is determined by setting $x = 0$. Then, $f(0) = \dfrac{1}{2(0)^2 - 9(0) - 5} = -\dfrac{1}{5}$. $\therefore$ the y-intercept is $-\dfrac{1}{5}$.
Vertical Asymptotes	Let the denominator be 0 and solve for x. Factor the denominator. $(2x + 1)(x - 5) = 0$ $x = -\dfrac{1}{2}, x = 5$ $\therefore$ the graph's vertical asymptotes are $x = -\dfrac{1}{2}$, 5. Also, note that the domain of the function is $x \neq -\dfrac{1}{2}, 5, x \in \mathbb{R}$.
Horizontal Asymptotes	If the degree of the numerator is less than the degree of the denominator, then the horizontal asymptote is the x-axis, $y = 0$.

Further Analysis of the Rational Function

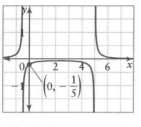

The vertical asymptotes are $x = -\dfrac{1}{2}$ and $x = 5$.

The maximum of the parabolic branch of the function (the middle section) is determined by finding the midpoint of the two vertical asymptotes. Then, the local maximum occurs at $x = 2\dfrac{1}{4}$.

The behaviour of the graph can be summarized by the table below.

Interval	$x < -\dfrac{1}{2}$	$-\dfrac{1}{2} < x < 2\dfrac{1}{4}$	$x = 2\dfrac{1}{4}$	$2\dfrac{1}{4} < x < 5$	$x > 5$
Sign of $f(x)$	$+$	$-$	$-$	$-$	$+$
Sign of Slope	$+$	$+$	0	$-$	$-$
Change in Slope	$+$	$-$		$-$	$+$

The graph

• is positive and increasing with an increasing rate of change for $x < -\dfrac{1}{2}$

• is negative and increasing with a decreasing rate of change for $-\dfrac{1}{2} < x < 2\dfrac{1}{4}$

• is negative and decreasing with an increasing rate of change for $2\dfrac{1}{4} < x < 5$

• is positive and decreasing with a decreasing rate of change for $x > 5$

• reaches a local maximum on the interval $-\dfrac{1}{2} < x < 5$ at $x = 2\dfrac{1}{4}$

A

1. Determine the equations of the vertical asymptotes for each function. Then, state the domain.

a) $f(x) = \dfrac{1}{(x - 3)(x + 4)}$

b) $g(x) = -\dfrac{2}{(x + 3)^2}$

c) $h(x) = \dfrac{1}{x^2 + 8x + 12}$

d) $k(x) = -\dfrac{4}{x^2 - 9}$

2. Copy and complete the tables to describe the behaviour of the function as x approaches each key value.

a) $f(x) = \dfrac{1}{(x - 1)(x + 3)}$

$x\rightarrow$	$f(x)\rightarrow$
1^-	
1^+	
-3^-	
-3^+	
$-\infty$	
$+\infty$	

b) $g(x) = \dfrac{1}{(2x + 1)(x - 2)}$

$x\rightarrow$	$f(x)\rightarrow$
$-\dfrac{1}{2}^-$	
$-\dfrac{1}{2}^+$	
2^-	
2^+	
$-\infty$	
$+\infty$	

3. For each rational function, determine

   i) y-intercepts

   ii) x-intercepts

   iii) horizontal asymptotes

   iv) vertical asymptotes

a)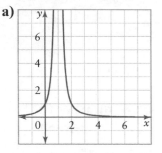

b)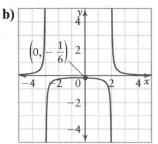

c)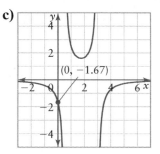

B

4. Determine a possible equation for each function in question 3.

5. Make a summary table with the headings shown for each graph in question 3.

Intervals	
Sign of Function	
Sign of Slope	
Change in Slope	

6. For each of the following functions

   i) state equations for the vertical and horizontal asymptotes

   ii) determine the x-intercepts and y-intercepts

   iii) describe the increasing and decreasing intervals

   iv) sketch a graph of the function

   v) state the domain and range

   a) $f(x) = \dfrac{1}{x^2 - 4x - 21}$

   b) $g(x) = -\dfrac{1}{x^2 - 4x + 4}$

   c) $h(x) = \dfrac{4}{x^2 - 25}$

7. Write an equation for a function that is the reciprocal of a quadratic and that has the following properties:

   i) horizontal asymptote $y = 0$

   ii) vertical asymptotes $x = -2$ and $x = 7$

   iii) $y > 0$ on the intervals $(-\infty, -2)$ and $(7, +\infty)$

8. a) For the function below, determine

   i) horizontal asymptotes

   ii) x-intercepts and y-intercepts

   iii) domain and range

   iv) intervals of increase and decrease

   b) Explain why there are no vertical asymptotes.

   c) Determine a possible equation for the graph.

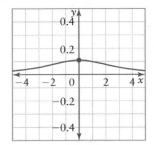

9. The function $g(x) = \dfrac{1}{f(x)}$ describes the quadratic reciprocal graphed in question 8.

   a) Determine the corresponding quadratic function $f(x)$ and sketch its graph.

   b) Compare the properties of the two graphs.

10. a) Sketch a function that satisfies each of the following:

   i) as $x \rightarrow 4^+$, $y \rightarrow \infty$

   ii) as $x \rightarrow 4^-$, $y \rightarrow -\infty$

   iii) as $x \rightarrow -4^-$, $y \rightarrow +\infty$

   iv) as $x \rightarrow -4^+$, $y \rightarrow -\infty$

   v) as $x \rightarrow \pm\infty$, $y \rightarrow 0$

   b) Determine a possible equation for the function described in part a).

C

11. As blood moves from the heart through the major arteries out to the capillaries and back through the veins, the systolic pressure continuously drops. The pressure is given by the function $P(t) = \dfrac{25t^2 + 125}{t^2 + 1}$, where P is measured in millimetres of mercury and t is measured in seconds.

   a) Determine the domain and range of the function.

   b) Where are the horizontal and vertical asymptotes?

   c) Sketch the graph of the function.

   d) Determine the rate of change of the blood pressure at each second for $0 < t < 10$. What does this tell you?

≪ **KEY CONCEPTS** ≫

Four Critical Properties of a Rational Function

Property	Example $f(x) = \dfrac{3x + 2}{4x - 1}$
X-intercepts	Let $f(x) = 0$ and solve for x. $\dfrac{3x + 2}{4x - 1} = 0$ gives $3x + 2 = 0$. $\therefore x = -\dfrac{2}{3}$. For a rational function, only the numerator determines x-intercepts.
Y-intercepts	The y-intercept is determined by setting $x = 0$. Then, $f(0) = \dfrac{3(0) + 2}{4(0) - 1} = -2$. $\therefore$ the y-intercept is -2.
Vertical Asymptotes	Let the denominator be 0 and solve for x. $4x - 1 = 0$ $x = \dfrac{1}{4}$ $\therefore$ the graph's vertical asymptote is $x = \dfrac{1}{4}$. Also, note that the domain of the function is $x \neq \dfrac{1}{4}, x \in \mathbb{R}$.
Horizontal Asymptotes	If the degree of the numerator is equal to the degree of the denominator, then the horizontal asymptote is $\dfrac{a}{c}$ (a and c are the leading coefficients of the numerator and denominator of the rational expression). Since the degrees are equal, the horizontal asymptote is $y = \dfrac{3}{4}$.

$$f(x) = \frac{3x + 2}{4x - 1}$$

For a rational function $f(x) = \frac{ax + b}{cx + d}$,

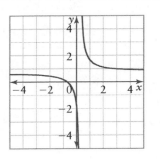

- the y-intercept is $\frac{b}{d}$

- the x-intercept is $-\frac{b}{a}$

- the vertical asymptote is $-\frac{d}{c}$

- the horizontal asymptote is $\frac{a}{c}$, where a and c are the leading coefficients of the binomials in the numerator and denominator, and the degree of each is the same

A rational function of the form $f(x) = \frac{ax + b}{cx + d}$ has the following key features:

- The equation of the vertical asymptote can be found by setting the denominator equal to zero and solving for x, provided the numerator does not have the same zero.

- The equation of the horizontal asymptote can be found by dividing each term in both the numerator and the denominator by x, and by investigating the behaviour of the function as $x \to \pm\infty$.

- The coefficient b acts to stretch the curve, but it has no effect on the asymptotes, domain, or range.

- The coefficient d shifts the vertical asymptote.

- The two branches of the graph of the function are equidistant from the point of intersection of the vertical and horizontal asymptotes.

A

1. Determine the equation of the vertical asymptote for each function.

   a) $f(x) = \frac{3x}{x - 7}$

   b) $g(x) = \frac{5x}{6 - 9x}$

   c) $h(x) = \frac{3x - 1}{x + 4}$

   d) $k(x) = -\frac{3x - 7}{x + 11}$

2. What is the domain of each function in question 1?

3. Determine the equation of the horizontal asymptote for each function.

   a) $f(x) = \frac{x}{x + 5}$

   b) $g(x) = \frac{5x}{6 - x}$

   c) $h(x) = -\frac{x + 3}{x - 3}$

   d) $k(x) = -\frac{3x - 2}{6 - 4x}$

4. What is the range of each function in question 3?

B

5. Sketch the graph of each function, and then summarize the increasing and decreasing intervals.

a) $f(x) = \dfrac{3x}{x - 7}$

b) $g(x) = -\dfrac{x}{5x - 1}$

c) $h(x) = \dfrac{2x - 1}{x + 2}$

d) $k(x) = -\dfrac{2 - 3x}{x - 5}$

6. For each rational function, determine

i) x-intercepts

ii) y-intercepts

iii) horizontal asymptotes

iv) vertical asymptotes

v) domain and range

a)
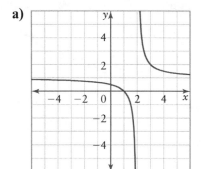

b)
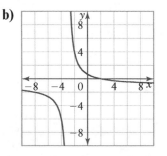

c)
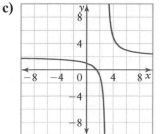

7. Determine an equation for each graph in question 6.

8. Determine an equation for the horizontal asymptote of each function. Then, determine an equation for the vertical asymptote and graph the function. State the domain and range. Summarize the key features of each function.

a) $f(x) = \dfrac{x}{x + 3}$

b) $g(x) = \dfrac{4x}{x + 1}$

c) $h(x) = -\dfrac{x - 1}{x + 6}$

d) $k(x) = \dfrac{5x + 3}{2x - 1}$

★9. Write an equation of a rational function that has a graph with all of the indicated properties.

i) x-intercept at 5

ii) y-intercept at $-\dfrac{5}{8}$

iii) vertical asymptote has equation $x = -\dfrac{8}{3}$

iv) horizontal asymptote has equation $y = \dfrac{1}{3}$

★10. a) Use long division to rewrite the function $f(x) = \dfrac{6x - 3}{2x + 1}$ as the sum of a constant and a rational function.

b) Explain how this method could be used to graph rational functions.

c) Use this method to sketch a graph of $f(x)$.

11. Use your method from question 10 to graph each function.

a) $f(x) = \dfrac{55x - 27}{5x + 14}$

b) $g(x) = -\dfrac{27x - 9}{9x + 4}$

12. Troy and Annie are graphing functions at the chalkboard. Troy is graphing $f(x) = \dfrac{7x - 2}{x}$ and Annie is graphing $g(x) = 7 - \dfrac{2}{x}$.

a) Determine the domain of each of the functions.

b) Identify the horizontal and vertical asymptotes for each of the functions.

c) Use Technology Sketch the graphs of each function and check using a graphing calculator.

d) Explain why these functions produce the same graph, and describe how to determine the important key features of each equation.

★**13.** Consider the function $y = \dfrac{3x}{x + 6}$.

a) Determine an equation for the vertical asymptote.

b) State the domain.

c) Determine an equation for the horizontal asymptote.

d) State the range.

e) Sketch the graph of the function.

f) Summarize the increasing and decreasing intervals.

g) Compare the slopes of the tangents at the points where

   i) $x = -5$ and $x = 15$

   ii) $x = -7$ and $x = -15$

C

14. The average cost per year in electricity for a widescreen television is approximately $18.

a) Assume that a new television costs $1299. Determine the total annual cost for a television that lasts for 10 years. (Assume the only costs associated with the television are its purchase cost and electricity.)

b) Develop a function that gives the annual cost of the television as a function of the number of years that the television is owned.

c) Sketch a graph of the function. What is an appropriate window?

d) Determine the asymptotes of this function.

e) Explain the meaning of the horizontal asymptote in terms of the television.

f) If a company offers a television that costs $1600, but says that it will last at least 20 years, is the television worth the difference in cost?

g) Describe the rate of change of the cost as the number of years increases.

15. A beach must be roped off to cover a rectangular area of 500 m². Since the side at the water's edge must be accessible, only three sides of the beach should be enclosed.

a) Determine an appropriate equation to determine the minimum amount of rope in terms of the width of the enclosed area.

b) Graph the function. What is the domain?

c) What dimensions require the least amount of rope?

★**16.** Describe how the graph of $y = \dfrac{3}{x - 5} - 8$ can be obtained from the graph of $y = \dfrac{1}{x}$.

17. Use Technology The concentration of a drug in the bloodstream is given by the equation $C(t) = \dfrac{5t}{0.01t^2 + 3.3}$, where t is the time, in minutes, and C is the concentration, in micrograms per millilitre.

a) Graph the function using technology.

b) Determine the maximum concentration and when it will occur.

c) Determine the effect of changing the values of the coefficients in the equation.

KEY CONCEPTS

- To solve rational equations algebraically, start by factoring the expressions in the numerator and denominator to find asymptotes and restrictions.

- Next, multiply both sides by the factored denominators, and simplify to obtain a polynomial equation. Then, solve using techniques from Chapter 2.

- For rational inequalities, note the following:
  - It can often help to rewrite with the right side equal to 0. Then, use test points to determine the sign of the expression in each interval.
  - If there is a restriction on the variable, you may have to consider more than one case. For example, if $\dfrac{a}{x - k} < b$, case 1 is $x > k$ and case 2 is $x < k$.

Example

Solve $\dfrac{x^2 - 3x - 4}{x^2 + 11x + 30} \geq 0$.

Factor the rational expression: $\dfrac{(x - 4)(x + 1)}{(x + 5)(x + 6)} \geq 0$

Solution

The x-intercepts are the factors of the numerator. Therefore, $x = 4, -1$.

The restrictions occur at $x = -5, -6$.

The function may change sign at the x-intercepts or at the vertical asymptotes. Thus, these values will be used to determine the intervals of the function.

The number line illustrates the intervals to test in the function.

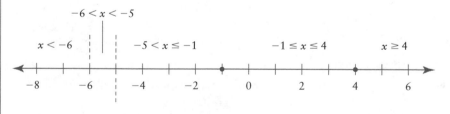

Interval	Test Value for x	Sign of Factors of $\dfrac{(x-4)(x+1)}{(x+5)(x+6)}$	Sign of Function $\dfrac{(x-4)(x+1)}{(x+5)(x+6)}$
$x < -6$	$x = -7$	$\dfrac{(-)(-)}{(-)(-)}$	$+$
$-6 < x < -5$	$x = -5.5$	$\dfrac{(-)(-)}{(-)(+)}$	$-$
$-5 < x < -1$	$x = -3$	$\dfrac{(-)(-)}{(+)(+)}$	$+$
-1	$x = -1$	$\dfrac{(-)(0)}{(+)(+)}$	0
$-1 < x < 4$	$x = 0$	$\dfrac{(-)(+)}{(+)(+)}$	$-$
4	$x = 4$	$\dfrac{(0)(+)}{(+)(+)}$	0
$x > 4$	$x = 5$	$\dfrac{(+)(+)}{(+)(+)}$	$+$

The inequality is satisfied over those intervals where the sign of the function is positive (+) or zero (0).

For the inequality $\dfrac{x^2 - 3x - 4}{x^2 + 11x + 30} \geq 0$, the solution is $x < -6$, $-5 < x \leq -1$, or $x \geq 4$.

$$f1(x) = \frac{x^2 - 3 \cdot x - 4}{x^2 + 11 \cdot x + 30}$$

A

1. Determine the x-intercepts of each function.

   a) $f(x) = \dfrac{-3x}{2x + 5}$

   b) $g(x) = \dfrac{6x - 5}{x^2 - 6x + 4}$

   c) $h(x) = \dfrac{x - 5}{x^3 + 7x^2 + 2x}$

   d) $k(x) = \dfrac{x^2 - 3x - 18}{x^2 - x - 6}$

2. Solve algebraically. Check each solution.

   a) $\dfrac{x - 3}{10} = 4x$

   b) $\dfrac{3}{x} - 2 = \dfrac{5}{x}$

   c) $\dfrac{3}{x + 2} - \dfrac{1}{x} = \dfrac{1}{5x}$

   d) $\dfrac{10}{x + 4} = \dfrac{15}{4(x + 1)}$

   e) $\dfrac{1}{x} = \dfrac{x + 3}{2x^2}$

   f) $\dfrac{x - 2}{x} = \dfrac{x - 4}{x - 6}$

   g) $\dfrac{x}{x - 2} + \dfrac{1}{x + 4} = \dfrac{2}{x^2 - 6x + 8}$

3. **Use Technology** Use graphing technology to solve each equation. Express answers to two decimal places.

   a) $\dfrac{1 + 3x}{x} = \dfrac{x^2}{x - 2}$

   b) $\dfrac{x^2 - 3x + 2}{x - 3} = \dfrac{x}{x + 2}$

   c) $\dfrac{5x - 1}{1 + 2x} = \dfrac{x + 4}{x - 3}$

   d) $\dfrac{3x - 1}{x^2 - 2} = \dfrac{4x^2 - 3}{x}$

4. Solve each inequality without using technology. Illustrate the solution on a number line.

   a) $\dfrac{3x + 1}{2x - 4} > 0$

   b) $\dfrac{x - 3}{x + 3} \le 5$

   c) $\dfrac{2x - 1}{5x + 3} \ge 0$

   d) $\dfrac{1}{x - 1} < \dfrac{-1}{x + 2}$

   e) $\dfrac{x - 8}{x} \le 3 - x$

   f) $\dfrac{2}{x + 3} \ge \dfrac{1}{x - 1}$

   g) $\dfrac{x^2 - x - 6}{x - 3} > 1$

   h) $\dfrac{x^2 - x - 2}{x^2 + x - 2} > 3$

5. **Use Technology** Solve each inequality using intervals. Check using technology.

   a) $\dfrac{(2x - 3)(x + 4)}{(x - 5)(x - 1)} \le 0$

   b) $\dfrac{(x - 2)(x - 1)}{(x - 3)(x - 4)^2} < 0$

   c) $\dfrac{x^2 - 16}{x^2 - 4x - 5} \le 0$

   d) $\dfrac{x^2 - 8x - 48}{x^2 + 6x} > 0$

   e) $\dfrac{x^2 + 58x - 120}{x^2 - 12x - 28} \ge 0$

   f) $\dfrac{2x^2 + x - 1}{x^2 - 4x - 4} \le 0$

B

6. Write a rational equation that cannot have $x = -2$ or $x = \dfrac{1}{2}$ as a solution. Explain your reasoning.

7. Determine the intervals where $\dfrac{2}{x + 1} > x$.

8. Solve and check.

a) $\frac{12}{x} + x - 8 = 0$

b) $\frac{1}{3x} + \frac{6x - 9}{3x} = \frac{3x - 3}{4x}$

c) $\frac{10}{x^2 - 1} + \frac{2x - 5}{x - 1} = \frac{2x + 5}{x + 1}$

d) $\frac{-4}{x - 1} = \frac{7}{2 - x} + \frac{3}{x + 1}$

e) $1 = \frac{1}{1 - x} + \frac{x}{x - 1}$

f) $\frac{7x}{3x + 3} - \frac{5}{4x - 4} = \frac{3x}{2x + 2}$

★9. Solve.

a) $\frac{2}{3x} + \frac{5}{6x} > \frac{3}{4}$

b) $5 + \frac{1}{x} > \frac{16}{x}$

c) $1 + \frac{5}{x - 1} \leq \frac{7}{6}$

d) $\frac{1}{2x + 1} + \frac{1}{x + 1} > \frac{8}{15}$

e) $\frac{x^2 + 3x + 2}{x^2 - 9} \leq 0$

f) $\frac{(-2x - 10)(3 - x)}{(x^2 + 5)(x - 2)^2} < 0$

★10. Prove that $\frac{x^2 - 2x + 5}{x^2 - 4x + 4} < 0$ has no real solutions.

11. Compare the solutions
$\frac{x^2 - 6x + 9}{x - 4} \leq \frac{2x - 1}{x + 3}$ and
$\frac{x^2 - 6x + 9}{x - 4} \geq \frac{2x - 1}{x + 3}$.

12. Rachael runs 2 km to her bus stop, and then rides 4.5 km to school. On average, the bus is 45 km/h faster than Rachael's average running speed. If the entire trip takes 25 min, how fast does Rachael run?

★13. The function $T(d) = \frac{518}{d - 10}$ gives the maximum time a diver can remain underwater and still surface at a steady rate with no decompression stops when the diver's depth is greater than 10 m. Assume that $T(d)$ represents time in minutes and d represents the diver's depth in metres. Determine the maximum depth the diver can go if the diver wants to dive for 60 min.

14. The ratio of $x + 3$ to $x - 5$ is greater than 40%. Solve for x.

★15. Solve $x + \frac{x^2 - 5}{x^2 - 1} = \frac{x^2 + x + 2}{x + 1}$.

16. Explain why $x + \frac{3}{x - 3} = 3 + \frac{3}{x - 3}$ has no solution.

17. Jordan has a sister who is three years older than he is, and a brother who is two years younger than he is. How old must Jordan be in order that the ratio of his sister's age to his brother's age is less than 2?

C
18. Determine all real solutions algebraically.

a) $\frac{2x^5 - 10x + 5}{x^3 + x^2 - 12x} = 0$

b) $\frac{x^3 - 4x + 1}{x^2 + x - 6} \geq 0$

19. Find two rational expressions that have a sum of $\frac{9 - 9x}{x^2 - 9}$.

20. If $\frac{3x}{5y} = 11$, find the value of $\frac{3x - 5y}{5y}$.

KEY CONCEPTS

Special Cases of Rational Functions

- When solving a problem, it is important to read carefully to determine whether a function is being analysed or an equation or inequality is to be solved.

- A full analysis will involve four components:
  - numeric (tables, ordered pairs, calculations)
  - algebraic (formulas, solving equations)
  - graphical
  - verbal (descriptions)

- When investigating special cases of functions, factor and reduce where possible. Indicate the restrictions on the variables in order to identify hidden discontinuities.

- When investigating new types of rational functions, consider what is different about the coefficients and the degree of the polynomials in the numerator and denominator. These differences could affect the stretch factor of the curve and the equation of the asymptotes, and they could cause other discontinuities.

Special Case: Discontinuities

A rational function such as $f(x) = \dfrac{2x^2 + 7x + 3}{2x + 1}$ appears to be linear because when it is factored and simplified, the denominator becomes 1.

$$f(x) = \frac{2x^2 + 7x + 3}{2x + 1} = \frac{(2x + 1)(x + 3)}{(2x + 1)} = x + 3$$

The restriction $x \neq -\dfrac{1}{2}$ leads to a "hole" or discontinuity in the graph.

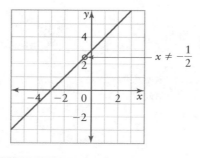

Special Case: Oblique Asymptotes

$$y = \frac{x^3 + 3x^2 - 4x + 2}{x^2 - 1}$$

The graph of the function has vertical asymptotes at $x = \pm 1$. It also has a "slant asymptote" which is found by long division.

Factoring by long division, $y = \dfrac{x^3 + 3x^2 - 4x + 2}{x^2 - 1} = x + 3 + \dfrac{-3x + 5}{x^2 - 1}$. The slant or oblique asymptote is $y = x + 3$.

A

⭐**1.** For an Ideal Gas, pressure, P, in kilopascals (kPa); volume, V, in litres (L); and temperature, T, in degrees Kelvin, are related by the equation $PV = 8.314nT$, where n is the number of moles of gas.

> To convert Celsius to Kelvin, add 273.

a) A 50-L cylinder is filled with argon gas to a pressure of 10 130.0 kPa at 30°C. How many moles of argon gas are in the cylinder?

b) What volume is needed to store 0.050 mol of helium gas at 202.6 kPa and 400K?

c) Sketch a graph of pressure versus volume for 1 mol of a gas assuming that the temperature is fixed.

d) What are the asymptotes of the graph?

e) What will happen to the pressure if the temperature is held fixed and the volume the gas occupies increases?

2. Sketch a graph of each function. Describe each special case.

a) $f(x) = \dfrac{-2x}{x(x + 3)}$

b) $g(x) = \dfrac{x^2 - 1}{x^2 - 7x - 8}$

c) $h(x) = \dfrac{x^2 - 6x}{x^2 - 8x + 12}$

d) $k(x) = \dfrac{x^2 - 9x + 20}{4x^2 - 21x + 5}$

e) $m(x) = \dfrac{x^2 + 2x - 8}{x + 4}$

f) $p(x) = \dfrac{x^2}{x^4 + 3x^2}$

g) $q(x) = \dfrac{x^3 + x^2 - 2}{4x^3 - 7x + 3}$

B

★**3.** According to the Law of Universal Gravitation, the attractive force (F) between two bodies is proportional to the product of their masses (m_1 and m_2), and inversely proportional to the square of the distance (r) between them. This force is represented by the equation $F(r) = \dfrac{Gm_1m_2}{r^2}$, where G is the gravitational constant 6.67×10^{-11}N.

a) Determine the force of gravitational attraction between Earth ($m = 5.98 \times 10^{24}$ kg) and an 80-kg student if the student is in an airplane 12 000 m above Earth's surface, a total distance of 6.39×10^6 m from Earth's centre.

b) Determine the force of gravitational attraction between two students standing 1 m apart if each student weighs 85 kg.

c) Sketch a graph of F if G, m_1, and m_2 are held constant. What are the restrictions on the function?

d) Describe what happens to F as the distance between the objects increases.

e) Compare your answers from parts a) and b). What can you conclude about the force of gravity in smaller objects?

4. A delivery company models its cost, C, in dollars per kilometre for a trip with the equation $C(x) = \dfrac{500}{4.50 + x}$, where x is the number of kilometres over its minimum trip of 4.5 km. Describe the change in the cost model represented by each of the following, and draw a graph for each.

a) $C(x) = \dfrac{700}{4.50 + x}$

b) $C(x) = \dfrac{500}{3.50 + x}$

c) $C(x) = \dfrac{700}{5.50 + x}$

★**5.** Consider the function $y = \dfrac{x^3 - 2x^2 - 5x + 6}{x^2 + 3x + 2}$.

a) Determine the vertical asymptotes.

b) Determine the x-intercepts and y-intercepts.

c) Does the function have any additional discontinuities? If so, explain.

d) Does the function have a horizontal or oblique asymptote? Explain how you determined this.

e) Graph the function.

6. Give a complete analysis of each function by determining key properties (see question 5). Graph each function.

a) $f(x) = \dfrac{4x^2 - 5}{2x^3 - 3x^2 + x}$

b) $g(x) = \dfrac{x^3 - 4x^2 + 6x + 5}{x - 2}$

c) $h(x) = \dfrac{x^3 - 1}{x^2 - 4}$

d) $k(x) = \dfrac{4x^2 + 4x - 3}{2x - 5}$

e) $m(x) = \dfrac{x - 4}{x^3 + 2x^2 - 23x - 60}$

f) $n(x) = \dfrac{2x^4 + 7x^3 + 7x^2 + 2x}{x^3 - x + 50}$

7. The kinetic energy of a moving particle is defined as the total work it can do in kilograms until it stops. For a particle at rest with mass m, the function $K = \dfrac{1}{2}mv^2$ finds in Joules the kinetic energy of the particle, or the work required to reach a velocity, v, in metres per second.

a) Determine an equation for mass of the particle based on its velocity and kinetic energy.

b) Sketch a graph of the function determined in part a) if the particle's kinetic energy is held constant.

c) Determine the mass (in kilograms) of a particle moving at 6.3 m/s with kinetic energy of 30 joules (J).

8. Creating a chemical solution requires precise measurements and mixing. For example, a chemist may have 35 L of a 12-mol hydrochloric acid (HCl) solution. The solution is diluted with 0.5-mol HCl solution in order to decrease the concentration. The concentration of the mixture can be modelled by the function $C(x) = \dfrac{420 + 0.5x}{35 + x}$, where x is the number of litres of 0.5-mol solution added.

a) Determine the vertical and horizontal asymptotes of $C(x)$. Explain their meaning in the context of the problem.

b) Write the function $C(x)$ as a transformation of the graph of $\frac{1}{x}$.

c) Write a function that models the concentration of a mixture that will dilute 50 L of a 12-mol solution by adding a 3-mol solution to it.

d) How many litres of the 3-mol solution must be added to the mixture described in part c) to create an 8-mol solution?

9. The volume of a rectangular prism with a square base is fixed at 500 cm³.

a) Determine the surface area of the prism as a function of the length of the side of the square.

b) Graph the surface area function.

c) Describe how the surface area changes as the side length approaches zero.

d) If the surface area needs to be at least 50 cm², what does the side length need to be?

10. The current in an electric circuit is given by the formula $I = \dfrac{t + 2}{15 - t}$, where t is the time, in seconds.

a) Describe what happens to the circuit as t approaches 15 s.

b) Determine any discontinuities in the graph.

★**11.** When Rosalyn empties her pool for the winter, she knows that the time required to empty it varies inversely as the rate, r, of pumping.

a) Write an equation that represents this situation where k is the constant.

b) Last fall, Rosalyn emptied her pool in 45 min at a rate of 1000 L/min. She now owns a new pump that can empty the pool at a rate of 900 L/min. How long will it take to empty the pool using this new pump?

★**12.** Use long division to prove that the function $f(x) = \dfrac{x^3 - 2x^2 - 5x + 10}{x + 2}$ has a parabolic asymptote.

C

13. Graph $f(x) = \dfrac{1}{x^2}$ after it has been translated 2 units to the right and down 5 units. What are its asymptotes? What is the equation of the transformed graph?

14. Determine the inverse of the function $f(x) = \frac{2}{x} + 3$. Is the inverse a function? Describe the similarities and differences.

15. Recall the Universal Gravitation law in question 3. Suppose that two objects attract each other with a gravitational force of 16 N.

a) If the distance between the two objects is doubled, what is the new force of attraction between the two objects?

b) If the mass of both objects is doubled, and if the distance between the objects remains the same, what would be the new force of attraction between the two objects?

Chapter 3: Challenge Questions

C1. A car travels at a constant speed and burns $g(x)$ litres of gas per kilometre, where x is the speed of the car in kilometres per hour and
$$g(x) = \frac{1280 + x^2}{320x}.$$

a) If fuel costs $1.29 per litre, find the cost function $C(x)$ that expresses the cost of the fuel for a 200-km trip as a function of the speed.

b) What driving speed will make the cost of fuel equal to $300?

c) What driving speed will minimize the cost of fuel for the trip?

C2. a) Find a rational function with domain $x \geq 0$ that has the same graph as
$$f(x) = \frac{x - 3}{|x| - 2}.$$

b) Find a rational function with domain $x < 0$ that has the same graph as
$$f(x) = \frac{x - 3}{|x| - 2}.$$

c) Explain why $f(x) = \frac{x - 3}{|x| - 2}$ has two vertical asymptotes. Confirm your answer by graphing the function.

C3. A cylindrical can with volume 60 cm^3 is to be designed to minimize the amount of material on the outside of the can. The can must be at least 1 cm high and at least 4 cm in diameter. Determine the optimal dimensions of the can.

C4. Ohm's Law states that the potential difference (voltage) across an ideal conductor is proportional to the current through it. The constant of proportionality is called the "resistance," R. The internal resistance of the circuit can be measured by the formula $E = IR$, where I is the current, in amperes (A); $R = x + 6.1$ ohms; x is the ohms of the resistor; and 6.1 is the internal resistance of the circuit.

a) Find I if $E = 1.6$ volts.

b) What is the domain of the function you found in part a)?

c) What is the maximum value of I?

d) Graph the function in part a). Is there a vertical asymptote?

e) What happens to I when the resistance is very large?

C5. The lens equation is $\frac{1}{f} = \frac{1}{d_i} + \frac{1}{d_0}$, where f is the focal length, d_i is the distance between the lens and the image, and d_0 is the distance between the lens and the object.

a) Write a rational equation to find the distance from the lens to the image.

b) If an object is 40 cm from the lens and the focal length is 12 cm, find the distance, d_i.

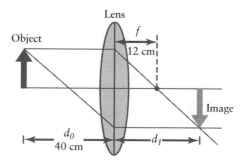

C6. Determine an equation for a rational function with a horizontal asymptote at 2, vertical asymptotes at ± 3, and y-intercept at -4.

C7. Wind chill describes the additional cooling that occurs when skin is exposed to wind. The equation is $W(v) = -0.17v^3 + 18.4v^2 - 584v - 239$ for $0 \leq v \leq 45$, where v is the wind speed in metres per second. The units for W are megajoules per square metres per hour. Determine the speed of the wind that gives a minimum wind-chill factor.

C8. A manufacturer sells x items per week at a price of $p(x) = 250 - 0.01x$ cents per item. It costs $C(x) = 60x + 10\,000$ cents to produce the x items. How many items should be produced to maximize profit? What range of items should be produced to ensure the manufacturer breaks even?

C9. Henry starts to walk south at a speed of 1.5 m/s, while Marion starts at the same point and walks east at a speed of 2 m/s. At what rate is the distance between Henry and Marion increasing 1 min later?

C10. Electric potential energy between two point charges with magnitude q_1 and q_2, in coulombs, is calculated according to the equation $E_e = \dfrac{kq_1q_2}{r}$, where k is known as Coulomb's constant, $9 \times 10^9\ N \cdot m^2/kg^2$, and r is the distance in metres between the charges.

  a) What will happen to the graph of electric potential energy versus charge separation when the sign of one of the charges changes?

  b) In what instances will electric potential energy be maximized?

C11. The frequency, N, of the sound heard by an observer can be measured by the Doppler Effect. N is given by function $N(u) = \dfrac{nv}{u + v}$, where n is the source of sound frequency moving away from an observer with a speed of u, and v is the speed of sound in the air. At 20°C, the speed of sound in air is 343.7 m/s. Determine the rate of change at which the observer loses the sound when its source is 50 Hz and it is moving away at a speed of 35 m/s.

C12. The cost, C, in thousands of dollars, of running a car wash can be modelled by the function $C(n) = \dfrac{3}{45 - n}$, where n is the average daily number of vehicles that use the car wash. The rate of change of the cost, in thousands of dollars, is given by $R(n) = \dfrac{3}{(45 - n)^2}$.

  a) Sketch a graph of each function.

  b) Determine the domain and range of each function and explain their meaning.

  c) Calculate the rate of change at $n = 25$ by finding the slope of the tangent to the function $C(n)$.

  d) Compare the rate of change from part c) to the rate of change function $R(n)$ when $n = 25$.

C13. The quotient of the cube of a number n and a number that is 4 less than the square of n can be modelled by the rational function $f(n) = \dfrac{n^3}{n^2 - 4}$.

  a) Find the equation of the oblique asymptote to the graph of $y = f(n)$.

  b) Determine vertical asymptotes, and x- and y-intercepts of $y = f(n)$.

  c) Determine an approximate minimum value of the quotient when $n > 2$.

  d) Determine an approximate maximum value of the quotient when $n < 2$.

C14. Given the function $g(x) = \dfrac{-5x}{x + 2}$, determine the coordinates of all points on the function where the slope of the tangent equals the slope of a secant line that passes through the points A $(2, -2.5)$ and B $(-1, 5)$.

By the end of this chapter, I will be able to:

- Determine the equations of the vertical and horizontal asymptotes of simple rational functions

- Determine the x- and y-intercepts of simple rational functions

- Determine the domain and range of simple rational functions

- Determine the rate of change at selected points of simple rational functions

- Sketch and label graphs of simple rational functions

- Solve rational equations using the properties of polynomial equations

- Solve simple rational inequalities using the properties of polynomial equations

- Determine and graph special cases of simple rational functions through investigation

- Solve contextual problems involving simple rational functions and equations

Chapter 4 Trigonometry

4.1 Radian Measure

The radian measure of an angle θ is defined as the length, a, of the arc that subtends the angle divided by the radius, r, of the circle.

$$\theta = \frac{a}{r}$$

For one complete revolution, the length of the arc equals the circumference of the circle, $2\pi r$.

$$\theta = \frac{2\pi r}{r}$$

$$= 2\pi$$

One complete revolution measures 2π radians.

- Therefore, 2π rad $= 360°$ or π rad $= 180°$.

- To convert degree measure to radian measure, multiply the degree measure by $\frac{\pi}{180}$ radians.

- To convert radian measure to degree measure, multiply the radian measure by $\left(\frac{180}{\pi}\right)°$.

> When angle rotation is positive, the motion is counter-clockwise, and, when the rotation is negative, the motion is clockwise.

Example – Orbital Motion

Earth's orbital radius around the Sun is 1.49×10^{11} m. If it travels $\frac{5\pi}{8}$ radians, calculate

  a) this angle in degrees

  b) the distance Earth has travelled in its orbit

Solution

a) Since π radians equal $180°$, multiply the angle by $\frac{180}{\pi}$.

$$\frac{5\cancel{\pi}}{8} \times \frac{180}{\cancel{\pi}} = \frac{900}{8} = 112.5°$$

Notice that the πs are cancelled out.

b) Distance is calculated by determining the arc length.

$$a = r\theta$$
$$a = (1.49 \times 10^{11})\frac{5\pi}{8}$$
$$= 2.92 \times 10^{11} \text{ m}$$

(Note that the calculation of arc length should be done using radian measure.)

Therefore, Earth has travelled 2.92×10^{11} m when it moves 112.5°.

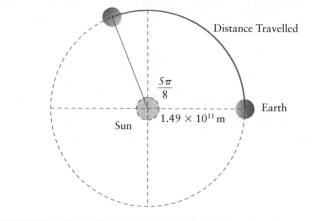

A

1. Convert the following angles to radian measure.

   a) 330°

   b) 60°

   c) 75°

   d) 135°

   e) 225°

   f) 1250°

2. Determine the exact measure for each angle below in degrees.

   a) π

   b) $\frac{\pi}{4}$

   c) $\frac{5\pi}{6}$

   d) $\frac{3\pi}{2}$

   e) $\frac{7\pi}{4}$

   f) $\frac{\pi}{2}$

   g) $\frac{19\pi}{16}$

   h) $\frac{2\pi}{9}$

3. Determine the approximate degree measure, to the nearest tenth, for each angle below.

   a) 1.02 rad

   b) 1.75 rad

   c) 3.79 rad

   d) 6.00 rad

4. Determine the exact radian measure for each angle.

   a) 10°

   b) 64°

   c) 202.5°

   d) 285°

5. The diameter of a circle is 22 cm. If the central angle measures 70°, find the length of the arc.

★ 6. An arc of 14.6 cm has a central angle of $\frac{\pi}{4}$ radians. Determine the radius of the circle.

7. Find the area of a sector of a circle that has a central angle of $\frac{13\pi}{18}$ and a radius of 12 cm. Round your answer to the nearest tenth.

B

8. Determine the angle formed by the hands of the clock at the following times in terms of degrees and radians.

  a) 3:00

  b) 5:30

  c) 7:20

  d) 10:50

9. How many radians are there in each of the following quantities?

  a) the second hand of a clock moving 40 s

  b) a long-distance runner doing 30.2 laps of a track

  c) Earth's rotation in 8 h

  d) Earth's orbit in 365 days

★ 10. Philadelphia and Ottawa share a common longitude at 79°. The latitude of Philadelphia is 39° and the latitude of Ottawa is 45°. Determine the distance between the cities, given that the radius of Earth is 6336 km.

11. Two gears work together. The smaller gear has a radius of 5 cm, and the larger gear has a radius of 12 cm. Determine the number of radians that the larger gear rotates when the smaller gear rotates 300°.

12. A pendulum is 40 cm long. If the end of the pendulum swings through a total distance of 13.5 cm, what is the measure, in radians, of the angle through which the pendulum swings?

13. If the radius of a circle doubles and the measure of the central angle remains the same, what happens to the length of the arc and the area of the sector?

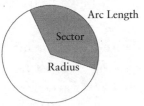

★ 14. The diagram below represents a yard that has the shape of a square with one corner cut off. A dog's leash is tied to a fence post at one end of the short "cut-off" side. The leash is 2.2 m long.

  a) Determine the total area of yard that the dog can reach while on the leash.

  b) How many times more space will the dog get if the length of the leash is increased by 0.5 m?

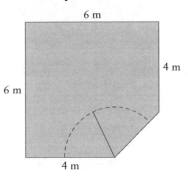

15. Erik rides his bike 4.5 km every morning.

  a) If the radius of the tire on his bike is 32 cm, determine the number of radians that the tire will rotate during the entire trip.

  b) Find the angular velocity in radians per second if the tire turns at 150 rev/min.

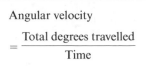

16. A carousel ride with a diameter of 16 m makes 16 rotations in 1 min.

    a) Find its angular velocity in radians per second.

    b) If the rider is on the carousel for 7 min, determine the total distance travelled.

17. A satellite with a circular orbit has an angular velocity of 0.0015 rad/s.

    a) How long will it take for the satellite to return to its starting position?

    b) What is the speed of the orbit if it orbits 1000 km above Earth's surface? (The radius of Earth is 6336 km.)

18. When an angle rotates clockwise from its initial position, it has negative rotation. Determine a positive coterminal angle for each of the following.

    a) $-\dfrac{\pi}{4}$ **d)** $-\dfrac{9\pi}{5}$

    b) $-\dfrac{5\pi}{6}$ **e)** $-\dfrac{11\pi}{3}$

    c) $-\dfrac{2\pi}{3}$ **f)** $-\dfrac{14\pi}{15}$

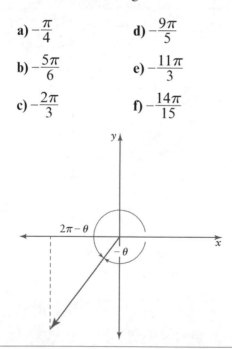

Centripetal acceleration occurs wherever motion is circular and constant. The instantaneous acceleration points toward the centre of the circular motion. The function $a_c = r\omega^2$ determines centripetal acceleration in m/s², where r is the radius of rotation in metres and ω is the angular velocity in rad/s.

C

19. In the Olympic hammer-throw event, an athlete swings the hammer in a circular arc. The speed of the hammer is constant at 1.61 r/s, and the hammer moves in an arc of radius 1.3 m. Determine the centripetal acceleration of the hammer's head.

20. A pulley makes 10 rotations in 3 s.

    a) Find the angular velocity in radians per second.

    b) If the pulley is 60 cm from its centre of rotation, what is its centripetal acceleration?

    c) How far does a point on the circumference travel in 1 s?

> An object that moves on a circular path has linear velocity $v = r\dfrac{\theta}{t}$, where $\dfrac{\theta}{t}$ is the angular velocity and r is the radius.

★ **21.** An airplane propeller rotates 20 times per second.

    a) Calculate the angular velocity of the propeller in rotations per minute and radians per second.

    b) If the propeller has a diameter of 2 m, what is its linear velocity?

22. A satellite rotates around Earth in 90 min.

    a) Determine its angular velocity in rotations per day and radians per day.

    b) The satellite is 35 000 km above Earth. What is its linear velocity?

23. Low Earth Orbiting (LEO) satellites typically orbit between 320 and 800 km above Earth. They must maintain a speed of 27 000 km/h so that they can stay at a constant distance from Earth.

    a) Find the angular velocity needed to maintain a LEO satellite at 320 km above Earth.

    b) A LEO satellite has an angular velocity of 3.8 radians per hour. Determine its distance above Earth.

KEY CONCEPTS

- You can use a calculator to calculate trigonometric ratios for an angle expressed in radian measure by setting the angle mode to radians.

- You can determine the reciprocal trigonometric ratios for an angle expressed in radian measure by first calculating the primary trigonometric ratios and then using the reciprocal key on a calculator.

  The reciprocal ratios are:

  $$\csc x = \frac{1}{\sin x}$$

  $$\sec x = \frac{1}{\cos x}$$

  $$\cot x = \frac{1}{\tan x}$$

Example

To evaluate $\csc \frac{\pi}{3}$, determine $\sin \frac{\pi}{3}$ and invert the ratio:

$\sin \frac{\pi}{3} = \frac{\sqrt{3}}{2}$; therefore, $\csc \frac{\pi}{3} = \frac{2}{\sqrt{3}}$

- You can use the unit circle and special triangles to determine exact values for the trigonometric ratios of the special angles $0, \frac{\pi}{6}, \frac{\pi}{4}, \frac{\pi}{3},$ and $\frac{\pi}{2}$.

Special Triangles

The triangles found in a geometry set are a 45°–45°–90° triangle and a 30°–60°–90° triangle. These triangles can be used to construct similar triangles with the same special relationships among the sides.

The Unit Circle

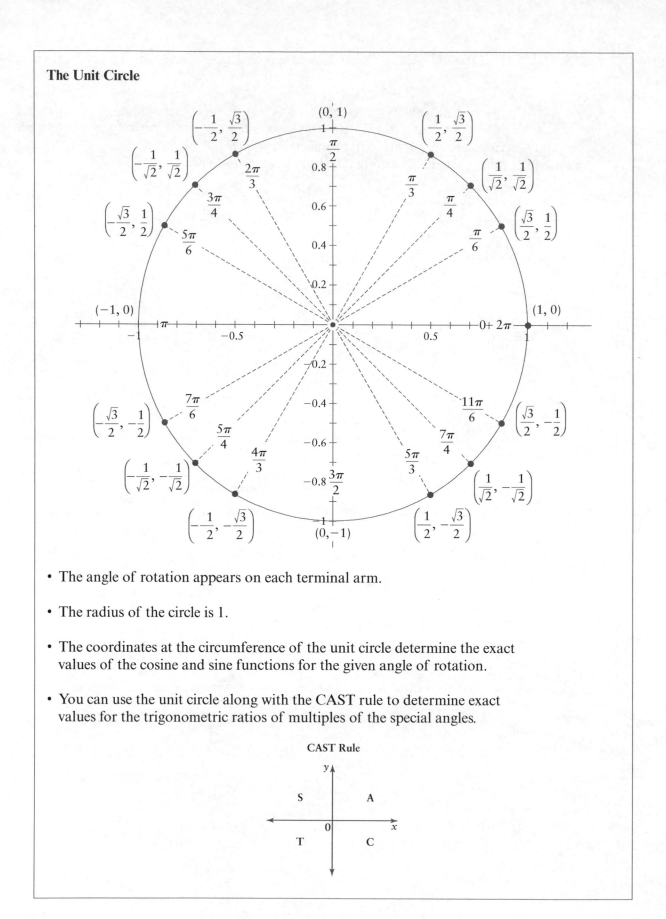

- The angle of rotation appears on each terminal arm.

- The radius of the circle is 1.

- The coordinates at the circumference of the unit circle determine the exact values of the cosine and sine functions for the given angle of rotation.

- You can use the unit circle along with the CAST rule to determine exact values for the trigonometric ratios of multiples of the special angles.

CAST Rule

A

1. a) Use a calculator to evaluate each of these trigonometric ratios, to four decimal places.

  i) cos 45°

  ii) tan 80°

  iii) sin 161°

  iv) cos 302°

 b) Use a calculator to evaluate each of these trigonometric ratios, to four decimal places. Reset your calculator to radians.

  i) cos 0.785   **iii)** sin 2.81

  ii) tan 1.396   **iv)** cos 5.271

 c) Note any similarities between the answers to parts a) and b). Explain why they occur.

2. Use a calculator to evaluate each trigonometric ratio, to four decimal places.

  a) $\cos \dfrac{3\pi}{4}$

  b) $\sin \dfrac{5\pi}{8}$

  c) $\tan \dfrac{\pi}{6}$

  d) $\sin \dfrac{11\pi}{6}$

3. Use a calculator to evaluate each trigonometric ratio below, to four decimal places.

  a) sec 9°

  b) cot 74°

  c) csc 200°

  d) sec 340°

4. Use a calculator to evaluate each trigonometric ratio below, to four decimal places.

  a) cot 0.51

  b) sec 0.92

  c) csc 4.17

  d) cot 6.00

5. Use a calculator to evaluate each trigonometric ratio below, to four decimal places.

  a) $\csc \dfrac{4\pi}{3}$

  b) $\cot \dfrac{\pi}{5}$

  c) $\sec \dfrac{2\pi}{9}$

  d) $\csc \dfrac{7\pi}{12}$

B

6. Use the unit circle to determine exact values of the primary trigonometric ratios for each angle below.

  a) $\dfrac{\pi}{3}$

  b) $\dfrac{5\pi}{4}$

  c) $\dfrac{7\pi}{6}$

  d) π

  e) $\dfrac{5\pi}{6}$

  f) $\dfrac{7\pi}{4}$

★**7.** Use the unit circle to determine exact values of the six trigonometric ratios for each angle below.

  a) $\dfrac{\pi}{6}$

  b) $\dfrac{5\pi}{3}$

  c) $\dfrac{3\pi}{4}$

  d) $\dfrac{5\pi}{6}$

  e) $\dfrac{11\pi}{6}$

  f) $\dfrac{2\pi}{3}$

★ **8.** The angle θ is in standard position with a terminal arm in the given quadrant. For each function, find the values of the remaining five functions for θ.

   a) $\sin \theta = -\dfrac{1}{5}$; quadrant IV

   b) $\tan \theta = 2$; quadrant III

   c) $\csc \theta = -2$; quadrant III

   d) $\sec \theta = \sqrt{3}$; quadrant I

9. Use the unit circle or special triangles to determine all possible trigonometric ratios that have the following values:

   a) $\dfrac{1}{\sqrt{3}}$

   b) $-\dfrac{\sqrt{3}}{2}$

   c) $\dfrac{2}{\sqrt{3}}$

   d) $-\sqrt{2}$

10. A kite is fastened to the ground by a string that is 45 m long. If the angle of elevation of the kite is $\dfrac{4\pi}{9}$, determine the kite's height above the ground.

★ **11.** Solve for the missing sides of the two right-angled triangles below. What are the horizontal and vertical displacements between the two triangles as the angle increases?

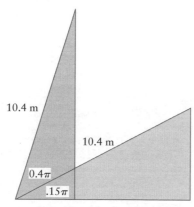

10.4 m

10.4 m

0.4π

$.15\pi$

12. a) Determine an exact value for each expression.

   i) $\cos \dfrac{2\pi}{3} \cos \dfrac{5\pi}{6} + \sin \dfrac{2\pi}{3} \sin \dfrac{5\pi}{6}$

   ii) $\sin \dfrac{5\pi}{6} \cos \dfrac{4\pi}{3} - \cos \dfrac{5\pi}{6} \sin \dfrac{4\pi}{3}$

   iii) $\dfrac{\tan \dfrac{7\pi}{3} - \tan \dfrac{5\pi}{3}}{1 + \tan \dfrac{7\pi}{3} \tan \dfrac{5\pi}{3}}$

   b) Use a calculator to verify your answers to part a).

13. Determine an expression using trigonometric ratios of special angles that simplifies to an answer of zero. You must use three different angles and three different ratios.

C

14. An angle in standard position coincides with the line $y = -1.5x$ and lies in the second quadrant. Find the six trigonometric functions of the angle.

15. Brett is enjoying a sunset at his cottage. As he sits outside on the deck, the angle of elevation to the sun changes from $\dfrac{\pi}{5}$ to $\dfrac{\pi}{6}$. If the sun is 146 million kilometres away from Earth, determine the vertical displacement of the sun over the given angle displacement. (Assume that the sun's distance from Earth remains constant.)

★ **16. a)** Determine an exact value for each expression below.

   i) $\dfrac{\sec \dfrac{\pi}{4} \cos \dfrac{2\pi}{3}}{\tan \dfrac{\pi}{6} \csc \dfrac{3\pi}{4}}$

   ii) $\sin \dfrac{5\pi}{4} - \cos \dfrac{11\pi}{6} \cot \dfrac{\pi}{3}$

   b) Use your calculator to check your answers to part a).

17. Determine the area of the intersection of the two triangles in question 11.

> ## KEY CONCEPTS
>
> - You can use a right triangle to derive equivalent trigonometric expressions that form the cofunction identities, such as $\sin x = \cos\left(\frac{\pi}{2} - x\right)$.
>
> - You can use the unit circle along with transformations to derive equivalent trigonometric expressions that form other trigonometric identities, such as $\cos\left(\frac{\pi}{2} + x\right) = -\sin x$.
>
> - Given a trigonometric expression of a known angle, you can use equivalent trigonometric expressions to evaluate trigonometric expressions of other angles.
>
> - You can use graphing technology to demonstrate that two trigonometric expressions are equivalent.
>
> | Trigonometric Identities Featuring $\frac{\pi}{2}$ | | | |
> |---|---|---|---|
> | **Cofunction Identities** | | | |
> | $\sin x = \cos\left(\frac{\pi}{2} - x\right)$ | $\cos x = \sin\left(\frac{\pi}{2} - x\right)$ | $\sin\left(x + \frac{\pi}{2}\right) = \cos x$ | $\cos\left(x + \frac{\pi}{2}\right) = -\sin x$ |
> | $\tan x = \cot\left(\frac{\pi}{2} - x\right)$ | $\cot x = \tan\left(\frac{\pi}{2} - x\right)$ | $\tan\left(x + \frac{\pi}{2}\right) = -\cot x$ | $\cot\left(x + \frac{\pi}{2}\right) = -\tan x$ |
> | $\csc x = \sec\left(\frac{\pi}{2} - x\right)$ | $\sec x = \csc\left(\frac{\pi}{2} - x\right)$ | $\csc\left(x + \frac{\pi}{2}\right) = \sec x$ | $\sec\left(x + \frac{\pi}{2}\right) = -\csc x$ |
>
> **Summary of Cofunction Identities**
>
>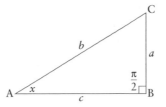
>
> $\angle C = \frac{\pi}{2} - x$
>
> $\sin x = \frac{a}{b}$ and $\cos\left(\frac{\pi}{2} - x\right) = \frac{a}{b}$
>
> Therefore, $\sin x = \cos\left(\frac{\pi}{2} - x\right)$
>
> Similar expressions can be derived for the other five trigonometric ratios.

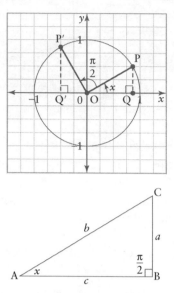

After a rotation of $\frac{\pi}{2}$, or 90°, counter-clockwise about the origin, the coordinates of the point (x, y) become $(-y, x)$.

The coordinates of P are $(\cos x, \sin x)$.

The coordinates of P′ are $\left[\cos\left(x + \frac{\pi}{2}\right), \sin\left(x + \frac{\pi}{2}\right)\right]$.

Because the angle has rotated counter-clockwise $\frac{\pi}{2}$,

$\cos\left(x + \frac{\pi}{2}\right) = -\sin x$, and $\sin\left(x + \frac{\pi}{2}\right) = \cos x$.

A

1. Given that $\sin\frac{\pi}{4} = \frac{\sqrt{2}}{2}$, use an equivalent trigonometric expression to show that $\cos\frac{\pi}{4} = \frac{\sqrt{2}}{2}$.

2. Given that $\sec\frac{\pi}{6} = \frac{2}{\sqrt{3}}$, use an equivalent trigonometric expression to show that $\csc\frac{\pi}{3} = \frac{2}{\sqrt{3}}$.

3. Given that $\tan\frac{\pi}{3} = \sqrt{3}$, use an equivalent trigonometric expression to show that $\cot\frac{\pi}{6} = \sqrt{3}$.

4. Given that $\cos\frac{2\pi}{9} = 0.766$, use an equivalent trigonometric expression to show that $\sin\frac{13\pi}{18} = 0.766$.

5. Given that $\sec\frac{5\pi}{4} = -\csc x$, first express $\frac{5\pi}{4}$ as a sum of $\frac{\pi}{2}$ and an angle, and then apply a trigonometric identity to determine the measure of angle x.

★6. Given that $\sin\frac{2\pi}{3} = \cos y$, first express $\frac{2\pi}{3}$ as a sum of $\frac{\pi}{2}$ and an angle, and then apply a trigonometric identity to determine the measure of angle y.

7. Given that $\tan\frac{7\pi}{8} = -\cot z$, first express $\frac{7\pi}{8}$ as a sum of $\frac{\pi}{2}$ and an angle, and then apply a trigonometric identity to determine the measure of angle z.

8. Given that $\sin \frac{2\pi}{5} = \cos x$, first express $\frac{2\pi}{5}$ as a difference between $\frac{\pi}{2}$ and an angle, and then apply a cofunction identity to determine the measure of angle x.

9. Given that $\csc \frac{3\pi}{10} = \sec y$, first express $\frac{3\pi}{10}$ as a difference between $\frac{\pi}{2}$ and an angle, and then apply a cofunction identity to determine the measure of angle y.

★10. Given that $\sin \frac{\pi}{12} \doteq 0.2588$, use equivalent trigonometric expressions to evaluate the following, to four decimal places.

   a) $\cos \frac{5\pi}{12}$

   b) $\cos \frac{7\pi}{12}$

11. Given that $\sec \frac{4\pi}{21} \doteq 1.21$, use equivalent trigonometric expressions to evaluate the following, to two decimal places.

   a) $\csc \frac{13\pi}{42}$

   b) $\csc \frac{29\pi}{42}$

B

12. Given that $\cos a = -\sin \frac{3\pi}{7}$ and that a lies in the second quadrant, determine the measure of angle a, to two decimal places.

13. Given that $\csc b = -\sec \frac{3\pi}{5}$ and that b lies in the first quadrant, use a co-function identity to determine the measure of angle b, to two decimal places.

★14. Given that $\sec x = -\csc 0.57$ and that x lies in the second quadrant, determine the measure of angle x, to two decimal places.

15. Given that $\tan y = \cot 1.52$ and that y lies in the first quadrant, determine the measure of angle y, to two decimal places.

16. Given that $\sin z = \cos 0.84$ and that z lies in the first quadrant, determine the measure of angle z, to two decimal places.

17. Use Technology

   a) Verify graphically that

   i) $\sin \left(\frac{\pi}{2} - x \right) = \cos x$

   ii) $\cos \left(\frac{\pi}{2} - x \right) = \sin x$

   b) Graph $\sin x$ and $\sin \left(\frac{\pi}{2} - x \right)$. Explain the differences you see in the functions. How do these functions verify the co-function identities graphed in part a)?

18. Using the trigonometric identities for $(\pi - x)$ and $(x + \pi)$ and given that $\cos \frac{\pi}{14} \doteq 0.9749$, find

   a) $\cos \frac{13\pi}{14}$

   b) $\cos \frac{15\pi}{14}$

19. Use a graph or unit circle to verify the following identities:

   a) $\sin (-x) = -\sin x$

   b) $\cos (-x) = \cos x$

   c) $\tan (-x) = -\tan x$

   Explain why you think this relationship exists. Do you think the same relationship exists for the reciprocal trigonometric identities?

20. Use Technology

   Use graphing technology to verify that $\cos(3\pi - x) = -\cos x$, where x lies in the first quadrant.

⭐**21.** Co-function angle identities are sometimes called correlated angle identities. Investigate the relationship among other correlated angles. Complete each statement below by determining an appropriate trigonometric function. The first one has been completed.

a) $\sin \alpha = \cos\left(\alpha - \dfrac{\pi}{2}\right)$

$= -\sin(\alpha - \pi)$

$= -\cos\left(\alpha - \dfrac{3\pi}{2}\right)$

b) $\cos \alpha = \underline{\qquad}\left(\alpha - \dfrac{\pi}{2}\right)$

$= \underline{\qquad}(\alpha - \pi)$

$= \underline{\qquad}\left(\alpha - \dfrac{3\pi}{2}\right)$

c) $\tan \alpha = \underline{\qquad}\left(\alpha - \dfrac{\pi}{2}\right)$

$= \underline{\qquad}(\alpha - \pi)$

$= \underline{\qquad}\left(\alpha - \dfrac{3\pi}{2}\right)$

d) $\csc \alpha = \underline{\qquad}\left(\alpha - \dfrac{\pi}{2}\right)$

$= \underline{\qquad}(\alpha - \pi)$

$= \underline{\qquad}\left(\alpha - \dfrac{3\pi}{2}\right)$

e) $\sec \alpha = \underline{\qquad}\left(\alpha - \dfrac{\pi}{2}\right)$

$= \underline{\qquad}(\alpha - \pi)$

$= \underline{\qquad}\left(\alpha - \dfrac{3\pi}{2}\right)$

f) $\cot \alpha = \underline{\qquad}\left(\alpha - \dfrac{\pi}{2}\right)$

$= \underline{\qquad}(\alpha - \pi)$

$= \underline{\qquad}\left(\alpha - \dfrac{3\pi}{2}\right)$

22. a) Repeat the exercise in question 21, using sums instead of differences. For example,

$\sin \alpha = \underline{\qquad}\left(\alpha + \dfrac{\pi}{2}\right)$

$= \underline{\qquad}(\alpha + \pi)$

$= \underline{\qquad}\left(\alpha + \dfrac{3\pi}{2}\right).$

b) How do these identities compare with the identities investigated in question 21?

23. Using the trigonometric identities for $\left(\dfrac{3\pi}{2} - x\right)$ and $\left(x + \dfrac{3\pi}{2}\right)$ and given that $\tan \dfrac{2\pi}{9} \doteq 0.8391$, find

a) $\cot \dfrac{23\pi}{18}$

b) $\cot \dfrac{31\pi}{18}$

24. a) Determine an exact value of a such that $\sec\left(3a - \dfrac{\pi}{4}\right) = -\csc\left(4a - \dfrac{\pi}{4}\right).$

b) Check your answer.

C

25. Simplify.

a) $\sin\left(\dfrac{\pi}{2} + x\right) - \cos\left(\dfrac{3\pi}{2} - x\right)$
$+ \sin\left(\dfrac{3\pi}{2} - x\right)$

b) $\dfrac{\cos(x + \pi)\cos\left(\dfrac{\pi}{2} + x\right)}{\cos(\pi - x)} - \dfrac{\sin\left(\dfrac{3\pi}{2} - x\right)}{\sec(\pi + x)}$

26. Determine whether or not

$\dfrac{\sin\left(x + \dfrac{\pi}{2}\right)}{\sin x} = \tan x.$

A compound angle expression is a trigonometric expression that depends on two or more angles.

- You can develop compound angle formulas using algebra and the unit circle.

- Once you have developed one compound angle formula, you can develop others by applying equivalent trigonometric expressions.

- The compound angle, or addition and subtraction, formulas for sine and cosine are

  $\sin (x + y) = \sin x \cos y + \cos x \sin y$

  $\sin (x - y) = \sin x \cos y - \cos x \sin y$

  $\cos (x + y) = \cos x \cos y - \sin x \sin y$

  $\cos (x - y) = \cos x \cos y + \sin x \sin y$

- You can apply compound angle formulas to determine exact trigonometric ratios for angles that can be expressed as sums or differences of special angles.

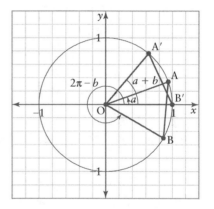

Addition Formula for Cosine

The unit circle can be used to show that the formula $\cos (x + y) = \cos x \cos y - \sin x \sin y$ is valid for all angles. Consider the unit circle shown.

Subtraction Formula for Cosine

The subtraction formula for cosine can be derived from the addition formula for cosine.

$\cos (x + y) = \cos x \cos y - \sin x \sin y$

$\cos (x + (-y)) = \cos x \cos (-y) - \sin x \sin (-y)$ Substitute $-y$ for y.

$\cos (x - y) = \cos x \cos (2\pi - y) - \sin x \sin(2\pi - y)$ From the unit circle, angle $-y$ is the same as angle $(2\pi - y)$.

$\cos (x - y) = \cos x \cos y - \sin x(-\sin y)$ $\cos (2\pi - y) = \cos y; \sin (2\pi - y) = -\sin y$

$\cos (x - y) = \cos x \cos y + \sin x \sin y$

Addition Formula for Sine

Recall the cofunction identities $\sin x = \cos\left(\frac{\pi}{2} - x\right)$ and $\cos x = \sin\left(\frac{\pi}{2} - x\right)$.
Apply these and the subtraction formula for cosine.

$\sin(x + y) = \cos\left[\frac{\pi}{2} - (x + y)\right]$ Apply a cofunction identity.

$\quad\quad\quad\; = \cos\left[\left(\frac{\pi}{2} - x\right) - y\right]$ Regroup the terms in the argument.

$\quad\quad\quad\; = \cos\left(\frac{\pi}{2} - x\right)\cos y + \sin\left(\frac{\pi}{2} - x\right)\sin y$ Apply the subtraction formula for cosine.

$\quad\quad\quad\; = \sin x \cos y + \cos x \sin y$ Apply cofunction identities.

Subtraction Formula for Sine

The subtraction formula for sine can be derived from the addition formula for sine, following the approach used for the subtraction formula for cosine.

$\sin(x + -y)) = \sin x \cos(-y) + \cos x \sin(-y)$ Substitute $-y$ for y.

$\sin(x - y) = \sin x \cos y + \cos x\,(-\sin y)$

$\sin(x - y) = \sin x \cos y - \cos x \sin y$

Compound-Angle Formulas for Tangent

$\tan(x + y) = \dfrac{\tan x + \tan y}{1 - \tan x \tan y}$

$\tan(x - y) = \dfrac{\tan x - \tan y}{1 + \tan x \tan y}$

Double-Angle Formulas

Addition and Subtraction formulas can be applied to develop the following double-angle formulas.

$\sin 2x = 2 \sin x \cos x$ $\cos 2x = \cos^2 x - \sin^2 x$

$\tan 2x = \dfrac{2 \tan x}{1 - \tan^2 x}$ $\cos 2x = 2 \cos^2 x - 1$

                                           $\cos 2x = 1 - 2 \sin^2 x$

A

1. Use the appropriate compound-angle formula to express each of the following as a single trigonometric function, and then determine an exact value for each.

   a) $\sin \dfrac{\pi}{2} \cos \dfrac{\pi}{4} - \cos \dfrac{\pi}{2} \sin \dfrac{\pi}{4}$

   b) $\sin \dfrac{2\pi}{3} \cos \pi + \cos \dfrac{2\pi}{3} \sin \pi$

   c) $\cos \dfrac{\pi}{6} \cos \dfrac{3\pi}{4} - \sin \dfrac{\pi}{6} \sin \dfrac{3\pi}{4}$

   d) $\cos \dfrac{\pi}{12} \cos \dfrac{7\pi}{4} + \sin \dfrac{\pi}{12} \sin \dfrac{7\pi}{4}$

2. Determine an exact value for $\cos \dfrac{\pi}{12}$ using a sum or difference formula for cosine. (*Hint:* Find two angles that have a sum or difference of $\dfrac{\pi}{12}$.)

3. Apply a compound-angle formula to each expression below, and then determine an exact value for each.

   a) $\sin\left(\dfrac{\pi}{2} + \dfrac{\pi}{12}\right)$

   b) $\sin\left(\dfrac{\pi}{2} - \dfrac{\pi}{12}\right)$

   c) $\cos\left(\dfrac{3\pi}{4} + \dfrac{\pi}{6}\right)$

   d) $\cos\left(\dfrac{3\pi}{4} - \dfrac{\pi}{6}\right)$

★**4.** Determine an exact value for $\sin\dfrac{13\pi}{36}$ using a sum or difference formula for sine.

5. Determine an exact value for $\tan\dfrac{19\pi}{24}$ using a sum or difference formula for tangent.

6. Use an appropriate compound angle formula to determine an exact value for each of the following:

a) $\cos\dfrac{7\pi}{12}$

b) $\sin\dfrac{11\pi}{12}$

c) $\sin\dfrac{\pi}{12}$

d) $\cos\left(-\dfrac{\pi}{12}\right)$

B

★**7.** Use sum or difference identities to determine an exact value for each trigonometric function below.

a) $\sin\dfrac{23\pi}{12}$

b) $\cos\dfrac{13\pi}{12}$

c) $\tan\dfrac{23\pi}{12}$

d) $\csc\dfrac{5\pi}{12}$

8. If x and y are acute angles such that $\sin x = \dfrac{1}{2}$ and $\sin y = \dfrac{1}{4}$,

a) determine the exact values for $\cos x$ and $\cos y$

b) use the results from part a) to determine an exact value for each of the following:

i) $\sin(x+y)$

ii) $\sin(x-y)$

iii) $\cos(x+y)$

iv) $\cos(x-y)$

9. If x and y are angles in the second quadrant such that $\sin x = \dfrac{2}{9}$ and $\cos y = -\dfrac{4}{5}$,

a) determine the exact value for $\cos x$ and $\sin y$

b) use the results from part a) to determine an exact value for each of the following:

i) $\sin(x+y)$

ii) $\sin(x-y)$

iii) $\cos(x+y)$

iv) $\cos(x-y)$

★**10.** Find the exact value of each of the following if $0 \le x \le \dfrac{\pi}{2}$ and $0 \le y \le \dfrac{\pi}{2}$:

a) $\sin(x-y)$ if $\cos x = \dfrac{3}{5}$ and $\sin y = \dfrac{24}{25}$

b) $\sin(x+y)$ if $\sin x = \dfrac{5}{13}$ and $\sin y = \dfrac{12}{13}$

c) $\cos(x+y)$ if $\cos x = \dfrac{2}{3}$ and $\sin y = \dfrac{10}{13}$

d) $\cos(x-y)$ if $\cos x = \dfrac{3}{5}$ and $\cos y = \dfrac{4}{5}$

e) $\tan(x+y)$ if $\cot x = \dfrac{6}{5}$ and $\sec y = \dfrac{3}{2}$

f) $\csc(x-y)$ if $\sec x = \dfrac{4}{3}$ and $\tan y = \dfrac{13}{5}$

11. Find and simplify an expression for $\sin\left(\dfrac{\pi}{3}-\alpha\right)$.

12. Verify that $\csc\left(\dfrac{3\pi}{2}+\theta\right) = -\sec\theta$, using a compound-sum formula.

13. Express $\cos\dfrac{13\pi}{4}$ as a trigonometric function of an angle in quadrant I.

14. The angle $2x$ lies in the third quadrant such that $\cos 2x = -\dfrac{6}{15}$.

   a) Sketch the location of angle $2x$.

   b) Determine the quadrant of angle x.

   c) Find an exact value for $\cos x$.

   d) Use a calculator to determine the measure of x, in radians.

   e) Use a calculator to verify your answer in part c).

15. Angle b lies in the second quadrant such that $\cos b = -\dfrac{3}{5}$.

   a) Determine an exact answer for $\sin b$ and $\tan b$.

   b) Determine an exact answer for $\cos 2b$.

   c) Determine an exact answer for $\sin 2b$.

   d) Determine an exact answer for $\tan 2b$.

   e) Use a calculator to determine an approximate measure for b, in radians, to two decimal places.

   f) In which quadrant does angle $2b$ lie? Justify your answer.

16. a) Use the half-angle formula
$$\sin \frac{x}{2} = \pm\sqrt{\frac{1 - \cos x}{2}} \text{ to find } \sin \frac{\pi}{12}.$$

   b) Check your answer to part a) by using another method to find $\sin \dfrac{\pi}{12}$.

C

17. An angle, x, lies in the second quadrant, and $\tan x = -\dfrac{4}{3}$. Determine $\sin 2x$ and $\cos 2x$.

18. Find $\sin 2x$ and $\cos 2x$ for each of the following:

   a) $\sin x = -\dfrac{3}{5}$ for $\pi \le x \le \dfrac{3\pi}{2}$

   b) $\cos x = -\dfrac{1}{\sqrt{2}}$ for $\dfrac{\pi}{2} \le x \le \pi$

   c) $\csc x = 4$ for $0 \le x \le \dfrac{\pi}{2}$

   d) $\tan x = -\dfrac{3}{2}$ for $\dfrac{\pi}{2} \le x \le \pi$

19. Find an expression for $\sin 3x$ by applying an addition formula for the sine function. Express your answer in terms of multiples and powers of $\sin x$.

20. Find an expression for $\cos 3x$ by applying an addition formula for the cosine function. Express your answer in terms of multiples and powers of $\cos x$.

21. The half-angle formula for sine is
$\sin \dfrac{x}{2} = \pm\sqrt{\dfrac{1 - \cos x}{2}}$. Use this formula to find an exact value for each of the following:

   a) $\sin \dfrac{\pi}{12}$

   b) $\sin \dfrac{3\pi}{8}$

22. Use compound-angle formulas to prove
$\cos x \cos y = \dfrac{1}{2}[\cos (x + y) + \cos (x - y)]$.

★**23.** A rocket is launched with velocity v at an angle of θ to the horizontal from the base of a hill that makes an angle of β with the horizontal. The range of the rocket, measured along the hill's slope, is given by $R = \dfrac{2v^2 \cos \theta \sin (\theta - \beta)}{g \cos^2 \beta}$. Determine an expression for the range if $\beta = \dfrac{\pi}{6}$.

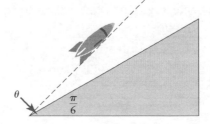

KEY CONCEPTS

- A trigonometric identity is an equation with trigonometric expressions that is true for all angles in the domain of the expressions on both sides.

- One way to show that an equation is not an identity is to determine a counter-example.

- To prove that an equation is an identity, treat each side of the equation independently and transform the expression on one side into the exact form of the expression on the other side.

Examples

Prove that $\csc 2x = \dfrac{\csc x}{2 \cos x}$.

Solution

L.S. $= \csc 2x$

$\quad = \dfrac{1}{\sin 2x}$ Use a reciprocal identity.

$\quad = \dfrac{1}{2 \sin x \cos x}$ Use the double-angle formula.

$\quad = \dfrac{1}{2} \times \dfrac{1}{\sin x} \times \dfrac{1}{\cos x}$ Write as separate rational expressions.

$\quad = \dfrac{1}{2} \times \csc x \times \dfrac{1}{\cos x}$ Use a reciprocal identity.

$\quad = \dfrac{\csc x}{2 \cos x}$ Combine into one term.

R.S. $= \dfrac{\csc x}{2 \cos x}$

L.S. = R.S.

Therefore, $\csc 2x = \dfrac{\csc x}{2 \cos x}$ is an identity.

Another way to verify an identity is to graph both sides of the equation.

For example, show that $\sin 2x = 2 \sin x \cos x$.

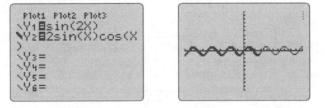

- The basic trigonometric identities are the Pythagorean identity, the quotient identity, the reciprocal identities, and the compound angle formulas. You can use these identities to prove more complex identities.

Pythagorean Identity

$\sin^2 x + \cos^2 x = 1$

Quotient Identity

$\tan x = \dfrac{\sin x}{\cos x}$

Reciprocal Identities

$\csc x = \dfrac{1}{\sin x} \qquad \sec x = \dfrac{1}{\cos x} \qquad \cot x = \dfrac{1}{\tan x}$

Compound-Angle Formulas

$\sin (x + y) = \sin x \cos y + \cos x \sin y$

$\sin (x - y) = \sin x \cos y - \cos x \sin y$

$\cos (x + y) = \cos x \cos y - \sin x \sin y$

$\cos (x - y) = \cos x \cos y + \sin x \sin y$

- Trigonometric identities can be used to simplify solutions to problems that result in trigonometric expressions. This is important in understanding solutions for problems in mathematics, science, engineering, economics, and other fields.

A

1. Simplify each expression.

   a) $\cos x \csc x \tan x$

   b) $\cos x \cot x + \sin x$

   c) $\dfrac{\cot x}{\cos x}$

   d) $(\sin x + \cos x)^2 + (\sin x - \cos x)^2$

2. Determine whether each of the following represents an identity.

   a) $\sin^2 x = (1 - \cos x)(1 + \cos x)$

   b) $\cos x \sin x \tan x + \cos^2 x = 1$

   c) $\sec x + \csc x = 1$

   d) $\sin x - \cos x = \dfrac{1}{\csc x - \sec x}$

   e) $(\csc x - \cot x)^2 = \dfrac{1 - \cos x}{1 + \cos x}$

   f) $\dfrac{\sec x - \cos x}{\tan x} = \sin x$

3. **Use Technology** Use graphing software to check your answers for question 2.

4. For the equations that are not identities in question 2, modify them so that they will become identities.

B

★**5.** Prove that

   a) $\tan^2 x + \sec^2 x = 1$

   b) $\cos x \tan^2 x = \sin x \tan x$

   c) $\tan 2x - \sin 2x = 2 \tan 2x \sin^2 x$

   d) $\sin 2x = \tan x(1 + \cos 2x)$

   e) $\sec 2x = \dfrac{\sec x \csc x}{2}$

   f) $\sin^2 x + \cos^2 x + \tan^2 x = \sec^2 x$

   g) $\dfrac{\cos^2 x - \sin^2 x}{\cos^2 x + \sin x \cos x} = 1 - \tan x$

6. Prove that each of the following is NOT a trigonometric identity by determining a counterexample. *Hint*: Find an angle that makes the equation false.

  a) $\sin x \cos x = \tan x$

  b) $\sin x + \cos x = 1$

  c) $\tan^2 x + \cot^2 x = 1$

  d) $\sec^2 x - 1 = \dfrac{\cos x}{\csc x}$

7. Apply a compound angle formula to verify the identity $\sin\left(\dfrac{\pi}{2} + \theta\right) = \cos \theta$.

8. Apply a compound-angle formula to determine an identity for each of the following:

  a) $\cos\left(\dfrac{3\pi}{2} - x\right)$

  b) $\sin\left(\dfrac{3\pi}{2} - x\right)$

  c) $\sin\left(\dfrac{3\pi}{2} + y\right)$

  d) $\cos\left(\dfrac{3\pi}{2} + y\right)$

9. Explain why it is not possible to determine identities for $\tan\left(\dfrac{3\pi}{2} - x\right)$ and $\tan\left(\dfrac{3\pi}{2} + y\right)$ using a compound angle formula. Propose an alternate method of determining identities for these expressions.

★10. Apply double-angle formulas to verify the identity $\sin\left(x - \dfrac{4\pi}{3}\right) = \dfrac{\sqrt{3}\cos x - \sin x}{2}$.

11. Apply double-angle formulas to verify the identity $\cos\left(2x + \dfrac{\pi}{2}\right) = -\sin 2x$.

12. Prove that $\cos\left(\dfrac{3\pi}{4} - x\right) - \sin\left(\dfrac{3\pi}{4} + x\right)$
$= \dfrac{-1}{\sqrt{2}}(\cos x - \sin x)$.

13. **a)** Apply double-angle formulas to verify the identity $\sin 4x = 2\sin 2x \cos 2x$.

  b) Conjecture an identity for $\sin 6x$ and $\sin 8x$. Do you think these identities will hold for all $\sin kx$, where k is a positive integer? Explain why or why not.

14. Use trigonometric identities to find all solutions for x below, given $0 \leq x \leq 2\pi$.

  a) $\sin 2x + \cos x = 0$

  b) $\sin 2x + \cos 2x = 0$

  c) $(\sin x - \cos x)^2 = 1$

  d) $\sin x \cos x + \dfrac{1}{2} = 0$

  e) $\tan x \sin 2x = 2 \sin^2 x$

  f) $\csc^2 \dfrac{x}{2} = 2 \sec x$

15. **a)** Use a compound angle formula to prove that $\tan(\pi - x) = -\tan x$.

  b) **Use Technology** Use graphing technology to illustrate the identity.

16. Prove that $\sin(\pi - x) - \tan(\pi + x)$
$= \dfrac{\sin x(\cos x - 1)}{\cos x}$.

17. **a)** Prove that $\dfrac{\sin 2x}{1 - \cos 2x} = \cot x$.

  b) **Use Technology** Illustrate the identity by graphing with technology.

18. Prove that $\dfrac{2 \csc 2x \tan x}{\sec x} = \sec x$.

19. **a)** **Use Technology** Use graphing technology to determine whether it is reasonable to conjecture that $\sin^4 x - \cos^4 x = 2 \sin^2 x + 1$ is an identity.

  b) If it appears to be an identity, prove the identity. If not, determine a counter-example.

C

★ **20.** The strength of the magnetic field in a wire can be modelled by $B = \dfrac{F \csc \theta}{I\ell}$, where F is the force on the wire, I is the current, ℓ is the length of the wire, and θ is the angle the wire makes with the magnetic field. Determine an identity for this expression by finding an equivalent trigonometric expression.

21. The intensity of light passing through a lens can be found using the formula $I = I_0 - \dfrac{I_0}{\csc^2 \theta}$, where I_0 is the intensity of light coming in, I is the intensity of the light that emerges or goes out of the lens, and θ is the angle between.

   a) Find and simplify an equivalent expression for $I = I_0 - \dfrac{I_0}{\csc^2 \theta}$.

   b) Suppose light passes through a polarized lens at angle $\dfrac{\pi}{4}$ to the original lens. How much less intense than the original light will the light now be?

22. Prove that $\sin(x + y)\sin(x - y) = \sin^2 x - \sin^2 y$.

23. The equation $\sin x \sin y = \dfrac{1}{2}[\cos(x - y) - \cos(x + y)]$ is called a Product to Sum formula.

   a) Show that this formula is an identity.

   b) Develop other Product to Sum formulas by determining a product that is equal to the following:

   i) $\dfrac{1}{2}[\cos(x + y) + \cos(x - y)]$

   ii) $\dfrac{1}{2}[\sin(x + y) - \sin(x - y)]$

   iii) $\dfrac{1}{2}[\sin(x + y) + \sin(x - y)]$

24. Develop Sum to Product formulas by determining a sum of two trigonometric functions that is equal to each of the following.
(*Hint*: Use the identities developed in question 28 as well as half-angle identities.)

   a) $\sin \dfrac{x + y}{2} \sin \dfrac{x - y}{2}$

   b) $\sin \dfrac{x + y}{2} \cos \dfrac{x - y}{2}$

   c) $\cos \dfrac{x + y}{2} \sin \dfrac{x - y}{2}$

   d) $\cos \dfrac{x + y}{2} \cos \dfrac{x - y}{2}$

25. Prove each of the following:

   a) $2 \sin 5x \cos 4x - \sin x = \sin 9x$

   b) $\dfrac{\sin x + \sin y}{\cos x - \cos y} = -\cot \dfrac{x - y}{2}$

   c) $\dfrac{\sin x - \sin 3x}{\cos x + \cos 3x} = -\tan x$

1. A lighthouse keeper sits at her post 30 metres above the water and sees a sailboat sailing directly towards her. As she watches, the angle of depression to the boat changes from 15° to 60°. How far has the boat travelled during that time?

2. The area of a circular sector that has been cut in a hay field is approximately 26 metres squared. What are the possible measures for the radius and central angle of the sector?

3. A child spins a hoop about her foot at an angular velocity of 4.1 radians per second. Determine the linear velocity of a point on the outside of the hoop if the diameter of the hoop is 85 centimetres from the centre of the rotating object.

4. The formula $C = 2\pi r \cos L$, where r is the radius of the Earth, and L is the latitude, determines the distance around Earth along a given latitude. How does the distance along a given latitude change as you go from the equator (0°) to each of the poles (90°)?

5. A highway curve is banked so that vehicles can safely negotiate the turn. To determine an appropriate banking angle θ of a car making a turn of radius r metres at a velocity of v metres per second, engineers use the equation $\tan \theta = \frac{v^2}{gr}$. The variable g is the acceleration due to gravity, which is a constant at 9.8m/s². A new exit ramp is designed with a radius of 210 metres. If the speed limit on the curve is 40 km/h, at what angle should the curve be banked? What adjustments should be made to the speed if the angle is increased?

6. The hypotenuse of a right-triangle is 10 centimetres in length. Find the measures of the angles in the triangle that will maximize the perimeter.

7. In calculus, you will be introduced to the difference quotient, $\frac{f(x + h) - f(x)}{h}$.

   a) Let $f(x) = \cos x$. Write and expand an expression for the difference quotient.

   b) Let $h = 0.1$. Evaluate the function.

   c) Graph the function you found in part b). What graph has a similar graph?

8. A position function of a particle that moves along the x-axis is given by $x = 2\pi t + \cos 2\pi t$, $0 \le t \le 5$.

   a) Graph the function using graphing technology.

   b) When is the particle moving left and right?

   c) When is the particle at rest?

   d) Determine the average rate of change over the first five seconds.

   e) Estimate the velocity of the particle for each second over the given interval.

9. What angle does the tangent line to the curve $y = \frac{1}{\sqrt{3}} \sin 3x$ at the origin make with the x-axis?

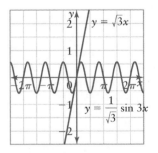

10. A voltage V being supplied to an electrical circuit at time t is $V = 100 \sin 50t + 50 \sin 100t$. Find the maximum and minimum values of V over one period.

By the end of this chapter, I will be able to:

- Convert degree measure to radian measure, in exact and approximate formats
- Convert radian measure to degree measure, in exact and approximate formats
- Determine arc lengths
- Determine angular velocity using both degree measure and radian measure
- Determine exact values for trigonometric ratios of special angles
- Use technology to determine values for trigonometric ratios
- Use equivalent trigonometric expressions to simplify calculations
- Apply the compound-angle formulas for sine and cosine
- Solve problems involving compound-angle formulas
- Prove trigonometric identities

Chapter 5 Trigonometric Functions

5.1 Graphs of Sine, Cosine, and Tangent Functions

Characteristics of the Sine, Cosine, and Tangent Functions

	Sine	Cosine	Tangent
Domain	Set of all real numbers	Set of all real numbers	Set of all real numbers, except for integral multiples of $\frac{\pi}{2}$
Range	All real numbers from -1 to 1, inclusive	All real numbers from -1 to 1, inclusive	All real numbers
Period	2π	2π	π
Symmetry	Odd function, that is $\sin(-x) = -\sin(x)$	Even function, that is $\cos(-x) = -\cos(x)$	Odd function, that is $\tan(-x) = -\tan(x)$
X-intercept	$..., -2\pi, -\pi, 0, \pi, 2\pi, 3\pi, ...$	$x = ..., \dfrac{-3\pi}{2}, \dfrac{-\pi}{2}, \dfrac{\pi}{2}, \dfrac{3\pi}{2}, \dfrac{5\pi}{2}, ...$	$x = ..., -2\pi, -\pi, 0, \pi, 2\pi, ...$
Y-intercept	0	1	0
Maximum Value	1, which occurs at $x = ..., \dfrac{-3\pi}{2}, \dfrac{\pi}{2}, \dfrac{5\pi}{2}, \dfrac{9\pi}{2}, ...$	1, which occurs at $x = ..., -2\pi, 0, 2\pi, 4\pi, 6\pi, ...$	
Minimum Value	-1, which occurs at $x = ..., \dfrac{-\pi}{2}, \dfrac{3\pi}{2}, \dfrac{7\pi}{2}, \dfrac{11\pi}{2}, ...$	-1, which occurs at $x = ..., -\pi, \pi, 3\pi, 5\pi, ...$	
Asymptotes			Vertical asymptotes occur at $x = ..., \dfrac{-3\pi}{2}, \dfrac{-\pi}{2}, \dfrac{\pi}{2}, \dfrac{5\pi}{2}, \dfrac{9\pi}{2}, ...$
Sketch of Graph			

A

1. Determine the maximum value, the minimum value, and the values of x where they occur for each function on the interval $x \in [-2\pi, 2\pi]$.

   a) $y = \sin x - 5$

   b) $y = \cos x + 7$

   c) $y = \sin x + 1$

   d) $y = \cos x - 3$

2. Sketch a graph of each function in question 1 on the interval $x \in [-2\pi, 2\pi]$.

3. Write an equation for each function.

   a) Sine function with an amplitude of $\frac{1}{2}$

   b) Cosine function with an amplitude of 3

   c) Sine function with an amplitude of 7, reflected in the x-axis

   d) Cosine function with an amplitude of $\frac{1}{4}$, reflected in the x-axis

4. Write an equation for each function.

   a) Sine function with a phase shift of $\frac{2\pi}{3}$

   b) Cosine function with a phase shift of $\frac{4\pi}{5}$

   c) Sine function with a phase shift of $\frac{-5\pi}{7}$

   d) Cosine function with a phase shift of $\frac{-11\pi}{7}$

5. Write an equation for each function.

   a) Sine function with a period of 4π

   b) Cosine function with a period of $\frac{\pi}{2}$

   c) Sine function with a period of $\frac{3\pi}{2}$

   d) Cosine function with a period of $\frac{5\pi}{4}$

B

6. A sine function has an amplitude of 5 and a period of 4π.

   a) Write an equation of the function in the form $y = a \sin kx$.

   b) Graph the function over two cycles.

7. A cosine function has a maximum value of 1 and a minimum value of -5.

   a) Determine the amplitude of the function.

   b) Determine the vertical translation.

   c) Write an equation of the function in the form $y = a \cos x + c$.

   d) Graph the function over two cycles.

8. One cycle of a sine function begins at $x = \frac{-2\pi}{3}$ and ends at $x = \frac{\pi}{3}$.

   a) Determine the period of the function.

   b) Determine the phase shift of the function.

   c) Write the equation of the function in the form $y = \sin k(x - d)$.

   d) Graph the function over two cycles.

★9. When seated, an average adult breathes in and out every 4 s. The average minimum amount of air in the lungs is 0.08 L, and the average maximum amount of air in the lungs is 0.82 L. Suppose the lungs have a minimum amount of air at $t = 0$, where t is the time, in seconds.

   a) Write a function that models the amount of air in the lungs.

   b) Graph the function.

   c) Determine the amount of air in the lungs at 5.5 s.

10. A boat is bobbing up and down on the water. The distance between the boat's highest and lowest points is 4 m. The boat moves from its highest point to its lowest point and back to its highest point every 30 s. Write a cosine function that models the movement of the boat in relation to the equilibrium point.

11. The mean average monthly temperature in Toronto, Ontario, is 8.6 °C. The temperature fluctuates 13.1 degrees above and below the mean temperature. If $t = 1$ represents January, the phase shift of the sine function is 4.

a) Write a model for the average monthly temperature in Toronto.

b) According to your model, what is the average temperature in March?

c) According to your model, what is the average temperature in August?

12. A weight hanging from a spring is set in motion by an upward push. It takes 10 s for the weight to complete one cycle of moving from its equilibrium position to 12 cm above, then dropping to 12 cm below its equilibrium position, and finally returning to that original position.

a) Find a sinusoidal function to represent the moving weight.

b) Sketch the graph of the function you wrote in part a).

c) Use the function determined in part a) to predict the height of the weight after 7 s.

d) In the first 10 s, when will the height of the weight be 9 cm below the equilibrium point?

13. A Ferris wheel completes one revolution every 90 s. The cars reach a maximum of 55 m above the ground and a minimum of 5 m above the ground. The height, h, in metres, above the ground can be modelled using a sine function of the form $y = a \sin kt + c$, where t represents time, in seconds.

a) Determine the amplitude of the function.

b) Determine the vertical translation of the function.

c) What is the desired period of the function?

d) Determine the value of k that results in the period desired in part c).

C

14. Use Technology

a) Determine the form of the graph of $y = \tan x - 3$. Verify your answer using graphing technology.

b) Determine the form of the graph of $y = 2 \tan x$. Verify your answer using graphing technology.

c) Determine the form of the graph of $y = \tan\left(x - \dfrac{\pi}{6}\right)$. Verify your answer using graphing technology.

d) Determine the form of the graph of $y = \tan 4x$. Verify your answer using graphing technology.

★**15.** Consider the graph of $y = \dfrac{1}{4}x$.

a) How many times will this graph intersect the graph of $y = \cos x$ if both are graphed on the same set of axes with no limits on the domain? Justify your answer.

b) Illustrate your answer graphically.

KEY CONCEPTS

Characteristics of the Reciprocal Trigonometric Functions

	Cosecant	**Secant**	**Cotangent**
Domain	Set of all real numbers except πn, where n is an integer	Set of all real numbers except $\frac{\pi}{2}n$, where n is an odd integer	Set of all real numbers, except for multiples of πn, where n is an integer
Range	All real numbers greater than or equal to 1, or less than or equal to -1	All real numbers greater than or equal to 1, or less than or equal to -1	All real numbers
Period	2π	2π	π
X-intercept	None	None	The x-intercepts are located at $\frac{\pi}{2}n$, where n is an odd integer
Y-intercept	None	1	None
Positive Turning Point	$y = 1$ when $x = \frac{\pi}{2} + 2\pi n$, where n is an integer	$y = 1$ when $x = \pi n$, where n is an even integer	
Negative Turning Point	$y = -1$ when $x = \frac{3\pi}{2} + 2\pi n$, where n is an integer	$y = -1$ when $x = \pi n$, where n is an odd integer	
Asymptotes	Vertical asymptotes occur at $x = \pi n$, where n is an integer	Vertical asymptotes occur at $x = \frac{\pi}{2}n$, where n is an odd integer	Vertical asymptotes occur at $x = \pi n$, where n is an integer
Sketch of Graph			

A

1. **Use Technology** Use graphing technology to determine all values of x in the interval $[0, 2\pi]$ such that $\csc x = -7$. Round your answers to two decimal places.

2. **Use Technology** Use graphing technology to determine all values of x in the interval $[0, 2\pi]$ such that $\sec x = 5$. Round your answers to two decimal places.

3. **Use Technology** Use graphing technology to determine all values of x in the interval $[0, 2\pi]$ such that $\cot x = -12$. Round your answers to two decimal places.

B

4. **a)** Describe the graph of $y = \csc x$ in terms of a transformation of the graph of $y = \sec x$.

   b) Is there more than one transformation that will accomplish this? Explain your answer.

5. **Use Technology**

   a) Use graphing technology to show that there is at least one value of x such that $\sec x = \cos^{-1} x$.

   > A reminder:
   > $y = \cos^{-1} x$
   > is the inverse function of
   > $y = \cos x$.

   b) Determine a value of x that makes the equation in part a) true.

   c) Verify your value from part b).

6. One of the world's longest suspension bridges is across the Humber Estuary in England. The towers of this bridge reach about 135 m above the level of the deck. The angles of elevation of the towers seen from the centre of the bridge and from either end are 10.80° and 18.65°, respectively. How long is the Humber Bridge?

★**7.** A lighthouse with a rotating beam is located 1200 m south of a coastal cliff that runs west to east.

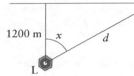

   a) Determine a relation for the distance from the lighthouse to the point where the light strikes the cliff in terms of the angle of rotation x.

   b) Determine an exact expression for this distance when $x = \dfrac{7\pi}{12}$.

   c) Sketch a graph of the relation in part a) on the interval $x \in [0, \pi]$.

8. One factor that affects daily temperature is the distance sunlight must pass through the atmosphere before it reaches Earth. To express this distance, the term air mass has been coined. Air mass 1 is the distance sunlight must pass through the atmosphere to reach sea level when the Sun is directly overhead. Air mass 2 is two times air mass 1; air mass 3 is three times air mass 1; and so on.

   a) Write an equation that expresses the air mass, a, as a function of the angle of inclination of the Sun, θ.

   b) Graph the function in part a).

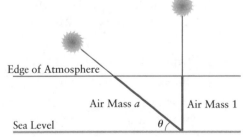

★9. A police cruiser is parked such that the beacon on its roof is 5 m from a brick wall. As the beacon rotates, a spotlight moves along the wall. Assuming that the beacon makes one complete rotation in 3 s, find an equation that expresses the distance, d, in metres, as a function of time.

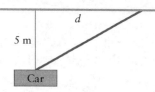

10. a) Explain the difference between $\cot \dfrac{1}{\sqrt{3}}$ and $\tan^{-1}\left(\dfrac{1}{\sqrt{3}}\right)$.

b) Determine a value for each expression in part a).

11. Use Technology Use graphing technology to determine whether it is reasonable to conjecture that $\sec^2 x = \csc^2 x$. If so, justify your conclusion. If not, use the graphs to determine a similar equation that is an identity.

12. A boat is in the water 150 m from a straight shoreline. There is a rotating beam on the boat.

a) Determine a reciprocal trigonometric relation for the distance, d, from the boat to where the light hits the shoreline in terms of the angle of rotation, x.

b) Determine an exact expression for the distance in part a) when $x = \dfrac{\pi}{6}$.

c) Determine an approximate value, to the nearest tenth of a metre, for the distance from part b).

d) Sketch a graph of the relation in part a) in the interval $x \in \left[0, \dfrac{\pi}{2}\right]$.

13. a) Sketch the function $y = \sec x$.

b) Determine the shape of each function, and then check by graphing.

  i) $y = 2 \sec x$

  ii) $y = \sec 3x$

  iii) $y = \sec x - 4$

  iv) $y = \sec(x + 2)$

14. a) Sketch the function $y = \cot x$.

b) Determine the shape of each function, and then check by graphing.

  i) $y = 4 \cot x$

  ii) $y = \cot 3x$

  iii) $y = \cot x + 5$

  iv) $y = \cot(x - 2)$

C

15. Suppose that you are carrying a fully-extended extension ladder horizontally and have to turn from a corridor 1 m wide to a corridor 1.5 m wide. To navigate the corner, you must shorten the ladder by reducing the extension as you make the turn. See illustration.

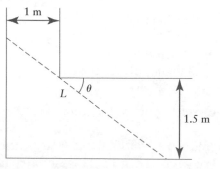

a) Show that the length, L, in metres, of the ladder as a function of the angle θ is $L = \sec \theta + 1.5 \csc \theta$.

b) Graph L, $0 < \theta < \dfrac{\pi}{2}$.

c) At what value of θ is L the least?

d) If the least value of L represents the maximum length that the ladder can be to get around the corner, how long is the ladder?

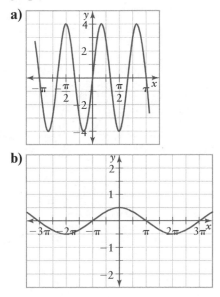

KEY CONCEPTS

The transformation of a sine or cosine function $f(x)$ has the general form
$g(x) = af[k(x - d)] + c$.

$\|a\| > 1$	is a vertical stretch
$0 > \|a\| > 1$	is a vertical compression
$a < 0$	is a reflection in the x-axis
$\|k\| > 1$	is a horizontal compression
$0 < \|k\| < 1$	is a horizontal expansion
$k < 0$	is a reflection in the y-axis
$d > 0$	is a phase shift to the right $\|d\|$ units
$d < 0$	is a phase shift to the left $\|d\|$ units
$c > 0$	is a vertical translation up $\|c\|$ units
$c < 0$	is a vertical translation down $\|c\|$ units

The period of the transformed function is given by $\dfrac{2\pi}{k}$.

A

1. Determine the amplitude and period of each sinusoidal function. Then, transform the graph of $y = \sin x$ to sketch a graph of each function.

a) $y = 4 \sin 9x$

b) $y = -2 \cos \frac{1}{2}x$

c) $y = 7 \sin \frac{1}{4}x$

d) $y = \frac{1}{2} \cos 6x$

e) $y = -3 \sin \frac{3}{4}x$

f) $y = \frac{3}{4} \cos \frac{4}{5}x$

2. Determine the equation in the form $y = a \sin kx$ or $y = a \cos kx$ for each graph.

a)

b)

3. Consider the function
$y = -\frac{1}{2}\sin\left[3\left(x + \frac{\pi}{6}\right)\right] - 5$.

   a) What is the amplitude?

   b) What is the period?

   c) Describe the phase shift.

   d) Describe the vertical translation.

   e) Sketch a graph of the function for two cycles.

4. Consider the function
$y = 7\cos\left[\frac{1}{2}\left(x - \frac{\pi}{4}\right)\right] + 3$.

   a) What is the amplitude?

   b) What is the period?

   c) Describe the phase shift.

   d) Describe the vertical translation.

   e) Sketch a graph of the function for two cycles.

B

5. Model the graph shown using a sine function.

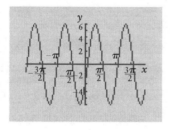

   a) From the graph, determine the amplitude, the period, the phase shift, and the vertical translation.

   b) Write an equation for the function.

   c) Graph the function from part b).

   d) Compare the graph in part c) to the given graph, and verify that the graphs match.

6. Model the graph shown using a cosine function.

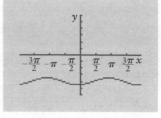

   a) From the graph, determine the amplitude, the period, the phase shift, and the vertical translation.

   b) Write an equation for the function.

   c) Graph the function from part b).

   d) Compare the graph in part c) to the given graph, and verify that the graphs match.

7. Determine an equation for each sine function. Check by graphing.

   a)

   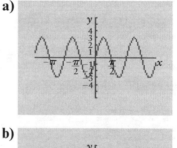

   b)

   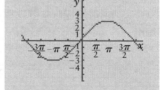

8. A cosine function has a maximum value of 4, a minimum value of −6, a period of $\frac{\pi}{2}$, and a phase shift of $\frac{\pi}{6}$ rad to the right.

   a) Write an equation for the function.

   b) Graph the function and verify that it has the properties given.

9. Determine an equation for each cosine function. Check by graphing.

a)

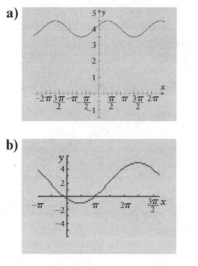

b)

10. Write the equation of a sine function that has the given characteristics.

a) Amplitude 2

Period π

Phase shift $\frac{\pi}{2}$ to the left

b) Amplitude 3

Period $\frac{\pi}{2}$

Phase shift $\frac{\pi}{3}$ to the right

11. Write the equation of a cosine function that has the given characteristics.

a) Amplitude $\frac{1}{2}$

Period 4π

Phase shift $\frac{\pi}{6}$ rad to the left

b) Amplitude 4

Period 4π

Phase shift π rad to the right

Vertical translation three units down

12. A sine function has a maximum value of 11, a minimum value of -1, a phase shift of $\frac{2\pi}{3}$ rad to the left, and a period of π.

a) Write an equation for the function.

b) Graph the function and verify that it has the properties given.

13. A cosine function has a maximum value of -3, a minimum value of -5, a phase shift of $\frac{\pi}{4}$ rad to the right, and a period of 4π.

a) Write an equation for the function.

b) Graph the function and verify that it has the properties given.

14. The water depth in a harbour is 21 m at high tide and 11 m at low tide. One cycle is completed approximately every 12 h.

a) Find an equation for the water depth as a function of the time, t hours, after low tide.

b) Draw a graph of the function for 48 h after low tide, which occurred at 2:00 p.m.

★15. A Ferris wheel with a radius of 14 m makes one complete revolution every 30 s. The bottom of the wheel is 2.5 m above the ground.

a) Draw a graph to show how a person's height above the ground varies with time during three revolutions, starting when the person gets on the Ferris wheel at its lowest point.

b) Find an equation for the graph.

c) Predict how the graph and the equation will change if the Ferris wheel turns more quickly.

16. An object suspended from a spring is oscillating up and down. The distance from the high point to the low point is 45 cm, and the object takes 4 s to complete 5 cycles. For the first few cycles, the motion is modelled by a sine function, where the distance from the mean position, $d(t)$, is measured in centimetres, with respect to time, in seconds.

a) Sketch a graph of this function for two cycles.

b) Write an equation that describes the distance of the object from its mean position as a function of time.

17. Model the graph shown using a sine function.

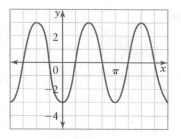

a) From the graph, determine the amplitude, the period, the phase shift, and the vertical translation.

b) Write an equation for the function.

c) Graph the function you found in part b) and compare it to the given graph. Verify that the two graphs match.

d) Determine a model for the above graph using a cosine function.

e) Verify that the graph of your equation in part d) matches the given graph.

C

18. In the theory of biorhythms, a sine function of the form $P = 50 \sin \omega t + 50$ is used to measure the percent, P, of a person's potential at a time, t, where t is measured in days and $t = 0$ is the person's birthday. Three characteristics are commonly measured:

    Physical potential: period of 23 days
    Emotional potential: period of 28 days
    Intellectual potential: period of 33 days

a) Find ω for each characteristic.

b) Graph all three functions.

c) Is there a time, t, when all three characteristics have 100% potential? When is it?

d) Suppose that you are 20 years old today ($t = 7305$ days). Describe your physical, emotional, and intellectual potential for the next 30 days.

19. Suppose that the length of time between consecutive high tides is approximately 12.5 h. On June 28, high tide occurred at 3:38 a.m. (3.633 3 h) and low tide occurred at 10:08 a.m. (10.133 3 h). Water heights are measured as the amounts above or below the mean low water mark. The height of the water at high tide was 8.2 m and the height of the water at low tide was −0.6 m.

a) Approximately when will the next high tide occur?

b) Find the sinusoidal function of the form $y = a \sin k(x - d) + c$ that fits the data.

c) Draw a graph of the function found in part b).

d) Use the function found in part b) to predict the height of the water at the next high tide.

★**20.** Sales of Ocean King boogie boards fluctuate sinusoidally from a low of 50 units per week each February 1($t = 1$) to a high of 350 units per week each August 1($t = 7$). Model the weekly sales, $s(t)$, of Ocean King boogie boards, where t is time in months.

a) Find an equation for the boogie board sales as a function of the time, t months.

b) Draw a graph of the function for a two-year period.

21. A Ferris wheel at an amusement park completes one revolution every 40 s. The wheel has a diameter of 16 m and its centre is 12 m above the ground. A rider boards on the lowest point on the wheel.

a) Model the height, h, in metres, above the ground of a rider using a sine function in the form $h = a \sin[k(t - d)] + c$, where t represents the time, in seconds.

b) Sketch a graph of the model over two cycles.

> ## KEY CONCEPTS
>
> Trigonometric equations can be solved
>
> - algebraically by hand or
> - graphically with technology
>
> To solve a trigonometric equation that is not an identity, find all values of the variable that make the equation true.
>
> There are often multiple solutions. Ensure that you find all solutions that lie in the domain of interest.
>
> Factoring can often solve quadratic trigonometric equations.

A

1. Determine approximate solutions for each equation in the interval $x \in [0, 2\pi]$ to the nearest hundredth radian.

    a) $\sin x - \frac{1}{2} = 0$

    b) $\cos x + 0.9 = 0$

    c) $\tan x - 1 = 0$

    d) $\sec x + 5 = 0$

    e) $3 \cot x + \sqrt{3} = 0$

    f) $\csc x + 3 = 0$

2. Determine exact solutions for each equation in the interval $x \in [0, 2\pi]$.

    a) $\sin x + \frac{\sqrt{2}}{2} = 0$

    b) $\cos x + \frac{\sqrt{3}}{2} = 0$

    c) $\tan x - \sqrt{3} = 0$

    d) $\cot x + 5 = 0$

3. Determine approximate solutions for each equation in the interval $x \in [0, 2\pi]$ to the nearest hundredth of a radian.

    a) $\sin^2 x - 0.49 = 0$

    b) $\cos^2 x - \frac{64}{144} = 0$

    c) $\tan^2 x - 121 = 0$

    d) $\sec^2 x - 4.9 = 0$

    e) $\cot^2 x - 3.6 = 0$

4. Determine exact solutions for each equation in the interval $x \in [0, 2\pi]$.

    a) $\sin^2 x - \frac{3}{4} = 0$

    b) $\cos^2 x - \frac{1}{4} = 0$

    c) $2 \tan^2 x - 12 = 0$

    d) $2 \csc^2 x - 8 = 0$

5. **Use Technology** Solve the following equations on the interval $x \in [0, 2\pi]$ using graphing technology.

    a) $x + 5 \cos x = 0$

    b) $x - 4 \sin x = 0$

    c) $\sin x + \cos x = x$

    d) $x^2 - 2 \cos x = 0$

6. Solve the following equations on the interval $x \in [0, 2\pi]$.

    a) $\sin x - \sin x \tan x = 0$

    b) $2 \cos^2 x + \cos x = 0$

    c) $2 \sin^2 x - \sin x - 1 = 0$

    d) $6 \cos^2 x + \cos x - 1 = 0$

    e) $8 \cos^2 x + 14 \cos x = -3$

    f) $\csc x - 3 \csc x \sec x = 0$

    g) $\sec^2 x + 2 \sec x - 8 = 0$

    h) $3 \sec^2 x - 5 \sec x - 2 = 0$

    i) $\csc^2 x + 5 \csc x - 6 = 0$

B

★**7.** A rain gutter is to be constructed of aluminum sheets 12 cm wide. Lengths 4 cm from each edge are marked off, then each length is bent up at an angle, θ. See the illustration. The area, A, of the opening as a function of θ is given by $A = 16 \sin \theta (\cos \theta + 1)$, $0° < \theta < 90°$.

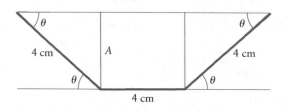

a) In Calculus, you would be asked to find the angle, θ, that maximizes A by solving the equation $2 \cos^2 \theta + \cos \theta - 1 = 0$, $0° < \theta < 90°$. Solve this equation for θ.

b) What is the maximum area, A, of the opening?

c) Graph A, $0° < \theta < 90°$, and find the angle, θ, that maximizes the area, A. Also, find the maximum area. Compare the results with the answers found earlier.

8. An object is propelled upward at an angle, θ, $45° < \theta < 90°$, to the horizontal with an initial velocity of v_0 metres per second from the base of a plane that makes an angle of $45°$ with the horizontal. See the illustration. If air resistance is ignored, the distance, R, that the object travels up the inclined plane is given by

$$R = \frac{v_0^2 \sqrt{2}}{32} (2 \sin \theta \cos \theta - 2 \cos^2 \theta).$$

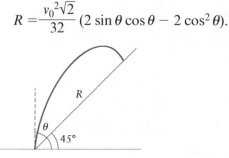

a) In Calculus, you would be asked to find the angle, θ, that maximizes R by solving the equation $2 \sin \theta \cos \theta + 1 - 2 \sin^2 \theta = 0$. Solve this equation for θ.

b) What is the maximum distance, R, if $v_0 = 32$ m/s?

c) Graph R, $45° < \theta < 90°$, and find the angle, θ, that maximizes the distance, R. Also, find the maximum distance. Use $v_0 = 32$ m/s. Compare the results with the answers found earlier.

9. The horizontal distance that a projectile will travel in the air is given by the equation $r = \frac{v^2}{g} \sin 2\theta$, where r is the range, in metres; v is the launch speed, in metres per second; g is the acceleration due to gravity, 9.8 m/s² ; and θ is the angle above the horizontal that the projectile is aimed at.

a) If you can throw a baseball with an initial speed of 34.8 m/s, at what angle of elevation, θ, should you direct the throw so that the ball travels a distance of 107 m before striking the ground?

b) Determine the maximum distance that you can throw the ball.

C

10. Determine the solutions for $2 \sec^2 x - \tan^4 x = -1$ in the interval $x \in [-2\pi, 2\pi]$.

★**11.** Determine the solutions for $\dfrac{1 + \sec x}{\sec x} = \dfrac{\sin^2 x}{1 - \cos x}$ in the interval $x \in [-2\pi, 2\pi]$.

12. In the study of heat transfer, the equation $x + \tan x = 0$ occurs.

a) Graph $y = -x$ and $y = \tan x$ for $x \geq 0$.

b) Find the first two positive solutions of $x + \tan x = 0$, correct to two decimal places.

KEY CONCEPTS

- The instantaneous rates of change of a sinusoidal function follow a sinusoidal pattern.

- Many real-world processes can be modelled with a sinusoidal function, even if they do not involve angles.

- Modelling real-world processes usually requires transformations of the basic sinusoidal functions.

A

★ **1.** The position of a particle as it moves horizontally is described by the given equation $s(t) = 12 \sin \frac{\pi t}{90} + 15$. If s is the displacement, in metres, and t is the time, in seconds, do the following:

  a) Determine the average Rate of Change of $s(t)$ in the following time intervals, rounded to three decimal places.

   i) 5 s to 10 s

   ii) 9 s to 10 s

   iii) 9.9 s to 10 s

   iv) 9.99 s to 10 s

  b) Estimate a value for the instantaneous rate of change of $s(t)$ at $t = 10$ s.

  c) What physical quantity does this instantaneous rate of change represent?

  d) When you expect the instantaneous rate of change of $s(t)$ to be the same as at $t = 14$ s?

B

2. The water depth in a harbour is 8 m at low tide and 20 m at high tide. One cycle is completed approximately every 12 h.

  a) Find an equation for the water depth, $d(t)$, in metres, as a function of the time, t, after high tide, which occurs at 3:00 a.m.

  b) Draw a graph of the function for 48 h after high tide.

c) Determine the average rate of change of $d(t)$ in the following time intervals, rounded to three decimal places.

   i) 8:00 a.m. to 9:00 a.m.

   ii) 8:30 a.m. to 9:00 a.m.

   iii) 8:40 a.m. to 9:00 a.m.

   iv) 8:50 a.m. to 9:00 a.m.

   v) 8:55 a.m. to 9:00 a.m.

   vi) 8:59 a.m. to 9:00 a.m.

d) Estimate a value for the instantaneous rate of change of $d(t)$ at $t = 9:00$ a.m.

e) What physical quantity does this instantaneous rate of change represent?

3. An electromotive force, E, in volts in a certain ac circuit can be modelled by $E = a \sin kt$. A graph of electromotive force versus time is shown.

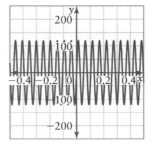

a) Use the graph to determine values for a and k.

b) Determine an equation for the electromotive force.

4. The average monthly temperatures in Brockton, Ontario, are represented in the following table. Since the data represent average monthly temperatures collected over many years, the data will not vary much from year to year and so will essentially repeat each year. In other words, the data are periodic.

Month	Average Monthly Temperature (°C)
January	−1.3
February	0.8
March	3.9
April	8.9
May	14.0
June	19.4
July	23.1
August	21.9
September	16.8
October	10.8
November	3.9
December	−0.6

a) Write a sine function to model the data.

b) Make a scatter plot of the data. Then, graph your model on the same set of axes. How well does it fit the data?

c) Check your model using a sinusoidal regression. How does the regression equation compare with the model?

d) Select a point on the graph where the instantaneous rate of change of the average monthly temperature appears to be a maximum.

e) Estimate the instantaneous rate of change of the average monthly temperature at this point.

f) What does this instantaneous rate of change of the average monthly temperature represent?

5. The following table shows, by year, the number, in millions, of unemployed people in a country's labour force.

Year	Unemployed (millions)
1996	9.539
1997	9.312
1998	9.237
1999	8.237
2000	7.701
2001	7.528
2002	8.047
2003	9.628
2004	10.613
2005	9.940
2006	8.996
2007	9.404

a) Make a scatter plot of the data.

b) Use the table and the graph to write a sinusoidal function to model the data.

c) Graph your model on the same set of axes as the scatter plot. Comment on the fit.

d) Check your model using a sinusoidal regression. How does the regression equation compare with the model?

e) Refer to the graph and select a point on the graph where the instantaneous rate of change of the population appears to be a minimum.

f) Estimate the instantaneous rate of change of the population at this point.

g) What does the instantaneous rate of change of the population represent?

6. A weight is suspended on a spring and set in motion such that it bobs up and down vertically. The graph shows the height, h, in centimetres, of the weight above a desk after time, t, in seconds. Use the graph to determine a model of the height versus time using a sine function.

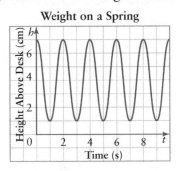

Weight on a Spring

a) Select a point on the graph where the instantaneous rate of change of the height appears to be a maximum.

b) Estimate the instantaneous rate of change of the height at this point.

c) What does this instantaneous rate of change of the height represent?

7. The height, h, in metres, of a seat above the ground as a Ferris wheel turns can be modelled using the function $h = 18 \sin\left(\frac{\pi t}{60}\right) + 20$, where t is the time, in seconds.

a) Determine the average rate of change of h in the following time intervals, rounded to three decimal places.

i) 6 s to 12 s

ii) 11 s to 12 s

iii) 11.9 s to 12 s

iv) 11.99 s to 12 s

b) Estimate a value for the instantaneous rate of change of h at $t = 12$ s.

c) Would you expect the instantaneous rate of change to be the same at $t = 3$ s? Justify your answer.

C

8. Sketch a graph of the inverse trigonometric relation $y = \cos^{-1} x$ such that the range covers the interval $[0, 2\pi]$.

a) Is this relation a function in this range? If so, explain how you know. If not, show how it can be made into a function by restricting the range.

b) Determine a value of x where the instantaneous rate of change appears to be a maximum.

c) Estimate the instantaneous rate of change for the value of x in part b).

9. Sketch the graph of the secant function on the interval $x \in [0, 2\pi]$.

a) For what values of x does the instantaneous rate of change appear to be equal to 0? reach a maximum value? reach a minimum value?

b) Plot the instantaneous rates of change on the same set of axes as the secant function.

c) Describe the pattern formed by the instantaneous rate of change of the secant function.

10. Consider the function $f(x) = \sin \theta$.

a) Find the instantaneous rate of change for the points $\theta = -\pi, \frac{-\pi}{2}, 0, \frac{\pi}{2}, \pi$

b) On a new graph, plot your answers to (θ, instantaneous rate of change). What function have you graphed?

c) Based on your result, what statement can be made about the instantaneous rate of change of $f(x) = \sin \theta$?

C1. A security camera is scanning a long, straight fence along one side of a military base. The camera is located 10 m from the centre of the fence. If d represents the distance along the fence from the centre and t is time, in seconds, then $d = 10 \tan \frac{\pi}{40} t$ models the point being scanned.

a) Graph the equation for $-20 \le t \le 20$.

b) Find the location that the camera is scanning at 3 s.

c) Find the location that the camera is scanning at 15 s.

C2. In Victoria, British Columbia, the first high tide was 3.99 m at 12:03 a.m. The first low tide of 0.55 m occurred at 6:24 a.m. The second high tide occurred at 12:19 p.m.

a) Find the amplitude of a sinusoidal function that models the tides.

b) Find the vertical shift of the sinusoidal function that models the tides.

c) What is the period of the sinusoidal function that models the tides?

d) Write a sinusoidal function to model the tides, using t to represent the number of hours, in decimals, since midnight.

e) According to your model, determine the height of the water at noon.

C3. Consider the graph of $y = \frac{x}{6}$.

a) How many times will this graph intersect the graph of $y = \cos x$ if both are graphed on the same set of axes with no limits on the domain? Justify your answer.

b) Illustrate your answers graphically.

C4. Consider the graphs $y = \sin^{-1} x$ and $y = \cos^{-1} x$. Name the y coordinate of the points of intersection of the two graphs.

★ **C5.** One energy-saving idea is to design houses with recessed windows on the side facing the sun. Sunlight will enter the window in winter when the sun's angle is low but it will be blocked in the summer when the angle is much higher. The highest angle of elevation of the Sun occurs at noon in mid-June when the angle of elevation, in degrees, is $23.5 + l$, where l is the latitude of the location.

a) Assume that the window shown is designed to block the sun's rays when the sun is at its highest elevation in the summer. Express the depth, d, in metres, of the recess as a function of latitude, l.

b) Draw the graph of d versus l.

c) Determine the value of d for your latitude.

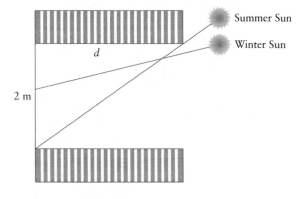

C6. **Use Technology** The position of a particle as it moves horizontally is described by the equation $s = 2 \sin t - \cos t$, $t \in [0, 2\pi]$, where s is the displacement, in metres, and t is the time, in seconds.

a) Using technology, graph the position of the particle relative to time.

b) At what time or times during the cycle is the instantaneous rate of change of the position equal to 0? At what times is it a minimum? Justify your answers.

C7. A wave travelling on a guitar string can be modelled by the equation $D = 0.5 \sin(6.5x)\sin(2500t)$, where D is the displacement, in millimetres, at the position x metres from the left end of the string at time t seconds. Find the first positive time when the point 0.5 m from the left end has a displacement of 0.01 mm.

C8. The equation
$$T(t) = 12.5 + 15.8 \sin\left(\frac{\pi}{6}t - \frac{2\pi}{3}\right) \text{ models}$$
the average monthly temperature of Toronto, Ontario. In this equation, t denotes the number of months with January represented by 1. During which two months is the average temperature 12.5°C?

C9. Determine solutions for $2 \tan^2 x - 3 \sec x = 0$ in the interval $x \in [-2\pi, 2\pi]$.

C10. Determine solutions for
$$\frac{1}{\sin x - \cos x} = \cos x + \sin x$$
in the interval $x \in [-2\pi, 2\pi]$.

C11. How many solutions in the interval $x \in [0, 2\pi]$ should you expect for the equation $a \sin(bx + d) + c = c + \frac{a}{2}$, if $a \neq 0$ and b is a positive integer?

C12. Determine an exact value for
$$\cos\left(\cos^{-1}\left(\frac{\sqrt{2}}{2}\right) - \frac{\pi}{2}\right).$$

C13. Engineers use the equation $\tan x = \frac{v^2}{224\,000}$ to calculate the angle at which a curved section of the highway should be banked. In the equation, x is the angle of the bank and v is the speed limit on the curve, in kilometres per hour.

a) Calculate the angle of the bank, to the nearest tenth of a degree, if the speed limit is 100 km/h.

b) The four turns at the Indianapolis Motor Speedway are banked at an angle of 9.2°. What is the maximum speed through these turns, to the nearest kilometre per hour?

C14. The following table gives the average population, in thousands, of a northern university town for each month throughout the year. The population is greater in the winter and smaller in the summer, and it repeats this pattern from year to year.

Month	Population (thousands)
January	10.5
February	9.3
March	7.8
April	6.0
May	4.9
June	4.5
July	4.7
August	5.8
September	7.6
October	9.4
November	10.6
December	10.9

a) Write a sine function to model the data.

b) Make a scatter plot of the data. Then, graph your model on the same set of axes. How well does it fit the data?

c) Check your model using a sinusoidal regression. How does the regression equation compare with the model?

d) At what time or times during the cycle is the instantaneous rate of change of the population equal to 0? At what times is it a maximum? Justify your answers.

By the end of this chapter, I will be able to:

- Determine amplitude, vertical translation, phase shift, and period of a sinusoidal function given its equation

- Determine the equation of a sinusoidal function given its amplitude, vertical translation, phase shift, and period

- Determine angles that have a given sine, cosine, tangent, cosecant, secant, or cotangent

- Solve linear and quadratic trigonometric equations

- Model real-world situations using reciprocal trigonometric equations

- Given a data set, model the data using a sinusoidal function

- Determine values for inverse trigonometric relations

Chapter 6 Exponential and Logarithmic Functions

6.1 The Exponential Function and Its Inverse

KEY CONCEPTS

An exponential function of the form $y = b^x$, $b > 0$, $b \neq 1$, has

- a repeating pattern of finite differences

- a rate of change that is increasing proportionally to the function for $b > 1$

- a rate of change that is decreasing proportionally to the function for $0 < b < 1$

An exponential function of the form $y = b^x$, $b > 0$, $b \neq 1$,

- has domain $\{x \mid x \in \mathbb{R}\}$ • has range $\{y \in \mathbb{R} \mid y > 0\}$

- has y-intercept of 1   • has horizontal asymptote at $y = 0$

- is increasing on its domain when $b > 1$

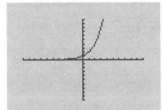

- is decreasing on its domain when $0 < b < 1$

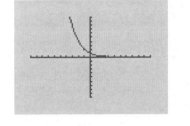

The inverse of $y = b^x$ is a function that satisfies $x = b^y$. This function

- has domain $\{x \in \mathbb{R}, x > 0\}$
- has range $\{y \in \mathbb{R}\}$
- has x-intercept of 1
- has vertical asymptote at $x = 0$
- is a reflection of $y = b^x$ about the line $y = x$
- is increasing on its domain when $b > 1$
- is decreasing on its domain when $0 < b < 1$

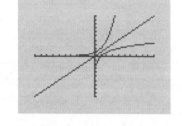
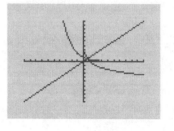

A

1. Consider the function $y = 2^x$.

   a) Identify the key features of the function

   i) domain and range

   ii) x-intercept, if it exists

   iii) y-intercept, if it exists

   iv) intervals for which the function is positive and intervals for which it is negative

   v) intervals for which the function is increasing and intervals for which it is decreasing

   vi) equation of the asymptote

   b) Sketch a graph of the function.

   c) On the same set of axes, sketch a graph of the inverse of the function.

   d) Identify the key features, as in part a) i) to iv), of the inverse of the function.

2. **a)** Which of the following is an exponential function? Explain how you know.

   i)

x	y
1	2
2	8
3	18
4	32

   ii)

x	y
1	5
2	25
3	125
4	625

   b) Write an equation for the data that is exponential.

3. Which of the following functions are exponential? For the exponential functions, write an equation to fit the data.

a)

x	y
1	3
2	5
3	7
4	9
5	11

b)

x	y
1	1.5
2	4.5
3	13.5
4	40.5
5	121.5

c)

x	y
1	5
2	11
3	21
4	35
5	53

d)

x	y
1	3.2
2	2.56
3	2.048
4	1.6384
5	1.3107

B

4. Use Technology Graph the function $y = 2.5^x$ over the domain $0 \le x \le 10$ using graphing technology.

a) Determine the average rate of change of y with respect to x for each interval. Round your answers to two decimal places.

  i) $x = 1$ to $x = 2$

  ii) $x = 2$ to $x = 3$

  iii) $x = 3$ to $x = 4$

  iv) $x = 4$ to $x = 5$

b) Estimate the instantaneous rate of change of y with respect to x at each of the endpoints in part a). Round your answers to two decimal places.

c) Describe how these rates are changing over the given domains.

5. Use Technology Graph the function $y = \left(\frac{3}{4}\right)^x$ over the domain $-10 \le x \le 0$ using graphing technology.

a) Determine the average rate of change of y with respect to x for each interval. Round your answers to two decimal places.

  i) $x = -5$ to $x = -4$

  ii) $x = -4$ to $x = -3$

  iii) $x = -3$ to $x = -2$

  iv) $x = -2$ to $x = -1$

  v) $x = -1$ to $x = 0$

b) Estimate the instantaneous rate of change of y with respect to x at each of the endpoints in part a). Round your answers to two decimal places.

c) Describe how these rates are changing over the given domains.

6. The atmospheric pressure, P, on a balloon or plane decreases with increasing height. This pressure, measured in millimetres of mercury, is related to the distance in kilometres, h, above sea level by the formula $P = 760(2.5)^{-0.145h}$.

   a) What is the pressure

   i) at sea level, $h = 0$?

   ii) at 500 m?

   iii) at 2 km?

   iv) at 5 km?

   b) Graph the function. Does it appear to be exponential? Explain your answer.

   c) Determine the average rate of change from sea level to 500 m.

   d) Estimate the instantaneous rate of change after

   i) 500 m

   ii) 1 km

7. Consider the function $f(x) = 3^x$.

   a) Sketch the graph of $f(x)$.

   b) Graph the line $y = x$ on the same set of Cartesian coordinates.

   c) Sketch the inverse of $f(x)$ on the same set of Cartesian coordinates.

   d) Identify the key features of both the graph and its inverse.

   i) domain and range

   ii) x-intercept, if it exists

   iii) y-intercept, if it exists

   iv) intervals for which the function is positive and intervals for which it is negative

   v) intervals for which the function is increasing and intervals for which it is decreasing

   vi) equation of the asymptote

8. Consider the function $g(x) = \left(\frac{1}{3}\right)^x$.

   a) Sketch the graph of $g(x)$.

   b) Graph the line $y = x$ on the same set of Cartesian coordinates.

   c) Sketch the inverse of $g(x)$ on the same set of Cartesian coordinates.

   d) Identify the key features of both the graph and its inverse.

   i) domain and range

   ii) x-intercept, if it exists

   iii) y-intercept, if it exists

   iv) intervals for which the function is positive and intervals for which it is negative

   v) intervals for which the function is increasing and intervals for which it is decreasing

   vi) equation of the asymptote

9. a) Copy the graph.

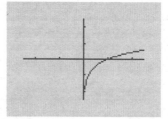

   b) Graph the line $y = x$ on the same grid.

   c) Graph the inverse of this function by reflecting in the line $y = x$.

   d) Write an equation for the inverse function.

10. The probability, P percent, of having an accident while driving a car is related to the alcohol level of the driver's blood by the formula $P = e^{kt}$, where k is the constant. Accident statistics show that the probability of an accident is 25% when the blood alcohol level is $t = 0.15$.

   a) Find k. Use $P = 25$.

   b) At what blood alcohol level is the probability of having an accident 50%?

11. The number of watts, w, provided by a space satellite's power supply after d days is given by the formula $w = 50(1.75)^{-0.004d}$.

a) How much power will be available after 30 days?

b) How much power will be available after 1 year (365 days)?

c) What is the power supply's average rate of change, in watts, between 30 days and 60 days? between 11 months and 12 months?

d) What is the value of the power supply's instantaneous rate of change, in watts, at 30 days? at 1 year?

12. A failure of o-ring seals caused the Challenger space shuttle disaster in 1986. After the disaster, there was a study of the 23 shuttle launches that had preceded the fatal flight. A mathematical model was developed involving the relationship between the Celsius temperature, x, around the o-rings and the number, y, of eroded or leaky primary o-rings. The model stated that $y = \dfrac{6}{1 + e^{-(5.085 - 0.114\,6x)}}$, where the number 6 indicates the 6 primary o-rings on the spacecraft.

a) What is the predicted number of eroded or leaky primary o-rings at a temperature of 37.5°C?

b) What is the predicted number of eroded or leaky primary o-rings at a temperature of 15.5°C?

c) What is the predicted number of eroded or leaky primary o-rings at a temperature of −7.5°C?

d) Use Technology Use a calculator to graph the equation. At what temperature is the predicted number of eroded or leaky o-rings 1? 2? 3?

e) What is the average rate of erosion of the o-rings from 37.7°C to 15.5°C? from 15.5°C to −7.5°C?

13. The deeper you are under water, the less sunlight reaches you. The percent of sunlight, P, that reaches a depth d, in metres, can be modelled by the function. $P = 100\,(0.85)^d$

a) Sketch a graph of P for the interval [0, 10].

b) Sketch the inverse of P.

c) Use your graph of the inverse of P to determine the depth at which the percentage of sunlight is 50%. Test your value for depth in the original equation for P.

d) Use your graph of P to calculate the average rate at which the sunlight is absorbed over the first 5 m.

e) Is the instantaneous rate at which sunlight is absorbed at a depth of 5 m greater

C

14. Complete the table of key features for $f(x)$ and its inverse.

	$f(x) = \left(\dfrac{1}{2}\right)^x$	Inverse of f
Domain		
Range		
x-Intercept		
y-Intercept		
Intervals for which $f(x)$ is positive		
Intervals for which $f(x)$ is increasing		
Equation of asymptote		

KEY CONCEPTS

The logarithmic function is the inverse of the exponential function.

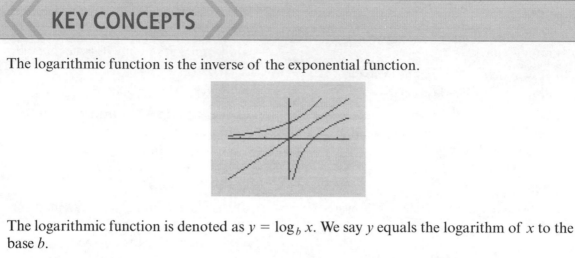

The logarithmic function is denoted as $y = \log_b x$. We say y equals the logarithm of x to the base b.

The function is defined only for $b > 0, b \neq 1$.

Exponential equations can be written in logarithmic form, and vice versa.

$y = b^x \iff x = \log_b y$
$y = \log_b x \iff x = b^y$

Exponential and logarithmic functions are defined only for positive values of the base that are not equal to one:

$y = b^x, b > 0, x > 0, b \neq 1$
$y = \log_b x, b > 0, y > 0, b \neq 1$

The logarithm of x to base 1 is only valid when $x = 1$, in which case y has an infinite number of solutions and is not a function.

Common logarithms are logarithms with a base of 10. It is not necessary to write the base for common logarithms: $\log x$ means the same as $\log_{10} x$.

A

1. Rewrite each equation in logarithmic form:

   a) $3^5 = 243$

   b) $\dfrac{1}{216} = 6^{-3}$

2. Evaluate without using a calculator.

   a) $\log_8 64$ **b)** $\log_2 \dfrac{1}{64}$

   c) $\log 100$ **d)** $\log 10^{-2.6}$

3. Rewrite each equation in exponential form:

   a) $\log_4 64 = 3$

   b) $y = \log 30$

4. Rewrite $125 = 5^x$ in logarithmic form.

5. Evaluate $\log_3\left(\dfrac{1}{27}\right)$.

6. Rewrite $\log_5 625 = 4$ in exponential form.

7. Rewrite each equation in logarithmic form.

   a) $9 = 3^2$

   b) $16 = 4^2$

   c) $6^{-2} = \dfrac{1}{36}$

   d) $\left(\dfrac{1}{3}\right)^3 = \dfrac{1}{27}$

   e) $7^x = y$

   f) $10^4 = 10\ 000$

   g) $\dfrac{1}{125} = 5^{-3}$

   h) $a = b^x$

8. Evaluate each logarithm.

   a) $\log_2 8$

   b) $\log_4 1024$

   c) $\log_3\left(\dfrac{1}{9}\right)$

   d) $\log_5\left(\dfrac{1}{625}\right)$

   e) $\log_{\frac{1}{2}} 16$

   f) $\log_{\sqrt{2}} 4$

   g) $\log_5 3125$

   h) $\log_3 2187$

   i) $\log_7 49^4$

   j) $\log_2 8^3$

9. Evaluate each common logarithm.

   a) $\log 100\ 000$

   b) $\log\left(\dfrac{1}{1000}\right)$

   c) $\log 0.001$

   d) $\log 10^{-9}$

   e) $\log 100$

   f) $\log\left(\dfrac{1}{10^7}\right)$

10. Rewrite in exponential form.

    a) $\log_2 8 = 3$

    b) $\log_3\left(\dfrac{1}{9}\right) = 2$

    c) $\log_a 3 = 6$

    d) $\log_3 2 = x$

    e) $\log_2 6 = x$

    f) $\log_2 x = 1.3$

    g) $\log_{\sqrt{2}} \pi = x$

    h) $\log_5 3x = 7y$

11. Sketch a graph of each function. Then, sketch a graph of the inverse of each function. Label each graph with its equation.

    a) $y = 3^x$

    b) $y = 5^x$

12. Estimate the value of each logarithm, correct to one decimal.

    a) $\log 117$

    b) $\log 0.123\ 4$

    c) $\log 14$

    d) $\log 2156$

    e) $\log 0.012$

    f) $\log 7500$

B

13. The number of visitors to a popular web site is tripling every month. The time, t, in days, for a number, N, of visitors to see the site is given by the equation $t = \dfrac{\log N}{\log 3}$. How long will it take until the number of visitors to the web site reaches each number?

    a) 1000

    b) 1 000 000

14. Johannes Kepler, a German mathematician and astronomer, developed an equation to determine how long a planet takes to revolve around the Sun based on the planet's distance from the Sun in kilometres. $T = 1.5 \log d - 0.7$. How long is the orbit around the Sun of

   a) Earth, if it is 150 000 000 km from the Sun?

   b) Neptune, if it is 4 473 million km from the Sun?

15. The function $D(t) = 93 \log t + 65$ relates the distance, in kilometres, that a particle travels in relation to the time, t, in seconds.

   a) If the particle travels for 45 s, estimate its distance travelled.

   b) If the particle travels for 798 km, estimate the time it takes to travel that far.

16. There are initially 5000 bacteria in a culture. The number of bacteria, N, doubles every hour, so the number of bacteria after t hours will be $N(t) = 5000(2)^t$.

   a) How many bacteria are present after 3 days?

   b) How long would it take to have 7 million bacteria?

   c) How long would it take to have 150 million bacteria?

17. The pH of a chemical solution is a measure of its acidity and is defined as $pH = -\log(H^+)$, where H^+ is the concentration of hydrogen ions in moles per litre.

   a) What is the pH value of a solution with a hydrogen concentration of 0.000 047 mol/L?

   b) Find the hydrogen concentration for a pH value of 11.

18. Our star, the Sun, appears billions of times brighter than the other stars because it is relatively near to us. Hence, astronomers are interested in comparing the brightness of stars if they could all be viewed from the same distance. The luminosity of a star refers to its brightness at a distance of 32.6 light years. By allowing for the Sun's magnitude and its distance from us, astronomers have established the following formula for the luminosity, L, of a star relative to the Sun: $\log L = 0.4(5 \log d - m) - 1.1$, where m is the magnitude of the star, and d is its distance from Earth in light years.

   a) How many times as luminous as the Sun are the stars in the table?

Some Stellar Distances		
Star	Magnitude	Distance (Light Years)
Sirius	−1.46	8.7
Vega	0.04	26.5
North Star	1.99	680.0
Deneb	1.26	1600.0

   b) The distance to the Sun is 1.55×10^{-5} light years. Verify that the luminosity of the Sun, as defined by the given equation, is 1.

19. The age of a bone can be determined from the fraction of carbon-14 that remains in the bone. The age is calculated by using the formula $A = -19\,000(\log R)$, where A is the age in years and R is the fraction of carbon-14 remaining.

   a) How old is a bone that has only $\frac{3}{4}$ of its original carbon-14?

   b) How old is a bone that has only 10% of its original carbon-14?

   c) Express the formula in exponential form.

   d) Use your answer to part c) to calculate the percent of carbon-14 remaining in a bone from an animal that died 100 years ago.

KEY CONCEPTS

The techniques for applying transformations to logarithmic functions are the same as those used for other functions.

$y = \log x + c$ translates up c units if $c > 0$

translates down c units if $c < 0$

$y = \log(x - d)$ translates right d units if $d > 0$

translates left d units if $d < 0$

$y = a \log x$ stretch vertically by a factor of $|a|$ if $|a| > 1$

compress vertically by a factor of $|a|$ if $|a| < 1$

reflect in the x-axis if $a < 0$

$y = \log kx$ compress horizontally by a factor of $\left|\dfrac{1}{k}\right|$ if $|k| > 1$

stretch horizontally by a factor of $\left|\dfrac{1}{k}\right|$ if $|k| < 1$, $k \neq 0$

reflect in the y-axis if $k < 0$

It is easier to perform multiple transformations in a series of steps:

Step 1: Ensure that the function is in the form $f(x) = a \log[k(x - d)] + c$.

Step 2: Apply any horizontal or vertical stretches or compressions.

Step 3: Apply any reflections.

Step 4: Apply any horizontal or vertical translations.

A

1. **a)** Graph the function
   $y = \log(x - 2) + 6$.

   b) State the key features of the function.

   i) domain and range

   ii) x-intercepts, if any exist

   iii) y-intercept, if it exists

   iv) equations of the asymptotes

2. **a)** Graph the function
   $y = -2 \log (3x + 6)$

   b) State the key features of the function.

   i) domain and range

   ii) x-intercepts, if any exist

   iii) y-intercept, if it exists

   iv) equations of the asymptotes

3. Match each equation with its graph.

   a) $y = \log x + 2$

   b) $y = \log x - 2$

   c) $y = \log(x - 2)$

   d) $y = \log(x + 2)$

i)

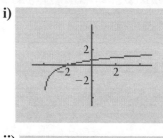

ii)

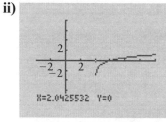

iii)

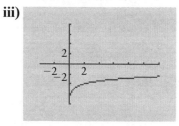

iv)

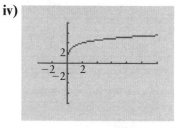

4. Let $f(x) = \log x$. Describe the transformation that would map f onto the following functions in each case.

   a) $y = \log(x + 3)$

   b) $y = \log(x - 2) + 4$

   c)

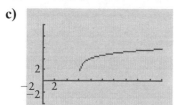

d)

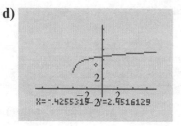

5. Sketch a graph of each function. Identify the key features of each.

   a) $y = \log x - 3$

   b) $f(x) = \log(x - 4)$

   c) $y = \log(x - 2) + 3$

   d) $f(x) = \log(x + 4) - 2$

6. Each of the following graphs can be generated by stretching or compressing the graph of $y = \log x$. Write an equation to describe each graph.

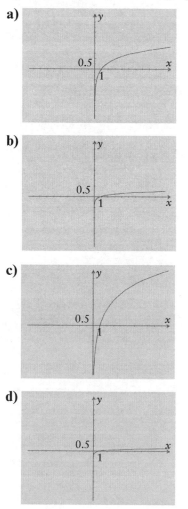

7. Sketch a graph of each function. For each, state the domain and the range.

    a) $y = \log x$

    b) $y = \log x - 2$

    c) $y = -2 \log x$

    d) $y = \log(-2x)$

    e) $y = \log\left(\frac{1}{2}x\right)$

    f) $y = \log(x - 2)$

8. Sketch a graph of each function.

    a) $f(x) = -2 \log(x + 3)$

    b) $f(x) = \log[2(x + 3)] - 4$

    c) $f(x) = 3 \log(-(x + 3))$

    d) $f(x) = \frac{1}{2} \log (2x + 6)$

B

9. a) A graph is produced by applying the following transformations, in order, to the graph of $y = \log x$.

    • reflection in the x-axis

    • horizontal stretch by a factor of 2

    • horizontal translation, left 5 units

    • vertical translation, down 3 units

    b) If steps 2) and 3) of the transformations were interchanged, what would the equation of the graph be?

10. Determine an equation for the graph shown.

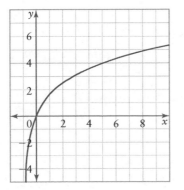

11. Let $f(x) = \log x$. Describe the transformation that would map f onto the following functions in each case.

    a) $y = \frac{1}{3} \log (x)$

    b) $y = \log\left(\frac{1}{4}x\right)$

    c)

    d)

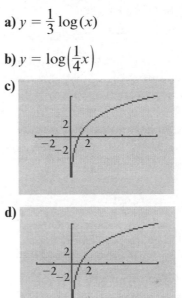

★12. a) Sketch a graph of each function.

    i) $y = -\log (x - 5)$

    ii) $f(x) = \log(-x) + 2$

    iii) $y = 2 \log (x + 4)$

    iv) $f(x) = \log\left(\frac{1}{3}x\right) - 2$

    b) For each function identify the following:

    i) the domain

    ii) the range

    iii) an equation for the asymptote

13. Sketch a graph of each function.

    a) $f(x) = 3 \log[5(x - 2)] + 1$

    b) $y = \log(-x - 3)$

    c) $f(x) = 4 \log(3x + 6) + 5$

    d) $y = -4 \log\left(\frac{1}{2}x - 5\right) - 2$

14. **Use Technology** Sketch the graph of $y = -4 \log(x + 5) - 2$ by hand. Then, check your answer using graphing technology.

15. The generation time for bacteria is the time that it takes for the population to double. The generation time, G, can be found using experimental data and the formula $G = \dfrac{t}{3.3 \log(f/b)}$ where t is the time period, b is the number of bacteria at the beginning of the experiment, and f is the number of bacteria at the end of the experiment. The generation time for mycobacterium tuberculosis is 16 h. How long will it take 4 of these bacteria to multiply into 1024 bacteria?

16. a) Graph the function
$$f(x) = 2 \log x + 3.$$

b) Graph the line $y = x$ on the same grid.

c) Graph the inverse function f^{-1} by reflecting f in the line $y = x$.

d) Determine the key features of f^{-1}.

  i) domain

  ii) range

  iii) equation of the asymptote

17. Graph each function.

  a) $y = \log_2 (x + 3) - 4$

  b) $y = -4 \log_2 (3x + 4) + 2$

★**18.** Suppose that the Tidbinbilla Deep Space Tracking Station in Australia received a signal, S, as a function of time that is given by
$$S = \tfrac{2}{5} \log(\cos x) - 3.$$

  a) What are the domain and range of this function? Explain your reasoning.

  b) Use Technology Graph this function using graphing technology.

  c) Do you think that the graph could be a code signal?

19. The growth of a $1000 investment at an interest rate of 6% per year compounded annually can be modelled by the function $n(A) = 40 \log A - 120$, where n is the number of years needed to grow to A dollars.

  a) Use the formula to calculate the number of years needed for the investment to

  i) double to $2000

  ii) triple to $3000

  b) Sketch a graph of n versus A for $0 \le A \le 3000$. Then, use your graph to estimate the value of the investment after 8 years.

  c) In real life there must be a restriction on the domain of this function. What is this restriction? Explain.

C

20. Describe how the graph of each function can be obtained using transformations of the graph of $y = \log x$.

  a) $y = -\log 2(x + 3)$

  b) $y = 3 \log(-x) + 4$

21. Use transformations to explain why $y = -\log(-x)$ and $y = \log x$ are inverses of each other.

22. Use Technology

  a) Compare the graphs of each pair of functions.

  i) $y = \log x + 1$ and $y = \log 10x$

  ii) $y = \log x + 2$ and $y = \log 10^2 x$

  iii) $y = \log x + 3$ and $y = \log 10^3 x$

  b) Use the pattern from part a) to graph $y = \log 10^4 x$, without using technology,

> ### ≪ KEY CONCEPTS ≫
>
> The power law of logarithms states that $\log_b x^n = n\log_b x$ for $b > 0$, $b \neq 1$, $x > 0$, and $n \in \mathfrak{R}$. This property can be used to solve equations with unknown exponents.
>
> Any logarithm can be expressed in terms of common logarithms using the change of base formula:
>
> $$\log_b m = \frac{\log m}{\log b}, b > 0, b \neq 1, m > 0$$
>
> This formula can be used to evaluate logarithms or graph logarithmic functions with any base.

A

1. Evaluate $\log_4 64^3$.

2. Solve for x: $5 = 2.5^x$.

3. Evaluate $\log_6 23$.

4. Graph the function $y = \log_3 x$.

5. An investment earns 12% interest, compounded annually. The amount, A, that the investment is worth as a function of time, t, in years, is given by $A = 1500(1.12)^t$.

   a) Use the equation to determine the value of the investment.

      i) initially, when $t = 0$

      ii) after 2 years

      iii) after 4 years

   b) How long will it take for the investment to

      i) double in value?

      ii) quadruple in value?

6. Evaluate.

   a) $\log_3 27^5$ c) $\log 1000^{-2}$

   b) $\log_5 15^2$ d) $\log 0.001^{\frac{1}{3}}$

7. Evaluate.

   a) $\log_8 \sqrt{16}$

   b) $\log_{125} 5^{12}$

   c) $\log_3 \left(\sqrt[3]{729}\right)^9$

   d) $\log_5 \left(\sqrt[4]{\dfrac{1}{125}}\right)^{12}$

8. Solve x to two decimal places.

   a) $5^x = 8$ c) $6(3)^{2x-3} = 18$

   b) $6^{3x} = 10$ d) $2(7)^{4x-5} = 30$

B

9. A guaranteed investment certificate (GIC) earns 5% interest, compounded annually. The amount, A, that the investment is worth as a function of time, t, in years, is given by $A = 1500(1.05)^t$.

   a) Use the equation to determine the value of the GIC.

      i) initially, when $t = 0$

      ii) after 2.5 years

      iii) after 5 years

   b) How long will it take for the investment to

      i) double in value?

      ii) quadruple in value?

10. Evaluate, correct to three decimal places.

a) $\log_5 67$ **d)** $-\log_{15} 5$

b) $\log_3 34$ **e)** $\log_{\frac{1}{3}} 20$

c) $\log_9 5$ **f)** $\log_{\frac{5}{7}} 9$

11. Write as a single logarithm.

a) $\dfrac{\log 9}{\log 4}$

b) $\dfrac{\log 12}{\log 5}$

c) $\dfrac{\log\left(\frac{1}{3}\right)}{\log\left(\frac{5}{7}\right)}$

d) $\dfrac{\log (x + 3)}{\log (x - 5)}$

12. Solve for x, correct to three decimal places.

a) $3 = \log 5^x$

b) $10\,000 = 100 \log 10^x$

c) $5 = \log_2 16^x$

d) $24 = 4 \log_3 5^x$

⭐**13.** An investment earns 12% compounded semi-annually. The amount, A, that the investment is worth as a function of time, t, in years, is given by $A(t) = 1200(1.06)^{2t}$.

a) What was the initial value of the investment? Explain.

b) How long will it take the investment to triple in value?

14. a) Evaluate $\log_3 27^7$ without using the power law of logarithms.

b) Evaluate the same expression by applying the power law of logarithms.

c) Which method do you prefer? Why?

⭐**15.** Suppose that the Ares 1 crew-launch vehicle is approaching the International Space Station (ISS) that is orbiting Earth. When Ares 1 is 250 km from the ISS, it must be slowed down, by controlled

braking. The time, t, in hours, required to reach a distance, d, in kilometres, from the ISS during controlled braking can be modeled by $t = \log_{0.5}\left(\dfrac{d}{250}\right)$. The docking sequence can be initialized when the craft is within 1 km of the station's docking bay.

a) How long after the controlled braking starts should the docking procedures begin?

b) What are the domain and range of this function? What do these features represent?

16. An investment pays 4% interest, compounded annually.

a) Write an equation that expresses the amount, A, of an investment of a function of time, t, in years.

b) Determine how long it will take for this investment to

i) triple in value

ii) quadruple in value

c) Determine the percent increase in value of the account after

i) 6 years

ii) 12 years

C

17. Use $\log_b x = \dfrac{\log_k x}{\log_k b}$ for any $x > 0$, $k > 0$, $b > 0$ to express each of the following terms of base 3 logarithms.

a) $\log_4 1024$

b) $\log 37$

18. An investment pays 5.5% interest, compounded semi-annually.

a) Write an equation to express the amount, A, of the investment as a function of time, t, in years.

b) Determine how long it will take for this investment to

i) double in value

ii) triple in value

<< **KEY CONCEPTS** >>

Logarithmic scales provide a convenient method of comparing values that typically have a very large range.

Several phenomena in the physical sciences can be described using logarithmic scales.

The pH scale is defined as pH $= -\log[H^+]$ pH $= -\log(H^+)$ where H^+ is the hydronium ion concentration in the substance.

A

⭐**1.** The pH scale is used to measure the acidity or alkalinity of a chemical solution. It is defined as pH $= -\log(H^+)$, where H^+ is the concentration of hydronium ions, measured in moles per litre.

   a) Hydrochloric acid has a hydronium ion concentration of approximately 100 mol/L. What is its pH?

   b) Battery acid has a hydronium ion concentration of 5×10^{-9} mol/L. What is its pH?

   c) A soft drink has a pH of approximately 3. What is the concentration of hydronium ions in a soft drink?

   d) What has a greater concentration of hydronium ions, soft drinking water with a pH of 5 or tomato juice with a pH of 4? by how much?

2. The pH of water in a small lake in northern Québec has dropped from 5.4 to 4.8 in the last three years. How many times more acidic is the lake now than it was three years ago?

3. When the pH of the water in a lake falls below 4.7, nearly all the species of fish in the lake are deformed or killed. How many times more acidic than clean rainwater, which has a pH of 5.6, is such a lake?

⭐**4.** The difference in sound levels, in decibels, can be found using the equation

$\beta_2 - \beta_1 = 10 \log\left(\dfrac{I_2}{I_1}\right)$, where I_1 and I_2 are the intensities of the two sounds, in watts per square metre.

   a) How many times more intense than a shout is the sound of maximum stereo output?

   b) The sound level of a normal conversation is approximately 60 dB. The sound level at a rock concert is about 10 500 times more intense. What is the sound level at the rock concert, in decibels?

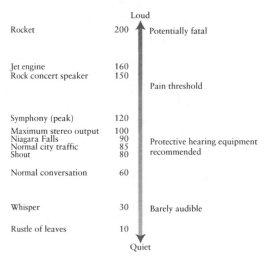

5. The magnitude, M, of an earthquake is measured using the Richter scale, which is defined as $M = \log\left(\frac{I}{I_0}\right)$, where I is the intensity of the earthquake being measured and I_0 is the intensity of a standard, low-level earthquake.

   a) How many times more intense than a standard earthquake is an earthquake measuring 4.2 on the Richter scale?

   b) What is the magnitude of an earthquake 50 000 times as intense as a standard earthquake?

6. Determine the pH of a solution with each hydronium ion concentration.

   a) 0.001   **c)** 10^{-5}

   b) 0.000 75   **d)** 4.3×10^{-8}

7. Determine the hydronium ion concentration, in moles per litre, of a solution with each pH.

   a) 15   **c)** 11.3

   b) 4   **d)** 6.2

Use the following information to complete questions 8 and 9.

The minimum intensity detectable by the human ear is $I_0 = 10^{-12}$ W/m^2 (watts per square metre), and is used as the reference point. The sound level corresponding to an intensity of I watts per square metre is $L = \frac{10 \log I}{I^0}$ or $L = \frac{10 \log I}{10^{-12}}$. This formula is used to determine the decibel rating of a sound.

8. Find the decibel ratings, in dB, of a whisper with an intensity in watts per square metre of $1.15 \times 10^{-10} \frac{\text{W}}{\text{m}^2}$.

9. Find the decibel ratings, in dB, of a teacher's voice with an intensity of $9 \times 10^{-9} \frac{\text{W}}{\text{m}^2}$.

10. A hair dryer has a sound intensity level of 70 dB and an air conditioner has a sound intensity level of 50 dB. How many times more intense is the sound from the hair dryer than the sound from the air conditioner?

11. How many times more intense is the sound of a jet engine than the sound of

   a) Niagara Falls?

   b) a rustle of leaves?

12 A power mower makes a noise that is measured at 106 dB. Ordinary traffic registers about 70 dB. How many times louder is the mower than the traffic?

B

13. An earthquake occurred that was 1 000 000 times more intense than I_0. What was the measure of this earthquake on the Richter scale?

14. In the South Pacific, there was an earthquake that measured 6.7 on the Richter scale.

   a) How many times more intense was this earthquake than a standard low-level earthquake?

   b) On July 22, 2001, an earthquake in St. Catharines, Ontario, measured 1.1 on the Richter scale. How many times less intense was the St. Catharines earthquake than the South Pacific earthquake?

15. The 1906 earthquake in San Francisco had a magnitude of 8.3 on the Richter scale. At the same time in Japan there was an earthquake that had a of magnitude of 4.8 that caused only minor damage. How many times more intense was the San Francisco earthquake than the Japan earthquake?

★**16.** In 1987, Canadian astronomer Ian Sheldon became the first person to observe a supernova in our galaxy since the invention of the telescope. Supernova 1987A increased in brightness by at least 200 times in the first day, and almost 1000 times in the first two days. What change occurred in the magnitude

a) in the first day?

b) in the first two days?

C1. The formula $D = 5e^{-0.4h}$ can be used to find the number of milligrams, D, of a certain drug that is in a patient's blood stream h hours after the drug has been administered. How many milligrams will be present after 1 h? after 6 h?

★**C2.** A model for the number of people, N, in a college community who have heard a certain rumour is $N = P(1 - e^{-0.15d})$ where P is the total population of the community and d is the number of days that have elapsed since the rumour began. In a community of 1000 students, how many students will have heard the rumour after 3 days?

C3. The number of watts, w, provided by a space satellite's power supply after d days is given by the formula $w = 50(1.75)^{-0.004d}$.

a) How much power will be available after 120 days?

b) How much power will be available after 5 years?

c) What is the power supply's average output, in watts, between 120 days and 150 days? between 24 months and 36 months?

d) What is the value of the satellite's instantaneous watts at 120 days? at 5 years?

C4. If an earthquake is 390 times as intense as an earthquake with a magnitude of 4.2 on the Richter scale, what is the magnitude of the more intense earthquake?

C5. The absolute magnitude of star A is −4.5 and that of star B is 0.2.

a) How many times as bright is star A than star B, to the nearest unit?

b) If the apparent magnitudes of two stars are −2.5 and 1.3, respectively, which star is closer to Earth? Justify your answer.

★**C6.** The approximate distance above sea level, d, in kilometres, is given by
$$h = \frac{-\ln\left(\dfrac{P}{760}\right)}{0.145}$$ where P is the atmospheric pressure, in mm of mercury.

a) Among the highest inhabited buildings in the world are those in the Indian Tibetan border fort of Basisi. If the atmospheric pressure at Basisi is 271.5 mm of mercury, how far above sea level is the fort?

b) Sir Edmund Hillary was the first person to reach the top of Mount Everest, 8850 m above sea level. Calculate the pressure loss that the mountaineer experienced from sea level to the top of the mountain.

c) Suppose that an aircraft is pressurized to sea level (about 760 mm of mercury) for the duration of a flight. What pressure difference must the jet withstand at 2.1 km above sea level?

C7. Another formula to calculate altitude takes temperature into account. If x is the atmospheric, or barometric, pressure measured in mm of mercury, then the formula for the altitude $h(x)$, measured in m above sea level, is $h(x) = (30T + 8000) \log \frac{P_0}{x}$. T is the temperature, in degrees Celsius, and P_0 is the barometric pressure at sea level, approximately 760 mm of mercury.

a) At what altitude is an aircraft if its instruments record an outside temperature of $-30\ °C$ and a barometric pressure of 241 mm of mercury?

b) Mount McKinley, in Alaska, is the highest peak in North America. What is the atmospheric pressure at the summit, altitude approximately 6970 m, if the air temperature is $-25\,°C$?

C8. The number of years, n, for a piece of machinery to depreciate to a known salvage value can be found using the formula $n = \dfrac{\log s - \log i}{\log(1 - d)}$ where s is the salvage value of the machinery, i is its initial value, and d is the annual rate of depreciation.

a) How many years will it take for a piece of machinery to decline in value from $90 000 to $10 000 if the annual rate of depreciation is 0.20 (20%)?

b) How many years will it take for a piece of machinery to loose half of its value if the annual rate of depreciation is 15%?

C9. Graph each function.

a) $f(x) = \log_3(x + 1) - 5$

b) $y = -2 \log_2(3x - 4) + 2$

C10. Given the exponential function $f(x) = a^x$ and $f^{-1}(x) = \log_a x$, where $a > 0$,

a) for what values of a do the graphs of $f(x) = a^x$ and $f^{-1}(x) = \log_a x$ intersect?

b) Describe as much as you can about the point of intersection of the graphs in part a).

C11. An investment pays 12% interest, compounded weekly.

a) Write an equation that expresses the amount, A, of the investment as a function of time, t, in years.

b) Determine how long it will take for this investment to

i) triple in value

ii) quadruple in value

c) Determine the present increase in value of the account after

i) 15 years

ii) 20 years

C12. Tensing invests $2500 in savings bonds at an interest rate of 8.5% per year, compounded semi-annually. How long will it take for this sum to increase to $3500?

C13. The sum of $1000 was invested for 4 years and the interest was compounded annually. If this investment amounts to $1463.33 after 4 years, what was the interest rate?

C14. A great earthquake in India had a Richter reading of 8.7. A slight tremor occurring in California had a magnitude of 2.5. How many times greater was the earthquake in India?

C15. An Alaskan earthquake was 4 times more intense than a San Francisco earthquake that had a magnitude of 3.4 on the Richter scale. What was the magnitude of the Alaskan earthquake on the same scale?

C16. Find the pH of a 1-L container of water with 0.000 000 1 mol of hydrogen ion.

C17. Find the hydrogen ion concentration of a mildly acidic solution with a pH of 4.2.

C18. Between 1997 and 2007, the annual average pH of precipitation in a northern Ontario town dropped from 5.6 to 4.3. How many times more acidic was the precipitation in 2007 than the precipitation in 1997?

C19. In chemistry, the equation $t = c \log_2 \dfrac{b(a - x)}{a(b - x)}$ is used where x is the concentration of a substance at time t, and a, b, c are constants. Solve this equation to express x as a function of t.

By the end of this chapter, I will be able to:

- Identify the nature of the rate of change and key features of an exponential function

- Identify the shape of the graph and key features of the inverse of an exponential function

- Identify the logarithmic function as the inverse of a corresponding exponential function

- Write an exponential equation in logarithmic form and vice versa

- Estimate and evaluate a logarithm

- Apply transformations to logarithmic functions

- Apply the power law of logarithms

- Solve for an unknown exponent of an exponential equation by applying the power law of logarithms

- Apply the change of base formula to evaluate a logarithm having any base

- Apply the change of base formula to graph a logarithmic function having any base

- Understand the nature of a logarithmic scale

- Solve a variety of problems involving logarithmic scales used in the physical sciences

Chapter 7 Tools and Strategies for Solving Exponential and Logarithmic Equations

7.1 Equivalent Forms of Exponential Equations

- Exponential functions and expressions can be expressed in different ways by changing the base.

Example

Express in terms of a power with a base of 3.

a) 81   b) 9^5 c) $\sqrt{9} \times \sqrt[7]{27}^5$ d) 17

Solution

a) $81 = 3^4$

b) $9^5 = (3^2)^5 = 3^{10}$

c) $\sqrt{9} \times \sqrt[7]{27}^5 = (3^2)^{\frac{1}{2}} \times (3^3)^{\frac{5}{7}}$

$\qquad\qquad = 3 \times 3^{\frac{15}{7}}$

$\qquad\qquad = 3^{\frac{22}{7}}$

d) $\qquad 3^x = 17$

$\qquad \log_3 3^x = \log_3 17$

$\qquad\qquad x = \log_3 17$

$\qquad\qquad 17 = 3^{\log_3 17}$

- Changing the base of one or more exponential expressions is a useful technique for solving exponential equations.

Example

Solve each equation.

a) $5^{x+3} = 125^x$ b) $3^{2x} = 243^{x-5}$

Solution

a) $5^{x+3} = 125^x$

$\quad 5^{x+3} = (5^3)^x$

$\quad 5^{x+3} = 5^{3x}$

$\quad x + 3 = 3x$

$\qquad 3 = 2x$

$\qquad x = \dfrac{3}{2}$

b) $3^{2x} = 243^{x-5}$

$\quad 3^{2x} = (3^5)^{x-5}$

$\quad 3^{2x} = 3^{5x-25}$

$\quad 2x = 5x - 25$

$\quad -3x = -25$

$\qquad x = \dfrac{25}{3}$

$\qquad x = 8\dfrac{1}{3}$

- Graphing technology can be used to solve exponential equations.

Example

Solve the equation $4^{x+1} = 2^{x-1}$ using a graphing calculator.

Solution

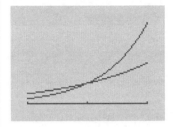

Solution is $\left(-4, \dfrac{1}{32}\right)$.

A

1. Write each expression with base 2.

   a) 16^4

   b) 4^7

   c) $\left(\dfrac{1}{8}\right)^3$

   d) 11

2. Write each expression with base 3.

   a) 9^4

   b) 27^7

   c) $\left(\dfrac{1}{9}\right)^3$

   d) $\dfrac{1}{5}$

3. Write each expression as a power of the base indicated.

   a) 64^3, base 4

   b) $\left(\dfrac{1}{4}\right)^5$, base 2

   c) 5^3, base 4

4. Write each expression as a single power of 3.

   a) $\sqrt[3]{81}$

   b) $\dfrac{\sqrt{27}}{\sqrt[4]{9}}$

5. **Use Technology** Solve. Check your answers by using graphing technology.

   a) $7^x = 49^{x+5}$

   b) $4^{t-3} = 32^{\frac{t+2}{3}}$

   c) $36^{3x-1} = 216^{5-x}$

6. a) Write 3^9 as a power of a number other than 3.

   b) Write 3^9 as a power with a base that is different from the one you chose in part a).

   c) Use a calculator to check that these powers are equivalent.

7. Write each expression as a single power of 4.

   a) $\left(\sqrt{256}\right)^5$

   b) $\sqrt[5]{64}$

   c) $\sqrt{1024} \times \left(\sqrt[5]{64}\right)^4$

   d) $\left(\sqrt{2}\right)^9 \times \left(\sqrt[4]{2}\right)^6$

8. **Use Technology** Solve. Check your answers using graphing technology.

   a) $2^{x+3} = 4^{2x-5}$

   b) $7^{w-2} = 49$

   c) $3^{x+2} = 9^{x-5}$

   d) $49^{4w+1} = 7^{2w+7}$

9. Use Technology Solve. Check your answers using graphing technology.

a) $9^{3x} = 27^{x-3}$

b) $4^{5x-1} = 8^{8x+7}$

c) $625^{4y+3} = 25^{y-2}$

d) $128^{2k-3} = 64^{k+3}$

B

★ **10.** Consider the equation $36^{4x} = 1296^{3x-7}$.

a) Solve this equation by expressing both sides as powers of a common base.

b) Solve the same equation by taking the common logarithm of both sides.

c) Which technique do you prefer? why?

11. Use Technology Solve. Check your answers using graphing technology.

a) $\sqrt{27} = 3^{x+5}$

b) $8^{k-2} = (\sqrt{128})^{2k}$

12. Consider the equation $10 = 3^x$.

a) Solve the equation for x by taking the common logarithm of both sides.

b) Use the result in part a) to show that $10 = 3^{\frac{1}{\log 3}}$.

c) Apply algebraic reasoning to show that $10 = 4^{\frac{1}{\log 4}}$.

13. Consider the equation $256^{3x} = 16^{x-2}$.

a) Solve this equation by expressing both sides as a power with base 4.

b) Solve the same equation by expressing both sides as a power with base 16.

c) **Use Technology** Solve the same equation using graphing technology.

d) Reflect on these methods. Which do you prefer? why?

14. Consider the equation $5^{3x-1} = 125^{2x}$.

a) Solve this equation by expressing both sides as powers of a common base.

b) Solve the same equation by taking the logarithm, base 5, of each side.

15. a) Solve. Give exact answers.

i) $5 = 10^x$

ii) $3 = 10^x$

iii) $7 = 10^x$

b) Use your answers to part a) to state a formula that could be used to solve $b = 10^x$ for x.

16. a) Solve $16^{3x+2} = 64^{5-3x}$ by expressing both sides of the equation as powers of 4.

b) Solve $16^{3x+2} = 64^{5-3x}$ by expressing both sides of the equation as powers of 2.

c) **Use Technology** Solve $16^{3x+2} = 64^{5-3x}$ by using graphing technology.

d) Which of the methods is "best"? Explain.

C

★ **17. a)** Solve each inequality.

i) $3^{2x} > 9^{x+3}$

ii) $8^{3x+5} < 32^{x+7}$

b) Use a sketch to help explain how you can use graphing technology to check your answers.

⟪ KEY CONCEPTS ⟫

- An equation maintains balance when the common logarithm is applied to both sides.

- The power law of logarithms ($\log_b x^n = n \log_b x$, $b > 0$, $x > 0$) is a useful tool for solving a variable that appears as part of an exponent.

Steps:

    1. Isolate the term containing the variable on one side of the equation.

    2. Take the base 10 logarithm of each side of the equation.

    3. Apply the power law of logarithms to rewrite the equation without exponents.

    4. Solve for the variable and check the results.

Example

Solve the equation $5^{3x-2} = 3^{x+5}$.

Solution

a)
$$5^{x-2} = 3^{x+5}$$
$$\log 5^{3x-2} = \log 3^{x+5}$$
$$(3x - 2)\log 5 = (x + 5)\log 3$$
$$3x\log 5 - 2\log 5 = x\log 3 + 5\log 3$$
$$3x\log 5 - x\log 3 = 5\log 3 + 2\log 5$$
$$x(3\log 5 - \log 3) = 5\log 3 + 2\log 5$$
$$x = \frac{5\log 3 + 2\log 5}{3\log 5 - \log 3}$$
$$x = 2.33$$

- When a quadratic equation is obtained, methods such as factoring and applying the quadratic formula are useful.

- Some algebraic methods of solving exponential equations lead to extraneous roots that are not valid solutions to the original equation.

Example

Solve the equation $5^{2x} - 5^x = 20$.

Solution
$$5^{2x} - 5^x = 20$$
$$(5^x)^2 - 5^x - 20 = 0$$
$$(5^x - 5)(5^x + 4) = 0$$

$$5^x - 5 = 0 \qquad 5^x + 4 = 0$$
$$5^x = 5 \qquad 5^x = -4$$
$$x = 1 \qquad \textit{extraneous}$$

A

1. Match each graph with its equation.

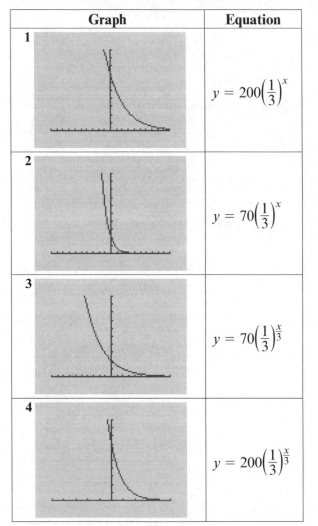

Graph	Equation
1	$y = 200\left(\frac{1}{3}\right)^x$
2	$y = 70\left(\frac{1}{3}\right)^x$
3	$y = 70\left(\frac{1}{3}\right)^{\frac{x}{3}}$
4	$y = 200\left(\frac{1}{3}\right)^{\frac{x}{3}}$

2. Solve for x. Round the answers to two decimal places.

   a) $2^x = 73$

   b) $8 = 1.4^x$

   c) $49 = 7(2.05)^x$

   d) $7 = 1.4^{x-3}$

   e) $0.75 = 1.3^{x+3}$

f) $25 = \left(\frac{1}{3}\right)^{2x}$

g) $14 = \left(\frac{1}{3}\right)^{\frac{x}{5}}$

h) $200 = 50\left(\frac{1}{4}\right)^{\frac{5}{x}}$

3. Use the decay equation for polonium-218, $A(t) = A_0\left(\frac{1}{2}\right)^{\frac{y}{3.1}}$, where A is the amount remaining after t minutes and A_0 is the initial amount.

   a) How much will remain after 120 s from an initial sample of 120 mg?

   b) How long will it take for this sample to decay to 25% of its initial amount of 120 mg?

   c) Would your answer to part b) change if the size and initial sample were changed? Explain why or why not.

4. Solve each equation. Leave answers in exact form.

   a) $3^x = 4^{x-2}$

   b) $7^{x+3} = 5^x$

   c) $9^{x-4} = 4^{x+2}$

   d) $8^{3x+5} = 5^{x+2}$

5. Find approximate values for your answers to question 4, correct to three decimal places.

6. Consider the equation $3^{2x} + 3^x - 12 = 0$.

   a) Write the equation in the form $az^2 + bz + c = 0$, where $z = 3^x$, and then identify the coefficients a, b, and c.

   b) Solve the equation using the quadratic formula.

   c) Identify any extraneous roots.

7. Consider the equation $7^{2x} = 2(7^x) + 3$.

   a) Write the equation in the form $az^2 + bz + c = 0$, where $z = 7^x$, and then identify the coefficients a, b, and c.

   b) Solve the equation using the quadratic formula.

   c) Identify any extraneous roots.

B

8. A bacteria culture starts with 3000 bacteria. After 3 h, the estimated count is 48 000. What is the doubling period?

★ **9.** A 50-mg sample of radioactive iodine decays to 23 mg after 12 min.

   a) Determine the half-life of the radioactive iodine.

   b) How long will it take for this sample to decay to 5 mg?

10. After 90 days, a sample of silver-110, Ag^{110}, has decayed to about 80% of its original size.

   a) Determine the half-life of Ag^{110}.

   b) Graph the amount of Ag^{110} remaining as a function of time.

   c) Describe how the graph would change if the half-life were

     i) shorter

     ii) longer

   d) Describe how the graph would change if the initial sample size were

     i) greater

     ii) less

★ **11.** Does the equation $3^{2x} - 5(3^x) - 6 = 0$ have any real solutions? Explain your answer.

12. Solve and check for any extraneous roots. Where necessary, round answers to two decimal places.

   a) $5(2)^{2-3x} = 50$

   b) $182 = 2(3)^{4x+3}$

   c) $9^{2x} + 4(9^x) = 21$

   d) $7^{2x} = 2(7^x) + 3$

   e) $6(2^{2x}) + 13(2^x) = 5$

   f) $12(4^{2x}) = -5(4^x) + 2$

13. Use Technology Check your solutions to question 12 using graphing technology.

14. Tenzin has purchased a minivan for $35 000. The value, V, in dollars, of the minivan as a function of time, t, in years, depreciates according to the function $V(t) = 35000\left(\frac{1}{2}\right)^{\frac{t}{3}}$. How long will it take for Tenzin's minivan to depreciate to

   a) half of its initial value?

   b) 15% of its initial value?

15. Pratheep bought a computer system for $2500. The value of the system depreciates at a rate of 20% each year.

   a) Determine an exponential function to model the value of the system over time.

   b) Graph the function you found in part a).

   c) Use the graph to determine the value of Pratheep's system three years from now.

   d) Verify your result from part c) algebraically.

16. To determine whether a person has a thyroid deficiency, a radioactive iodine with a half-life of 8.2 days is injected into the bloodstream. A healthy thyroid is able to absorb all of the radioactivity. The amount, R, of radioactivity present after t days can be modelled by the relationship $R(t) = R_0\left(\frac{1}{2}\right)^{\frac{t}{8.2}}$, where R_0 is the initial dose. How long will it take for 87.5% of the iodine to be absorbed into a healthy person's body?

17. A sample of radioactive iodine-131 atoms has a half-life of about 8 days. A formula that models the number of iodine-131 atoms that remain is $P = P_0\left(2^{\frac{-t}{8}}\right)$, where P is the number of iodine-131 atoms that remain after time, t, in days, and P_0 is the number of iodine-131 atoms that are initially present. Suppose that 1 000 000 iodine-131 atoms are initially present.

a) How long will it take until there is

  i) half of the initial value of iodine-131 atoms?

  ii) 10% of the initial value of iodine-131 atoms?

b) Sketch a graph of the decay formula.

c) Suppose that the iodine-131 decays more slowly than the current half-life of 8 days. What effect will this have on the

  i) equation?

  ii) graph?

⭐**18.** One day, a movie trailer to the new James Bond film was posted on the Internet. Suppose that 5000 people see the video on the first day after it is posted and that the number doubles every day after that.

a) Write an expression to describe the number of people who have seen the trailer t days after it is posted.

b) One week later, a second trailer is posted. Suppose that 3500 people see this trailer the first day after it is posted and that this number triples every day after that. Write an expression to describe the number of people who have seen the second trailer t days after it is posted.

c) Set the two expressions from part a) and part b) equal and solve for t using tools and strategies of your choice. What does this solution mean?

19. The population of a colony of bacteria grows according to the formula $P(t) = 4(1.40)^{\frac{t}{24}}$, where P is the population, in thousands, and t is the time, in hours.

a) How long does it take the population to reach 10 000, to the nearest hour?

b) Calculate the time it takes for the population to double, to the nearest hour.

20. The maximum height that a ball reaches after bounce number n is given by the equation $H = 2.0(0.90)^n$, where H is the height, in metres.

a) What is the ball's maximum height after the fifth bounce?

b) What is the first bounce after which the maximum height is less than 10 cm?

21. Rewrite the equation $P(t) = 4(1.40)^{\frac{t}{24}}$ with base 1.40 replaced with 2.

22. The general equation for population growth is $P(t) = P_0\left(1 + \frac{R}{100}\right)^{\frac{t}{t_0}}$, where R is the growth rate, in percent, over time period t_0. Suppose a population grew from 10 000 to 25 000 in 6 years. If time is measured in years, calculate

a) the yearly growth rate

b) the growth rate per decade (10 years)

C

23. A radioactive substance has a half-life of 15 days.

a) Develop an equation for the amount of radioactive substance left as a function of time for the given scenario.

b) Find the domain and the range of this function.

> ### KEY CONCEPTS

- The product law of logarithms states that $\log_b x + \log_b y = \log_b(xy)$ for $b > 0$, $b \neq 1$, $x > 0$, $y > 0$.

- The quotient law of logarithms states that $\log_b x - \log_b y = \log_b\left(\frac{x}{y}\right)$ for $b > 0$, $b \neq 1$, $x > 0$, $y > 0$.

- The laws of logarithms can be used to simplify expressions and solve equations.

Example

Express as a single logarithm.

a) $\log_{10} 12 + \log_{10} 7 - \log_{10} 3$

b) $\log_a b + \log_a (7c) + \log_a (3b) - \log_a c$

c) $\log(x^2 + 2x - 3) - \log(2x + 6)$

Solution

a) $\log_{10} 12 + \log_{10} 7 - \log_{10} 3 = \log_{10} \dfrac{(12 \times 7)}{3}$

$$= \log_{10} 28$$

b) $\log_a b + \log_a (7c) + \log_a (3b) - \log_a c = \log_a \dfrac{21cb^2}{c}$

$$= \log_a 21b^2$$

c) $\log(x^2 + 2x - 3) - \log(2x + 6) = \log \dfrac{x^2 + 2x - 3}{2x + 6}$

$$= \log \dfrac{(x + 3)(x - 1)}{2(x + 3)}$$

$$= \log \dfrac{(x - 1)}{2}$$

Example

Express as a single logarithm. Then, evaluate.

a) $\log_{10} 8 + \log_{10} 1.25$

b) $\log_2 80 - \log_2 5$

c) $\log 40 + \log 5 - \log 2$

d) $\log_7 245 + \log_7 \dfrac{1}{5}$

Solution

a) $\log_{10} 8 + \log_{10} 1.25 = \log_{10}(8 \times 1.25)$
$$= \log_{10} 10$$
$$= 1$$

b) $\log_2 80 - \log_2 5 = \log_2 \dfrac{80}{5}$
$$= \log_2 16$$
$$= 4$$

c) $\log 40 + \log 5 - \log 2 = \log \dfrac{40 \times 5}{2}$
$$= \log 100$$
$$= 2$$

d) $\log_7 245 + \log_7 \dfrac{1}{5} = \log_7\left(245 \times \dfrac{1}{5}\right)$
$$= \log_7 49$$
$$= 2$$

Example

Write as a sum or difference of logarithms. Simplify if possible.

a) $\log_3 8$

b) $\log_2(x^2 \, yz^4)$

c) $\log_b\left(\dfrac{x^2}{yz^3}\right)$

Solution

a) $\log_3 4 + \log_3 2$

b) $2\log_2 x + \log_2 y + 4\log_2 z$

c) $2\log_b x - \log_b y - 3\log_b z$

A

1. Simplify, using the laws of logarithms.

   a) $\log 8 + \log 5$

   b) $\log 56 - \log 7$

   c) $\log_2 8 + \log_2 3$

   d) $\log_5 80 - \log_5 16$

2. Use a calculator to evaluate each result in question 1, correct to three decimal places.

3. Simplify each algebraic expression. State any restrictions on the variables.

   a) $\log(2x) + \log(3y) + \log z$

   b) $\log_2 x + \log_2(3y) - 5\log z$

   c) $3\log a + 4\log y - 2\log z$

   d) $2\log(3x) + 3\log y - \dfrac{1}{2}\log(4w)$

4. Evaluate, using the product law of logarithms.

   a) $\log_3 9 + \log_3 729$

   b) $\log_5 4 + \log_5(31.25)$

   c) $\log_4 32 + \log_4 256$

   d) $\log 25 + \log 4 + \log 10$

5. Evaluate, using the quotient law of logarithms.

a) $\log_3 13\,122 - \log_3 2$

b) $\log_5 4375 - \log_5 7$

c) $\log_4 36\,864 - \log_4 9$

d) $\log 2800 - \log 4 - \log 7$

6. Evaluate, using the laws of logarithms.

a) $\log_3 12 - \log_3 4$

b) $\log_4 24 + \log_4 \dfrac{64}{3} - \log_4 32$

c) $\log_5 \sqrt{225} - \log_5 \sqrt{9}$

d) $\dfrac{1}{2} \log_3 225 - \log_3 5 + 3 \log_3 3$

7. Evaluate, using the laws of logarithms.

a) $\log_4 12 - \log_4 3$

b) $3 \log 6 + 2 \log 5 - \log 54$

8. Write $\log_3 5 + 2 \log_3 (x - 2)$ as a single logarithm.

9. Write $\log \left(\dfrac{ab^4}{\sqrt[4]{c}} \right)$ as sums and differences of logarithms. Simplify, if possible.

10. Simplify and state restrictions necessary on the variable.

a) $\log (x^2 - 4x - 12) - \log (3x - 18)$

b) $\log (x^3 - 27) - \log (x - 3)$

11. Write as a sum or difference of logarithms. Simplify, if possible.

a) $\log_5 (xy)$

b) $\log_8 \left(\dfrac{a}{b} \right)$

c) $\log_2 40$

d) $\log_6 120$

B

12. Simplify. State any restrictions on the variables.

a) $\log \left(\dfrac{\sqrt{x}}{x^2} \right)$

b) $\log \left(\dfrac{x^5}{\sqrt[3]{x}} \right) + \log (x^2)^4$

c) $\log \sqrt[3]{x^4} + \log \sqrt{x} + \log (\sqrt{x})^6$

d) $4 \log x - 5 \log \sqrt{x} + \dfrac{1}{2} \log x^8$

☆ **13.** Simplify. State any restrictions on the variable.

a) $\log (x^2 - 9) - \log (x + 3)$

b) $\log (x^2 - 11x + 28) - \log (x - 7)$

c) $\log (x^2 + 5x - 36) - \log (3x - 12)$

d) $\log (2x^2 + 7x + 6) - \log (x^2 - 4)$

14. Simplify. State any restrictions on the variables.

a) $\log (m^5) - \log (m^2) + \log m$

b) $\log (\sqrt[3]{p}) + \log (\sqrt{p}) + \log (\sqrt[6]{p})$

c) $\log (x^2 - 5x - 6) - \log (x - 3)$

d) $\log (6x^2 + 5x - 6) + \log (2x - 3)$
     $- \log (4x^2 - 9)$

15. Use Technology

a) Graph the function $f(x) = \log x$.

b) Graph the function $g(x) = 2f(x)$.

c) Graph the function $h(x) = f(x^2)$.

d) How are the functions $g(x)$ and $h(x)$ related? What law of logarithms does this illustrate?

16. Use the laws of logarithms to write y as a function of x for each of the following. Then, state the domain of the function.

a) $\log (xy) = 2 \log (x - 3)$

b) $\log (y) + 3 = \log (y + 1) + \log (x)$

c) $\log \left(\dfrac{x^2}{y} \right) = 2 \log (x + 5)$

17. Prove that $\dfrac{1}{\log_x 10} + \dfrac{1}{\log_y 10} = \dfrac{1}{\log_{xy} 10}$.

$\left(\text{Hint: recall that } \log_n m = \dfrac{\log m}{\log n}\right)$

18. a) Graph the functions $f(x) = 7 \log x$ and $g(x) = 5 \log x$.

  b) Graph the difference of these two functions $r(x) = f(x) - g(x)$.

  c) Graph the function $s(x) = \log x^2$.

  d) How are the functions $r(x)$ and $s(x)$ related? What law of logarithms does this illustrate?

19. Ifra, a recent business school graduate, has been offered entry-level positions with two firms. Firm A offers a starting salary of $45 000 per year, with a $2500 per year increase guaranteed each subsequent year. Firm B offers a starting salary of $37 000, with a 7% increase every year after that.

  a) After how many years will Ifra earn the same amount at either firm?

  b) At which firm will she earn more after

   i) 10 years?

   ii) 20 years?

  c) What other factors might affect Ifra's choice? Explain how these factors may influence her decision.

20. Energy is needed to transport a substance from outside a living cell to inside the cell. This energy, E, is measured in kilocalories per gram molecule. It is given by the relationship
$E = 1.4 \log \dfrac{C_1}{C_2}$, where C_1 represents the concentration of the substance outside the cell, and C_2 represents the concentration inside the cell.

  a) Find the energy needed to transport the exterior substance into the cell if the concentration of the substance inside the cell is

   i) double the concentration outside the cell

   ii) triple the concentration outside the cell

  b) What is the sign of E if $C_1 < C_2$? Explain what this means in terms of the cell.

21. The formula for the gain in voltage of an electronic device is

$A_v = 20 \,(\log V_0 - \log V_i)$, where V_0 in the output voltage and V_i is the input voltage.

  a) Write a simplified form of this formula, expressing the right side as a single logarithm.

  b) Verify the gain in voltage for $V_0 = 22.8$ and $V_i = 14$ using both versions of the formula.

C

☆ **22.** Use the product law of logarithms and the power law of logarithms to prove the quotient law of logarithms,
$\log_a \dfrac{p}{q} = \log_a p - \log_a q$, where $a > 0$,
$a \neq 1, p > 0, q > 0$.

KEY CONCEPTS

- It is possible to solve an equation involving logarithms by expressing both sides of a logarithm of the same base: if $a = b$, then $\log a = \log b$, and if $\log a = \log b$, then $a = b$.

- When a quadratic equation is obtained, methods such as factoring or applying the quadratic formula may be useful.

- Some algebraic methods of solving logarithmic equations lead to extraneous roots that are not valid solutions to the original equations.

Example

Find the roots of each equation.

a) $\log(5 - x) = 3$

b) $\log_4(2x + 6) = 3$

Solution

a) $\log(5 - x) = 3$

$$5 - x = 10^3$$
$$5 - x = 1000$$
$$x = -995$$

b) $\log_4(2x + 6) = 3$

$$2x + 6 = 4^3$$
$$2x + 6 = 64$$
$$2x = 58$$
$$x = 29$$

Example

Solve. Identify and reject any extraneous roots.

a) $\log(x + 2) - 1 = -\log(x - 1)$

b) $\log \sqrt[5]{x^2 - 21x} = \frac{2}{5}$

c) $\log_9(x - 5) + \log_9(x + 3) = 1$

Solution

a) $\log(x + 2) - 1 = -\log(x - 1)$

$\log(x + 2) + \log(x - 1) = 1$

$$(x + 2)(x - 1) = 10$$
$$x^2 - x + 2x - 2 = 10$$
$$x^2 + x - 12 = 0$$
$$(x + 4)(x - 3) = 0$$
$$x + 4 = 0 \qquad x - 3 = 0$$
$$x = -4 \qquad x = 3$$

extraneous

b)
$$\log \sqrt[5]{x^2 - 21x} = \frac{2}{5}$$
$$(x^2 - 21x)^{\frac{1}{5}} = 10^{\frac{2}{5}}$$
$$x^2 - 21x = 100$$
$$x^2 - 21x - 100 = 0$$
$$(x - 25)(x + 4) = 0$$
$$x - 25 = 0 \qquad x + 4 = 0$$
$$x = 25 \qquad x = -4$$

extraneous

c) $\log_9(x - 5) + \log_9(x + 3) = 1$
$$\log_9(x - 5)(x + 3) = 1$$
$$(x - 5)(x + 3) = 9$$
$$x^2 - 2x - 15 = 9$$
$$x^2 - 2x - 24 = 0$$
$$(x - 6)(x + 4) = 0$$
$$x - 6 = 0 \quad x + 4 = 0$$
$$x = 6 \qquad x = -4$$

extraneous

A

1. **Use Technology** Find the roots of each equation. Check your solutions using graphing technology.

   a) $\log(x - 5) = 1$

   b) $\log(x - 35) = 2$

   c) $15 = 5\log(x + 73)$

   d) $1 - \log(x + 4) = 0$

   e) $\log(x - 6) = 2$

   f) $8 - 4\log 3n = 0$

2. Solve.

   a) $\log_4(x + 9) = 2$

   b) $6 = \log_2(3x - 12)$

   c) $3 - \log_3(x - 17) = 0$

   d) $12 = \log_5(x + 150) + 9$

   e) $\log_8(t + 2) - 1 = 0$

   f) $\log_3(n^2 - 2n - 6) = 2$

3. **Use Technology** Solve. Identify and reject any extraneous roots. Check your solutions using graphing technology.

   a) $\log_4(x - 3) + \log_4(x + 3) = 2$

   b) $\log x^4 - \log 3 = \log(3x^2)$

   c) $\log(v - 2) = 1 + \log(v + 2)$

   d) $2 + \log x = \log(x - 9)$

   e) $\log_2(x + 3) + \log_2(x - 3) = 4$

   f) $\log_7(x + 1) + \log_7(x - 5) = 1$

4. **Use Technology** Solve $\log_5(2x - 1) = 2$. Verify the solution to the equation using graphing technology. Explain your method.

B

5. **Use Technology** Solve. Check the extraneous roots. Check your results using graphing technology.

   a) $\log_9 \sqrt{x^2 - 6x} = \dfrac{1}{2}$

   b) $\log \sqrt{x^2 + 21x} = 2$

★ 6. Solve. Identify any extraneous roots.

   a) $\log_{11} x + \log_{11}(x + 1) = \log_{11} 6$

   b) $\log(3x + 6) = 1 + \log x$

   c) $\log_2(x + 7) - \log_2(2x) = 3$

7. **Use Technology** Find the roots of each equation, correct to two decimal places, using graphing technology. Sketch the graphical solutions.

   a) $\log(x + 3) = 1 - \log x$

   b) $2 \log(x + 3) = \log(4x) - 5$

★ 8. An airplane altimeter is a gauge that indicates the height of the plane above the ground. The gauge works based on air pressure, according to the formula $h = 18\,400 \log \dfrac{P_0}{P}$, where h is the height of the airplane above the ground in metres, P is the air pressure at height h, and P_0 is the air pressure at ground level. Air pressure is measured in kilopascals (kPa).

   a) Air pressure at the ground is 102 kPa. If the air pressure outside the airplane is 32.5 kPa, what is the height of the airplane?

   b) How high would the airplane have to be flying for the outside air pressure at that height to be half of the air pressure at ground level?

   c) If the weather changes, then the air pressure at ground level may change. How do pilots take this into account?

9. Another formula to calculate altitude or atmospheric pressure takes temperature into account. If x is the atmospheric pressure (measured in millimetres of mercury), then the formula for the altitude $h(x)$, measured in metres above sea level, is $h(x) = (30T + 8000) \log\left(\dfrac{P_0}{x}\right)$, where T is the temperature, in degree Celsius at altitude $h(x)$, and P_0 is the atmospheric (barometric) pressure at sea level which is approximately 760 mm of mercury.

   a) At what height is a small airplane whose instruments record an outside temperature of 0^0 C and a barometric pressure of 300 mm of mercury?

   b) What is the barometric pressure outside a passenger aircraft flying at an altitude of 10 000 metres if the outside air temperature is -100^0 C?

   c) What is the barometric pressure at the summit of Mount Everest, which has an elevation of approximately 8900 metres, if the air temperature is 5^0 C?

C

10. Solve the equation $3 \log(x - 15) = \left(\dfrac{1}{4}\right)^x$.

11. Solve the equation $\dfrac{\log(28 - x^3)}{\log(4 - x)} = 7$.

- Different technology tools and strategies can be used to construct mathematical models that describe real situations.

- A good mathematical model
    - is useful for both interpolating and extrapolating from given data in order to make predictions
    - can be used, in conjunction with other considerations, to aid in decision making

- Exponential and logarithmic equations often appear in contexts that involve continuous growth or decay.

Example

A bacterial culture has been growing steadily for several hours. The table below gives the growth of the culture at 5-h intervals, beginning at 9:00 a.m.

Time (hours)	Amount of Bacteria
0	140
5	1415
10	2000
15	2828
20	4000
25	5656
30	8000

a) Create a scatter plot to illustrate this growth trend.

b) Construct a quadratic model to fit the data.

c) Construct an exponential model to fit the data.

d) Which model is better? why?

e) When will the amount of bacteria reach 5000?

Solution

a)

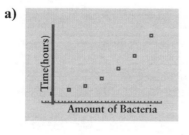

b) $y = 7.47x^2 + 0.76x + 1117.74$

$R^2 = 0.997\ 19$

c) $y = 1000(1.07)^x$

$R^2 = 0.999\ 99$

d) The exponential model is better. It fits the data better and its regression coefficient is closer to 1.

e) $5000 = 1000(1.07)^x$

$5 = 1.07^x$

$\ln 5 = x \ln 1.07$

$x = \dfrac{\ln 5}{\ln 1.07}$

$x = 23.78$

There would be 23.78 growth intervals of 5 h each. Therefore, the amount of bacteria will reach 5000 after 118.9 h.

Example

The compound interest formula modelling the future amount, A, of an investment with initial principal, P, is $A = P(1 + i)^n$, where I is the interest rate per compounding period, in decimal form, and n is the number of compounding periods. Sasha wishes to invest $1500 in a Registered Education Savings Plan that earns 12% interest, compounded quarterly.

a) Write an equation for the value of the investment as a function of time, in years.

b) Determine the value of the investment after 5 years.

c) How long will it take for the investment to double in value?

Solution

a) $A = 1500(1 + 0.03)^{4x}$

b) $A = 1500(1 + 0.03)^{4x}$

$A = 1500(1.03)^{4 \times 5}$

$A = 1500(1.03)^{20}$

$A = \$2709.17$

c) $\quad A = 1500(1 + 0.03)^{4x}$

$3000 = 1500(1 + 0.03)^{4x}$

$2 = (1.03)^{4x}$

$\ln 2 = 4x \ln 1.03$

$x = \dfrac{\ln 2}{4 \times \ln 1.03}$

$x = 5.86$

It will take about 5.86 years, or 5 years and 10 months, for the investment to double in value.

1. Sasha has a 100-g sample of a radioactive material. He records the amount of radioactive material every week for 6 weeks and obtains the following data.

Week	Weight (g)
0	100
1	88.3
2	75.9
3	69.4
4	59.1
5	51.8
6	45.5

a) Draw a scatter diagram with the week as the independent variable.

b) Find the exponential function of best fit. Express the function of best fit in the form $A = A_0 e^{kt}$.

c) Use the solution to part b) to estimate the time it takes until l50 g of material are left.

d) Use the solution to part b) to predict how much radioactive material will be left after 50 weeks.

e) **Use Technology** Use a calculator to verify the exponential function of best fit.

2. The number of students who were home-schooled in Canada in selected years is shown in the table below.

School Year	Number of Children
1983	925
1985	1830
1988	2250
1990	3010
1992	4700
1993	5880
1994	7350
1995	8000
1996	9200
1997	11 000

a) Draw a scatter diagram with the school year as the independent variable.

b) Find the exponential function of best fit. Express the function of best fit in the form $A = A_0 e^{kt}$.

c) Use the solution to part b) to estimate the time it takes until there are 15 000 children home-schooled in a year.

d) Use the solution to part b) to predict how many students will be home-schooled in 2020.

e) **Use Technology** Use a calculator to verify the exponential function of best fit.

B

⭐ 3. A $2500 investment earns 5% interest compounded semi-annually.

a) Write an equation for the value of the investment as a function of time, in years.

b) Determine the value of the investment after 5 years.

c) How long will it take for the investment to double in value?

4. Refer to question 3. Suppose that a penalty for early withdrawal of 3% of the initial investment is applied if the withdrawal occurs within the first 5 years.

a) Write an equation for the adjusted value of the investment as a function of time.

b) Describe the effect this adjustment would have on the graph of the original function.

5. The table below shows the population growth of rabbits living in a warren.

Time (years)	Number of Rabbits
1	12
2	15
3	19
4	23
5	29
6	37
7	46

a) Create a scatter plot of the rabbit population over time.

b) Perform the following types of regression to model the data:

  i) linear

  ii) quadratic

  iii) exponential

c) Record the equation for the line or curve of best fit in each case.

d) Assuming that the rabbit population had been steadily growing for several months before the collection of data, which model best fits the situation? why?

e) Use the model to predict when the population will reach 100.

f) Do you think this trend will continue indefinitely? Explain why or why not.

6. The population of a species of animal in a nature reserve grows by 12.2% each year. Initially, there are 200 of that species.

a) Write an equation for the population of the species as a function of time, in years.

b) After 20 years, an epidemic kills all but 200 of the species. After the epidemic, the population grows as it did before. What will be the equation modelling the population after the epidemic?

c) Sketch the graph of the population for $0 \le t \le 30$.

C

★ **7.** Newton's Law of Cooling states that the temperature of a heated object will decrease exponentially over time towards the temperature of the surrounding medium. That is, the temperature, u, of a heated object at a given time, t, obeys the law $u(t) = T + (u_0 - T)e^{kt}$, where T is the constant temperature of the surrounding medium, u_0 is the initial temperature of the heated object, and k is a negative number.

a) An object is heated to 100°C and is then allowed to cool in a room that has an air temperature of 21°C. If after 5 min the temperature of the object is 80°C, when will its temperature be 50°C?

b) A thermometer reading -5°C is brought into a room with a constant temperature of 21°C. If the thermometer reads 15°C after 3 min, what will it read after being in the room for 5 min? for 10 min?

8. The difference in two sound levels, β_1 and β_2, in decibels (dB), is given by the logarithmic equation

$$\beta_2 - \beta_1 = 10 \log\left(\frac{I_2}{I_1}\right), \text{ where } \frac{I_2}{I_1} \text{ is the}$$

ratio of their intensities.

a) The sound level of a jet at take off is 140 dB, while the level of a normal conversation is 50 dB. What is the ratio of the intensities of the sound level of the jet versus the level of normal conversation?

b) What is the loudness of a jackhammer (in use) if it is known that this sound has an intensity 10 times that of sound due to heavy city traffic (90 dB)?

Chapter 7: Challenge Questions

C1. Write each as a power of 6.

a) 216

b) $\dfrac{1}{36}$

c) $\sqrt[5]{6^7}$

C2. Solve each equation. Check your answers using graphing technology.

a) $4^{5x} = 32^{x+2}$

b) $9^{2x+1} = 27^{x-7}$

C3. The half-life of a substance is 80 days. Initially, there are 500 mg of this substance.

a) How much of the substance will remain after 60 days?

b) When will 100 mg of the substance remain?

C4. Solve exactly.

a) $4^{x-2} = 7^x$

b) $2^{x-3} = 3^{x+7}$

C5. The equation $y = a(2)^{bt}$ models an exponential relation.

a) Explain what the restriction is on b. Why does t not have the same restriction?

b) For what values of b will the equation model an exponential growth? Explain why.

c) For what value of b will the equation model an exponential decay? Explain why.

C6. Solve each equation. Check for extraneous roots.

a) $2^{2x} + 7(2^x) + 12 = 0$

b) $2(5^{2x}) - 7(5^x) = 15$

c) $4^{2x} + 9(4^x) + 14 = 0$

d) $7^{2x} + 3(7^x) = 10$

C7. Scientists who study Atlantic salmon have found that the oxygen consumption, O, of a yearling salmon is given by the function $O = 100\left(3^{\frac{3s}{5}}\right)$, where s is the speed that the fish is travelling in metres per second.

a) What is the oxygen consumption of a fish that is travelling at 3 m/s?

b) If a fish has travelled 1.2 km in an hour, what is its oxygen consumption?

C8. Evaluate, using the laws of logarithms.

a) $\log_7 49 + \log_7 343$

b) $\log_5 1125 - \log_5 9$

c) $2\log 5 + \log 4$

d) $3\log 4 + 2\log\left(\dfrac{5}{4}\right)$

C9. Write as a single logarithm.

a) $\log_8 7 + 2\log_8 3 - \log_8 3$

b) $\log_a b + c\log_a d - r\log_a s$

C10. Write as a sum or difference of logarithms. Simplify, if possible.

a) $\log_4 \dfrac{a^2 b}{\sqrt{c}}$

b) $\log_9\left(\sqrt[3]{y^2 + y}\right)$

C11. Simplify and state any restrictions on the variables.

a) $\log(2x + 10) - \log(x^2 - 25)$

b) $\log(2x^2 + 7x + 6) - \log(2x^2 - 7x - 15)$

C12. Solve.

a) $\log_3(5 - x) = 3$

b) $1 - \log_3(4x - 15) = 0$

C13. Solve $\log_6(x + 3) + \log_6(x - 2) = 1$. Check for extraneous roots.

C14. The percent, P, of caffeine remaining in your bloodstream is related to the elapsed time, t, in hours, by $t = 5\left(\dfrac{\log P}{\log 0.5}\right)$.

a) How long will it take for the amount of caffeine to drop to 25% of the amount consumed?

b) Suppose you drank a cup of coffee after dinner at 5:00 p.m. What percent of the caffeine will remain in your body when you go to bed at 10:30 p.m.?

C15. Use the product and quotient laws of logarithms to prove the power law of logarithms $\log_a(p^c) = c \log_a p$, where $a > 0$, $a \neq 1$, $p > 0$, $q > 0$, and $p, q \in (0, \infty)$, and $c \in \Re$.

C16. Show that if $\log_b a = c$ and $\log_y b = c$, then, $\log_a y = c^{-2}$.

C17. Solve for x and check your solution.

a) $\log_2 x + \log_4 x + \log_8 x + \log_{16} x = 25$

b) $2(5^{6x}) - 9(5^{4x}) + 13(5^{2x}) - 6 = 0$

C18. The following data represent the amount of money an investor has in an investment account each year for 10 years. She wishes to determine the effective rate of return on her investment.

Year	Value of Account
1999	$10 000
2000	$10 573
2001	$11 260
2002	$11 733
2003	$12 424
2004	$13 269
2005	$13 968
2006	$14 823
2007	$15 297
2008	$16 539

a) Draw a scatter diagram with the year as the independent variable.

b) Find the exponential function of best fit. Express the function of best fit in the form $A = A_0 e^{kt}$.

c) Use the solution to part b) to predict the value of the account in the year 2020.

d) Use the solution to part b) to predict how long it will take to have $25 000 in the account.

e) Use Technology Use a calculator to verify the exponential function of best fit.

C19. A savings bond offers interest at a rate of 8.8% compounded semi-annually. Suppose that a $1500 bond is purchased.

a) Write an equation for the value of the investment as a function of time, in years.

b) Determine the value of the investment after 12 years.

c) How long will it take for the investment to triple in value?

d) Describe how the shape of the graph of this function would change if

i) a bonus of 5% of the principal was added after 5 years had passed

ii) the size of the initial investment were doubled

C20. On average, the number of items, N, per day, on an assembly line, that a quality assurance trainee can inspect is $N = 45 - 26(0.74)^t$, where t is the number of days worked.

a) After how many days of training will the employee be able to inspect 43 items?

b) The company expects an experienced quality assurance employee to inspect 50 items per day. After the training period of 20 days is complete, how close will the trainee be to the experienced employee's quota?

By the end of this chapter, I will be able to:

- Write a power using different bases

- Solve equations involving exponential expressions using a variety of methods (change of base, algebraic manipulation, use of graphing technology)

- Identify and reject extraneous roots to equations involving exponential expressions

- Solve problems involving exponential equations

- Apply the product and quotient laws of logarithms

- State restrictions on variables for expressions involving logarithms

- Solve equations involving logarithmic expressions using a variety of methods (rewrite numbers as logarithms, apply laws of logarithms, use of graphing technology)

- Solve problems involving logarithmic equations

- Construct and evaluate mathematical models involving exponential and logarithmic relationships

- Apply exponential and logarithmic models to solve contextual problems

Chapter 8 Combining Functions

8.1 Sum and Difference of Functions

KEY CONCEPTS

- Some combined functions are formed by adding or subtracting two or more functions.

- The superposition principle states that the sum of two or more functions can be found by adding the ordinates (y-coordinates) of the function at each abscissa (x-coordinate). For example, the sum of $f(x) = 2x$ and $f(x) = x - 1$ is $f(x) = 3x - 1$, which is calculated by adding the y values at every x value.

- The superposition principle also applies to the difference of two functions.

- The domain of the sum or difference of functions is the domain common to the component function.

Example

Determine an equation for the function $h(x) = f(x) + g(x)$ in each case. Then, graph $h(x)$ and state the domain and range of the function.

a) $f(x) = 5x + 2, g(x) = 6$

b) $f(x) = x^2 - 1, g(x) = x$

Solution

a) $h(x) = f(x) + g(x)$

$h(x) = 5x + 2 + 6$

$h(x) = 5x + 8$

The domain is $\{x \in \mathbb{R}\}$ and the range is $\{y \in \mathbb{R}\}$.

b) $h(x) = f(x) + g(x)$

    $h(x) = x^2 - 1 + x$

    $h(x) = x^2 + x - 1$

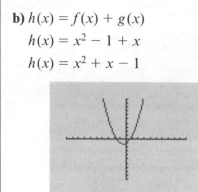

The domain is $\{x \in \mathbb{R}\}$ and the range is $\{y \in \mathbb{R} \mid y \geq -1.25\}$.

Example

Student Council is selling prom tickets. The cost to rent the hall is $1500, plus a meal cost of $45 per ticket. The Council has decided to sell the tickets for $60 each.

a) Write an equation to represent

   • the total cost, C, as a function of the number, n, of prom tickets sold

   • the revenue, R, as a function of the number, n, of prom tickets sold

b) Graph the functions in part a) on the same set of axes. Identify the point of intersection and explain the meaning of its coordinates.

c) Profit, P, is the difference between revenue and expenses. Develop an algebraic and graphical model for the profit function.

d) Under what circumstances will Student Council lose money? make money?

e) Identify the domain and range of the cost, revenue, and profit functions in the context of this problem.

Solution

a) $C(n) = 1500 + 45n$

    $R(n) = 60n$

b)

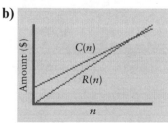

The point of intersection is (100, 6000). This represents the break-even point where the prom would be making money.

c) Profit = Revenue − Costs

$$P(n) = 60n - (1500 + 45n)$$

$$P(n) = 15n - 1500$$

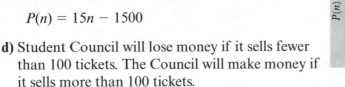

d) Student Council will lose money if it sells fewer than 100 tickets. The Council will make money if it sells more than 100 tickets.

e) Cost function: $C(n) = 1500 + 45n$

The domain is $\{n \in \mathbb{R} \,|\, n \geq 0\}$ and the range is $\{C(n) \in \mathbb{R} \,|\, C(n) \geq 1500\}$.

Revenue function: $R(n) = 60n$

The domain is $\{n \in \mathbb{R} \,|\, n \geq 0\}$ and the range is $\{R(n) \in \mathbb{R} \,|\, R(n) \geq 0\}$.

Profit function: $P(n) = 15n - 1500$

The domain is $\{n \in \mathbb{R} \,|\, n \geq 0\}$ and the range is $\{P(n) \in \mathbb{R} \,|\, P(n) \geq -1500\}$.

A

1. For each pair of functions, find

   i) $y = f(x) + g(x)$

   ii) $y = f(x) - g(x)$

   iii) $y = g(x) - f(x)$

   a) $f(x) = 6x$ and $g(x) = x - 4$

   b) $f(x) = -3x + 7$ and $g(x) = -2x + 3$

   c) $f(x) = x^2 - 2$ and $g(x) = 4$

   d) $f(x) = 2x^2 + 3x - 7$ and $g(x) = 5x - 2$

2. Let $f(x) = 6x + 7$ and $g(x) = 2x - 5$.

   a) Determine an equation for the function $h(x) = f(x) + g(x)$. Then, find $h(-2)$.

   b) Determine an equation for the function $h(x) = f(x) - g(x)$. Then, find $h(4)$.

   c) Determine an equation for the function $h(x) = g(x) - f(x)$. Then, find $h(-3)$.

3. Let $f(x) = 2x^2 + 3$ and $g(x) = 5x - 7$.

   a) Determine an equation for the function $h(x) = f(x) + g(x)$. Then, find $h(0)$.

   b) Determine an equation for the function $h(x) = f(x) - g(x)$. Then, find $h(-5)$.

   c) Determine an equation for the function $h(x) = g(x) - f(x)$. Then, find $h(6)$.

4. Copy each graph of $f(x)$ and $g(x)$. Then, apply the superposition principle to graph $y = f(x) + g(x)$. Give the domain and range of $y = f(x) + g(x)$.

a)

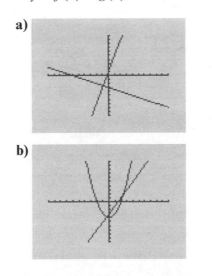

b)

5. For each graph in question 4, use the superposition principle to graph $y = f(x) - g(x)$.

★ **6.** Let $f(x) = |x|$ and $g(x) = 5$.

a) Graph each of the following:

i) $y = f(x) + g(x)$

ii) $y = f(x) - g(x)$

iii) $y = g(x) - f(x)$

b) Explain how you could also produce each of these combined functions by applying transformations to the graph of $f(x) = |x|$.

c) Give the domain and range of each combined function.

7. Let $f(x) = \cos x$ and $g(x) = 2^x$. Work in radians.

a) Sketch these functions on the same set of axes.

b) Sketch a graph of $y = f(x) + g(x)$.

c) Sketch a graph of $y = f(x) - g(x)$.

d) Check your answers using graphing technology.

B

8. A bicycle courier has a fixed delivery cost of $12.50 per day, plus a variable cost of $0.25/package. He earns $4.25 per package he delivers, in revenue. The maximum number of packages that he can deliver in a day is 27.

a) Write an equation to represent

• the total cost, C, as a function of the number, p, of packages delivered

• the revenue, R, as a function of the number, p, of packages delivered

b) Graph $C(p)$ and $R(p)$ on the same set of axes.

c) Identify the break-even point and explain what its coordinates mean.

d) Develop an algebraic and graphical model for the profit function, $P(p) = R(p) - C(p)$.

e) Identify the domain and range in the context of this problem for $C(p)$, $R(p)$, and $P(p)$.

f) What is the maximum daily profit the courier can earn?

9. Refer to question 8. The bicycle courier has found a way to improve the efficiency of his operation that will allow him to either reduce his fixed cost to $10.25 per day *or* reduce his variable cost to $0.15/package.

a) Which of these two options has the more favourable effect on

i) the break-even point?

ii) the potential maximum daily profit?

b) What advice would you give the bicycle courier?

★ **10.** Lara is going on a summer camping vacation, the first part to be spent canoeing, the second part to be completed by hiking. The time Lara will spend canoeing is given by the function $T_c(x) = \dfrac{(x^2 + 4)^{\frac{1}{2}}}{3}$, and the time she will spend hiking is given by the function $T_h(x) = \dfrac{12 - x}{5}$.

a) Sketch graphs of these functions on the same set of axes.

b) Graph the combined function $T_c(x) + T_k(x)$.

c) Identify the domain and range of $T_c(x) + T_k(x)$.

11. Consider the combined function $T(x) = f(x) + g(x) + h(x)$, where $f(x) = 3x + 1$, $g(x) = 2x^2$, and $h(x) = 3^x$.

a) Graph $f(x)$, $g(x)$, and $h(x)$ on the same set of axes. Use colours or different line styles to easily distinguish the curves.

b) Graph the combined function $T(x)$.

c) The function $T(x)$ appears to converge with one of the three component functions. Which one is it?

d) Explain the result in part c) by considering the rates of change of the component functions.

12. Let $f(x) = x - 4$ and $g(x) = x + 7$.

   a) Write an expression for $-g(x)$.

   b) Graph $f(x)$ and $-g(x)$ on the same set of axes.

   c) Add these functions to produce $f(x) + [-g(x)]$.

   d) Graph $f(x)$ and $g(x)$ together on another set of axes.

   e) Subtract these functions to produce $f(x) - g(x)$ and compare this result to the one obtained in part c).

13. A computer manufacturing company produces laptop computers for $175 per unit, plus a fixed operating cost of $750 000. The company sells the laptops for $599.00 per unit.

   a) Determine a function, $C(x)$, to represent the cost of producing x units.

   b) Determine a function, $S(x)$, to represent sales of x units.

   c) Determine a function that represents the company's profit.

14. Let $f(x) = mx^2 + 7x + 8$ and $g(x) = 3x^2 - nx + 3$. The functions are combined to form the new function $h(x) = f(x) + g(x)$. Points $(1, 18)$ and $(-1, 14)$ satisfy the new function. Determine $f(x)$ and $g(x)$.

15. Consider two functions, f and g. Explain why the domains of f and g must be the same in order to add or subtract the functions.

16. Describe how to determine the type of function for $(f + g)(x)$ if we know the degree of $f(x)$ and the degree of $g(x)$.

17. a) Sketch graphs of $f(x) = \sin x$ and $g(x) = \cos x$ on the same set of axes. Use the domain $-3\pi \le x \le 3\pi$.

   b) Use the principle of superposition to sketch a graph of $y = f(x) + g(x)$.

   c) Determine the equation of $y = f(x) + g(x)$. Express your answer as a sine function.

   d) Sketch a graph of $y = f(x) - g(x)$.

   e) Determine the equation of $y = f(x) - g(x)$. Express your answer as a sine function.

C

18. Let $f(x) = \sin x$ and $g(x) = x$.

   a) Use graphing technology to graph $f(x)$ and $g(x)$ on the same set of axes. Work in radians.

   b) Predict the shape of $h(x) = f(x) + g(x)$. Sketch a graph of your prediction.

   c) Use graphing technology to check your prediction.

   d) Hide $f(x)$ so that only $g(x)$ and $h(x)$ are visible. How many intersection points do there appear to be?

   e) Describe what you notice about where the line $g(x) = x$ intersects the graph of $h(x)$.

   f) Consider the curvature (up versus down) of $h(x)$. Explain why this is so.

KEY CONCEPTS

- A combined function of the form $y = f(x)g(x)$ represents the product of two functions, $f(x)$ and $g(x)$.

- A combined function of the form $y = \dfrac{f(x)}{g(x)}$ represents the quotient of the two functions, $f(x)$ and $g(x)$, for $g(x) \neq 0$.

- The domain of the product and quotient of functions is the domain common to the component functions. The domain of a quotient function, $y = \dfrac{f(x)}{g(x)}$, is further restricted by excluding any values that make the denominator, $g(x)$, equal to zero.

- Products and quotients of functions can be used to model a variety of situations.

Example

Let $f(x) = 2x + 3$ and $g(x) = 2x^2 + x - 3$. Determine an equation for each combined function. Sketch a graph of the combined function and state its domain and range.

a) $y = f(x)g(x)$

b) $y = \dfrac{f(x)}{g(x)}$

Solution

a) $y = f(x)g(x)$

$y = (2x + 3)(2x^2 + x - 3)$

$y = 4x^3 + 2x^2 - 6x + 6x^2 + 3x - 9$

$y = 4x^3 + 8x^2 - 3x - 9$

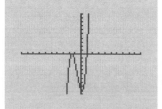

The domain is $\{x \in \mathbb{R}\}$ and the range is $\{y \in \mathbb{R}\}$.

b) $y = \dfrac{f(x)}{g(x)}$

$y = \dfrac{2x + 3}{2x^2 + x - 3}$

$y = \dfrac{2x + 3}{(2x + 3)(x - 1)}$

$y = \dfrac{1}{x - 1}$

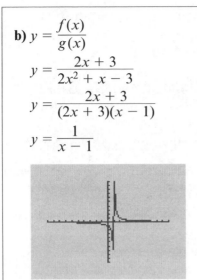

The domain is $\left\{ x \in \mathbb{R} \middle| x \neq \dfrac{-3}{2}, 1 \right\}$ and the range is $\{ y \in \mathbb{R} | y \neq 0 \}$.

Example

The cost, C, in thousands of dollars, for Widgets-R-Us to produce x thousand of its widgets is given by the function $C(x) = 230 + 0.24x + 0.000\,1x^2$. The revenue, R, from the sales of its widgets is given by the function, $R(x) = x\,D(x)$, where $D(x)$ is the demand function, that is, the price for a widget when x widgets are sold.

a) Write the function that represents the company's profits on sales of x of the widgets.

b) Graph the cost, revenue, and profit functions.

c) What is the company's profit on the sale of 1000 widgets?

Solution

a) Profits = Revenue − Costs

$\qquad P(x) = xD(x) - C(x)$

$\qquad P(x) = 0.98x - 0.000\,2x^2 - (230 + 0.24x + 0.000\,1x^2)$

$\qquad P(x) = -0.000\,3x^2 + 0.74x - 230$

b)

```
  y
1500          C(x) = 230 + 0.24x + 0.000 1x
                   R(x) = x(0.98 − 0.000 2x)
1000

 500
        P(x) = R(x) − C(x)

  0   1000 2000 3000 4000  x
```

c) $\qquad P(x) = -0.000\,3x^2 + 0.74x - 230$

$\qquad P(1000) = -0.000\,3(1000)^2 + 0.74(1000) - 230$

$\qquad P(1000) = 210$

In this example, the profit on the sale of 1000 widgets is $210.

A

1. Let $f(x) = x + 3$ and $g(x) = x^2 - 9$. Develop an algebraic and graphical model for each combined function. Then, give the domain and range of the combined function. Identify any holes or asymptotes.

   a) $y = f(x)g(x)$

   b) $y = \dfrac{f(x)}{g(x)}$

   c) $y = \dfrac{g(x)}{f(x)}$

2. Let $u(x) = \sin x$ and $v(x) = 0.5^x$. Develop an algebraic and a graphical model for each combined function. Then, give the domain and range of the combined function. Identify any holes or asymptotes.

   a) $y = u(x)v(x)$

   b) $y = \dfrac{u(x)}{v(x)}$

   c) $y = \dfrac{v(x)}{u(x)}$

B

3. A small town initially has a population of 1500 people. The population, P, of people grows as a function of time, t, in years, as $P(t) = 1500(1.5)^t$. The surrounding farms supply the town with food. The amount, F, of food is decreasing as the size of the farms is decreasing because of urban sprawl, according to the function $F(t) = 5000(0.25)^t$.

   a) Graph the functions $P(t)$ and $F(t)$ on the same set of axes. Describe the nature of these functions.

   b) Determine the domain and range of these functions.

   c) Identify the point of intersection of these two curves. Determine the coordinates, to two decimal places, and explain what they mean. Call this point in time the crisis point.

   d) Graph the function $y = F(t) - P(t)$. Explain the significance of this function.

   e) What is the t-intercept of the function $y = F(t) - P(t)$? How does this relate to the crisis point?

   f) Comment on the validity of the mathematical model for $P(t)$ for t values greater than this intercept.

4. Refer to the equations from question 3.

   a) Graph the function $y = \dfrac{F(t)}{P(t)}$ on a different set of axes. What does this function represent? Describe the shape of this function.

   b) What are the coordinates of this function at the crisis point? Explain the meaning of these coordinates.

   c) Describe the living conditions of the people in the town before, at, and after the crisis point.

★5. Let $f(x) = \sqrt{x^2 - 4}$ and $g(x) = \cos x$.

   a) Graph $f(x)$ and describe its shape. Is this function even, odd, or neither?

   b) Graph $g(x)$ on the same set of axes. Is this function even, odd, or neither?

   c) **Use Technology** Predict the shape of $y = f(x)g(x)$. Sketch a graph of your prediction. Then, check your prediction using graphing technology.

   d) Give the domain and range of $y = f(x)g(x)$.

6. Refer to the functions in question 5.

   a) Graph $y = \dfrac{g(x)}{f(x)}$. Is this function even, odd, or neither? Give the domain and range.

   b) Graph $y = \dfrac{f(x)}{g(x)}$. Is this function even, odd, or neither? Give the domain and range.

7. Alex has decided to breed rabbits. The initial population was 12 rabbits and is growing at a rate of 55% per year. The population, P, as a function of time, t, in years, can be modelled by the function $P(t) = 12(1.55)^t$. However, Alex has to feed the rabbits. The amount of food that can sustain the hutch is given by the equation $F(t) = 16 + 0.05t$.

   a) Graph $P(t)$ and $F(t)$ on the same set of axes and describe the trends.

   b) Graph the function $y = F(t) - P(t)$, and describe the trend. Does the hutch enjoy a food surplus or suffer from a food shortage? Explain. What about in years to come?

   c) Identify the coordinates of the maximum of $y = F(t) - P(t)$ and explain what they mean.

8. The food production per capita in question 7 is the amount of food per rabbit.

   a) Graph the function $y = \dfrac{F(t)}{P(t)}$ and describe its trend.

   b) At what time is the food production per capita a maximum for the rabbit hutch? Does this point coincide with the maximum in part c) of question 7? Explain the result.

   c) What does it mean when $\dfrac{F(t)}{P(t)} > 1$ and $\dfrac{F(t)}{P(t)} < 1$? When are these conditions projected to occur in the rabbit hutch?

C

★9. Consider the functions $f(x) = 3^{-x}$ and $g(x) = x^2$. Sketch a graph of the function $y = f(x)g(x)$ and describe its key features. Explain its end behaviour.

10. Let $f(x) = x - 3$ and $g(x) = x^2 - 4x + 3$.

   a) Determine each combined function.

   i) $y = f(x) - g(x)$

   ii) $y = \dfrac{f(x)}{g(x)}$

   b) State the domain and range of $y = \dfrac{f(x)}{g(x)}$.

11. At the Canadian National Exhibition there is a swing ride that can be modelled by the function $s(t) = 5\cos(4t) \times 0.85^t$, where s is the horizontal displacement from the rest position in metres, as a function of time, t, in seconds.

   a) What was the initial horizontal displacement of the swing?

   b) Sketch how the shape of the graph would change if

   i) the air resistance were reduced

   ii) the length of the swing were lengthened.

   Justify your answers with mathematical reasoning.

12. The algebraic tests used to decide whether a function is even or odd are as follows.

   • A function f is even provided $f(-x) = f(x)$.

   • A function f is odd provided $f(-x) = f-(x)$.

   a) Suppose f and g are both odd. Prove that $y = f(x)g(x)$ is even.

   b) Suppose f is even and g is odd. Prove that $y = f(x)g(x)$ is odd.

   c) Suppose f and g are both even. Prove that is $y = f(x)g(x)$ even.

   d) Is the product of functions in any way analogous to the multiplication of numbers when it comes to evenness and oddness? Explain.

13. Let $f(x) = 3x^2 + mx - 1$ and $g(x) = nx^2 + 2x + 4$. The functions are combined to form a new function $h(x) = f(x) \times g(x)$. Points $(1, 33)$ and $(-1, -3)$ satisfy the new function. Determine $f(x)$ and $g(x)$.

KEY CONCEPTS

- $f(g(x))$ denotes a composite function, that is, one in which the function $f(x)$ depends on the function $g(x)$. This can also be written as $(f \circ g)(x)$.

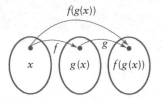

- To determine an equation for a composite function, substitute the second function into the first, as read from left to right. To determine $f(g(x))$, substitute $g(x)$ for x in $f(x)$.

- To evaluate a composite function $f(g(x))$ at a specific value, substitute the value into the equation of the composite function and simplify, or evaluate $g(x)$ at the specific value and then substitute the result into $f(x)$.

Example

Let $f(x) = 3x^2$ and $g(x) = x - 2$. Determine an equation for each composite function, graph the function, and give its domain and range.

a) $y = f(g(x))$

b) $y = g(f(x))$

c) $y = f(f(x))$

d) $y = g(g(x))$

e) $y = g^{-1}(g(x))$

Solution

a) $y = f(g(x))$

$\quad y = 3(x - 2)^2$

$\quad y = 3(x^2 - 4x + 4)$

$\quad y = 3x^2 - 12x + 12$

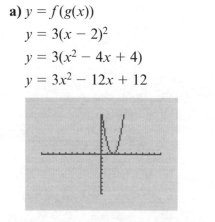

The domain is $\{x \in \mathbb{R}\}$ and the range is $\{y \in \mathbb{R} \mid y \geq 0\}$.

b) $y = g(f(x))$

$y = 3x^2 - 2$

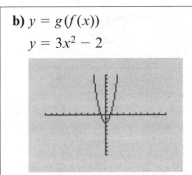

The domain is $\{x \in \mathbb{R}\}$ and the range is $\{y \in \mathbb{R} | y \geq -2\}$.

c) $y = f(f(x))$

$y = 3(3x^2)^2$

$y = 3(9x^4)$

$y = 27x^4$

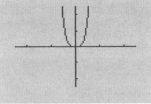

The domain is $\{x \in \mathbb{R}\}$ and the range is $\{y \in \mathbb{R} | y \geq 0\}$.

d) $y = g(g(x))$

$y = (x - 2) - 2$

$y = x - 4$

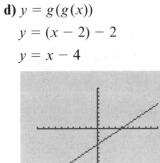

The domain is $\{x \in \mathbb{R}\}$ and the range is $\{y \in \mathbb{R}\}$.

e) $y = g^{-1}(g(x))$

$y = (x - 2) + 2$

$y = x$

The domain is $\{x \in \mathbb{R}\}$ and the range is $\{y \in \mathbb{R}\}$.

A

1. An Internet service provider has modelled its projected number of business subscribers as $B(t) = 50t + 2500$, and the projected average number of Internet connections per business subscriber as $C(t) = 0.004t^2 + 3.2$, where t is the time, in weeks, over the next year. The projected total number of business Internet connections is then $N(t) = B(t) \times C(t)$.

   a) Determine the growth rate of the number of business connections after t weeks.

   b) Determine the growth rate of the number of business connections after 12 weeks.

2. Let $f(x) = x - 2$ and $g(x) = (x - 1)^2$. Determine a simplified algebraic model for each composite function.

   a) $y = f(g(x))$ b) $y = g(f(x))$

   c) $y = f(f(x))$ d) $y = g(g(x))$

   e) $y = f^{-1}(f(x))$

3. Graph each composite function in question 2. Give the domain and range.

4. **Use Technology** Check your answers to question 3 using graphing technology.

★5. Let $f(x) = x^2 - 3x + 5$ and $g(x) = \dfrac{1}{x - 2}$. Evaluate:

   a) $g(f(1))$ b) $f(g(4))$

B

6. In the Student Council election, the popularity, P, as a percent of voters, of Candidate A can be modelled by a function of time, t, in days throughout the campaign, as $P(t) = 50 - 0.4t$. The popularity, $R(t)$ of the opposing Candidate B can be modelled by a composite function of $P(t)$, $R(P(t)) = 40 + 0.65(50 - P(t))$.

   a) Graph $P(t)$ and describe the trend.

   i) What is the popularity of Candidate A at the beginning of the campaign?

   ii) What is the rate of change of this function, and what does it mean?

   iii) Can you tell if these are the only two candidates in the election? If you can, explain how. If you cannot, describe what additional information is required.

   b) Graph $R(t)$ and describe the trend.

   i) What is the popularity of Candidate B at the beginning of the campaign?

   ii) What is the rate of change of this graph? what does it mean?

   iii) If it can be assumed that these are the only two candidates running for election, which candidate do you think will win? Does your answer depend on something? Explain.

   c) Assume that there are at least three candidates running in the election.

   i) Graph the composite function $V(t) = 100 - [P(t) + R(t)]$. What does this graph represent? Describe the trend.

   ii) Assuming that this is a three-candidate election, and that there is no undecided vote, can you tell who will win this election? Explain.

   iii) Repeat part c) assuming that there are four candidates.

7. Let $f(x) = x^4$.

   a) Determine $f^{-1}(x)$

   b) Determine $f(f^{-1}(x))$

   c) Determine $f^{-1}(f(f^{-1}(x)))$

   d) Compare your answers to parts b) and c).

   e) Determine $f(f^{-1}(2)), f(f^{-1}(4))$, and $f(f^{-1}(-2))$. What do you notice?

8. Let $f(x) = x^3$, $g(x) = x^5$, and $h(x) = \cos x$. Work in radians.

   a) Predict what the graph of $y = f(h(x))$ will look like, and sketch your prediction.

   b) Check your prediction using graphing technology.

   c) Is the function in part a) periodic? Explain.

   d) Identify the domain and range.

9. a) Repeat question 8 for $y = g(h(x))$.

   b) Compare $y = f(h(x))$ and $y = g(h(x))$. How are these functions similar? different?

10. In an electric circuit, the current through a resistor, in amperes, is given by $I = 4.85 - 0.001t^2$, and the resistance, in ohms, is given by $R = 15.00 + 0.11t$, where t is the time, in seconds. The voltage, V, in volts, across the resistor is the product of the current and the resistance.

    a) Determine an equation for the voltage as a function of time.

    b) Sketch a graph of this function.

    c) How long will it take for the voltage to reach 77 V, to the nearest second?

★11. A manufacturing company models its weekly production of alarm clocks since 2007 by the function $N(t) = 300 + 75t$, where t is the time, in years, since 2007, and N is the number of alarm clocks. The size of the company's workforce can be modelled by the composite function $W(N) = 2\sqrt{N}$.

    a) Write the size of the workforce as a function of time.

    b) State the domain and range of the new function and sketch its graph.

C

12. To rent a sailboat for an evening cruise costs $C(h) = 2500 + 50h$, where h is the number of hours of the cruise. During the

month of June, when there are a number of proms, the sailboat's rental company is offering a 5% discount.

    a) Write the new cost equation for an evening cruise including the discount.

    b) If a prom committee has raised $2600, how long can they cruise at the new price?

13. Let $f(x) = 2x^3$, $g(x) = 4x - 7$, and $h(x) = \frac{-1}{x}$.

    a) Determine a simplified algebraic model for each composite function.

    i) $f(g(x))$

    ii) $h(g(x))$

    iii) $g^{-1}(h(x))$

    b) Evaluate $f(h(-1))$.

14. Let $f(x) = |x|$, $g(x) = \sin x$, and $h(x) = x^3$. Work in radians.

    a) What is the domain of $f(x)$?

    b) Use this information to predict the shape of the graph of the composite function $y = f(g(x))$. Sketch your prediction.

    c) Check your prediction in part b) using graphing technology. Give the domain and range of $y = f(g(x))$.

    d) Use your result in part c) to predict the shape of the graph of the composite function $y = f(h(x))$. Sketch your prediction.

    e) Check your prediction in part d) using graphing technology. Give the domain and range of $y = f(h(x))$.

15. Let $f(x) = 25 - x^2$ and $g(x) = \frac{1}{x - 9}$.

    a) Determine the domain and range of $y = f(g(x))$.

    b) Determine the domain and range of $y = g(f(x))$.

    c) Use graphing technology to verify your answers in parts a) and b).

≪ KEY CONCEPTS ≫

- Solutions to problems involving combined functions can sometimes lead to a range of acceptable answers. When this happens, techniques for solving inequalities are applied.

- There are a number of ways to graphically illustrate an inequality involving a combined function.

- Algebraic and graphical representations of inequalities can be useful for solving problems involving combined functions.

A

1. Let $f(x) = 2x$ and $g(x) = x^2 - 1$.

   a) Graph the functions on the same set of axes. Identify the points of intersection.

   b) Illustrate the regions for which

   i) $f(x) > g(x)$

   ii) $g(x) > f(x)$

2. Solve $\cos x > 2^x$.

3. Talk-Us's cost, C, for shipping and storing n cell phones can be modelled by the function $C(n) = n + \dfrac{100}{n}$, where n represents years.

   a) Graph this function and explain its shape. What is the domain of interest for this problem?

   b) Determine the maximum and minimum number of cell phones that can be ordered at any one time to keep costs below $55, assuming that inventory has fallen to zero.

   c) What is the optimum order size that will minimize storage costs?

   d) Why might this be the best number to order?

Use the following information to answer questions 4 and 5.

Revenue and cost functions for the Howard's Hamburgers restaurant chain are shown on the graph.

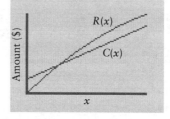

4. **a)** Suppose that Howard's Hamburgers found a way to reduce its variable cost to $0.35. How would this affect

   i) the minimum and maximum number of burgers the chain could sell?

   ii) the maximum potential profit?

   b) Sketch a graph to illustrate your explanation.

5. a) Suppose that, instead of the variable cost being reduced, the restaurant chain's fixed costs increase by $225 000. How would this affect

   i) the minimum and maximum number of burgers the chain could sell?

   ii) the maximum potential profit?

   b) Sketch a graph to illustrate your explanation.

6. The graph of two functions is shown.

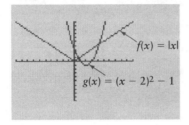

$f(x) = |x|$

$g(x) = (x - 2)^2 - 1$

   a) For what values of x is

   i) $f(x) > g(x)$?

   ii) $f(x) < g(x)$?

   b) Sketch the graph of $y = f(x) - g(x)$ on the interval $(0, 5)$.

   c) For what region is $f(x) - g(x) > 0$? Explain how this corresponds to your answer to part a).

7. Let $u(x) = -2x + 3$ and $v(x) = \left(\frac{1}{2}\right)^x$.

   a) Graph these functions on the same set of axes.

   b) Graph the combined function $y = \dfrac{u(x)}{v(x)}$.

   c) Explain how $y = \dfrac{u(x)}{v(x)}$ can be used to identify the regions where

   i) $u(x) > v(x)$

   ii) $u(x) < v(x)$

★8. Let $f(x) = -x^3 - x^2 + 17x - 15$ and $g(x) = (x - 5)^2 - 18$.

   a) Graph these functions on the same set of axes.

b) Identify, by inspecting the graphs, the intervals for which

   i) $f(x) > g(x)$

   ii) $g(x) > f(x)$

9. Solve question 8b) using two other methods.

10. Solve $\cos x > x^2$.

11. Solve $x^3 > \left(\frac{1}{4}\right)^x$.

Use the following information to answer questions 12 to 14. The owner of a local amusement park needs to identify the optimum price for admission tickets to maximize his profits. The number, N, of people who attend the amusement park is a function of the price, p, in dollars. $N(p) = -(p + 5)(p - 17)$, assuming the minimum ticket price is $12.00.

B

12. a) Graph $N(p)$.

   b) Identify the region for which $N(p) > 0$. What does this suggest about the maximum realistic ticket price? Explain your answer.

   c) Identify the domain and range for which $y = N(p)$ has meaning.

13. The revenue generated, R, in dollars, is $R(p) = N(p) \times p$, where p is the number of tickets sold.

   a) Graph the function $R(p)$ on a graphing calculator.

   b) For what region is $R(p) > 0$? Does this result agree with the result found in question 12b)?

   c) Do the maxima of $N(p)$ and $R(p)$ occur at the same value of p? Explain why or why not.

   d) What does $R(p)$ suggest that the optimum ticket price is? Explain.

14. The cost, C, of running the amusement park can be modelled by a composite function of $N(p)$, $C(p) = 75 + 12N(p)$.

  a) Graph the function $C(p)$ on a graphing calculator.

  b) Graph the combined function $y = R(p) - C(p)$. What does this function represent?

  c) Identify the region for which $R(p) - C(p) > 0$. What is the significance of this region?

  d) Do the maxima of $y = R(p)$ and $y = R(p) - C(p)$ occur for the same value of p? Explain why or why not.

  e) Identify the optimum ticket price for the amusement park and determine the maximum profit per ticket.

C

15. The Parkdalian Pen Company estimates that the cost of manufacturing x pens is $C(x) = 6000 + 0.8x$ and the revenue is $R(x) = \dfrac{1}{10\,000}(30\,000x - x^2)$.

  a) Graph $R(x)$ and $C(x)$ on the same set of axes.

  b) How many points of intersection does this system have? Explain their significance.

  c) Identify the region where $R(x) > C(x)$. Why is this region important?

  d) Maximum profit occurs when $R(x)$ exceeds $C(x)$ by the greatest amount. Use the superposition principle to graph the function $P(x) = R(x) - C(x)$.

  e) Use this function to determine

   i) the optimum number of units sold

   ii) the maximum profit per unit sold

   iii) the total profit, if the optimum number of units are sold

f) Reflect on the shapes of the revenue and cost curves. Suggest some reasons why they are shaped like this.

★**16.** Stephanie makes and sells jewellery for the gift shop at the museum. Stephanie makes n necklaces in a given week and sells them for $25 - n$ dollars per necklace. Her costs include a fixed cost of $55 plus $3.50 per necklace made. Assume that Stephanie sells all of the necklaces that she makes.

  a) Write an equation to represent her total weekly cost.

  b) Write an equation to represent her total weekly revenue.

  c) Write an inequality to express the conditions with which Stephanie will make a profit.

  d) How many necklaces should Stephanie make each week in order to make a profit?

  e) What is the optimum number of necklaces Stephanie should make in order to earn maximum profit? How much will she earn if she does this?

17. The projected population, P, of a town can be modelled by the function $P(t) = 1500(1.025)^t$, where t is the time, in years, from now. The expected number, N, of people who can be supplied by the local water services can be modelled by the function $N(t) = 4200 + 45.2t$.

  a) Determine $y = N(t) - P(t)$ and sketch the graph.

  b) Explain what the function in part a) represents.

  c) When is $N(t) - P(t) < 0$? Explain what this means.

  d) Determine $y = \dfrac{N(t)}{P(t)}$ and sketch its graph.

  e) Explain what the function in part d) represents.

┌──┐
│ ≪ **KEY CONCEPTS** ≫   │
└──┘

- A variety of real world situations can be modelled using combined functions

- To develop a model consisting of a combined function, consider
  - the component functions that could be combined to form the model
  - the nature of the rate of change of the component function
  - the other key features of the graph or equation that fit the given scenario

Example

The following table lists one octave of the frequencies of commonly used notes in North American music, rounded to the nearest hertz (Hz). This is called the Chromatic scale.

Note	Frequency (Hz)
C	262
C#	277
D	294
D#	311
E	330
F	349
F#	370
G	392
G#	415
A	440
A#	466
B	494
High C	524
High D	588
High F#	740
High G	784
High A	880

The graph of a pure note can be modelled by the function $I(t) = \sin(2\pi f t)$, where I is the sound intensity; f is the frequency of the note, in hertz; and t is the time, in seconds.

a) Graph the intensity functions for D and high D. Then, graph the combined function of these two notes struck together on domain $[-0.001, 0.005]$. Describe the resultant waveform.

b) The G-major triad is formed by striking the following notes simultaneously:

    G   B   D

Graph the combined function for these notes struck together. Explain why these notes sound good together.

c) Graph the intensity functions for D and G# and the combined function for these two notes struck together. Explain why these notes are discordant (i.e. do not sound good together).

Solution

a)

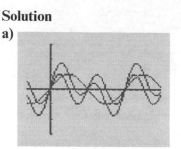

The resultant waveform is a smooth curve that is similar to the initial waveforms.

b)

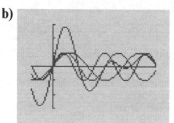

The notes of the G-major triad sound good together because the resultant curve of the combined function is similar to the waveforms graphed for the individual notes.

c)

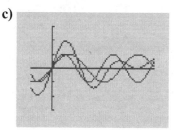

The notes D and G# do not sound good together because the resultant curve of the combined function does not follow the waveforms graphed for the individual notes.

1. A D-major triad can be expanded into other D-major chords by adding additional notes of the triad from the next octave.

   a) Graph the combined function formed by the following notes being struck simultaneously:

       D   F#   A   High F#   High G

   b) Compare this waveform to the one for the D-major triad.

2. A power chord is formed by dropping the major third (or F# note) from the D-major triad.

   a) Graph each D power chord.

     i) D   A

     ii) D   A   High A

   b) Compare these waveforms to those of the D-major triad and the D-major chord.

3. A skier is skiing down a 200 m hill at a constant speed of 2 m/s through a series of moguls, or small hills. The constant slope of the hill was -2. Assuming that the moguls measure 0.80 m from crest to trough and are roughly 6 m apart, develop an algebraic and a graphical model of the height of the skier versus time.

Use this graph of the path of the bungee jumper to answer questions 4 to 6.

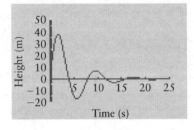

4. Copy the graph of this curve. Sketch how the path of the jumper would change if she dropped from

   a) a greater height

   b) a lower height

5. Sketch how the path of the jumper would change is she were attached to

   a) a longer cord

   b) a shorter cord

6. Sketch how the path of the jumper would change if she were attached to

   a) a springier cord

   b) a stiffer cord

7. A skier is skiing down a hill at a constant speed. His height versus time graph is shown.

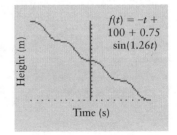

Sketch how the graph would change if the moguls were

a) shorter

b) farther apart

★8. A skier is going up and down the same hill at regular intervals. On each run, she skis at an average speed of 1.5 m/s from the top of the hill to the bottom, waits in the chairlift line for about 3 min, and then travels up the chairlift at a speed of 0.75 m/s.
Assume that this hill has no moguls.

   a) Develop a graphical model of the skier's height versus time over the course of several ski runs.

   b) Explain what is happening during each region of the graph for one cycle.

   c) How might you develop an algebraic model to describe this motion?

9. Refer to question 8. Adjust your graph from part a) to illustrate the effect on the skier's height function in each scenario.

   a) After her first run, the lift breaks and she spends an extra 5 min waiting in the lift line.

   b) On her second trip up the chairlift, the lift is stopped for 2 min so that the lift operator can help some new skiers onto the lift.

   c) On her third trip down the hill, the skier tripled her speed.

B

10. The data shown models the growth of a field mouse population where the mice have no predators.

Year	Mice Population
1973	630
1976	2 097
1978	5 275
1979	8 185
1980	12 320
1983	35 487
1986	66 265
1993	91 780
1998	92 875
2004	92 752
2008	93 205

a) Using 1973 as year 0, create a scatter plot of the number of mice, N, versus time, t, in years.

b) Determine a line or curve of best fit, using a method of your choice (e.g., regression analysis, sliders, systematic trial). Justify the type of function that you chose.

c) Write an equation for $N(t)$.

d) There is an outlier in 1993 that does not appear to fit the trend very well. What effect does removing the outlier have on the model for $N(t)$? Does this effect appear to be significant?

★**11.** While testing the speed of a car in kilometres per hour, $v(t)$ was measured.

Time, t	Kilometres Per Hour, $v(t)$
0	50
1	55
2	62
3	71
4	82
5	95
6	110

The rate of gas consumption for this car, c litres per kilometre, at a speed of $v(t)$ kilometres per hour, is represented by

$$c(v) = \left(\frac{v(t)}{450} - 0.09\right)^2 + 0.18.$$

a) Create a scatter plot of kilometres, $v(t)$, versus time, t, in hours.

b) Determine a line or curve of best fit, using a method of your choice. Justify the type of function that you chose.

c) Write an equation for $v(t)$.

d) Determine algebraically $c(v(t))$.

12. Relative motion uses the superposition principle. Consider the position of a person relative to the ground as she runs back and forth in a train while the train itself is also moving.

a) Suppose the runner's motion relative to the train is $x_1(t) = -\cos(0.2\pi t)$, where x_1 is in metres and t is in seconds. If the train is moving at a constant speed of 1 m/s, its position is $x_2(t) = y$.

  i) Predict what the motion of the runner would look like from the vantage point of a person standing on the ground beside the train as it went by. Sketch a graph of this motion.

  ii) Graph $y = x_1(t) + x_2(t)$ to check your answer to part a). Work in radians, and use technology.

b) Repeat part a) but with the train accelerating from rest, so that $x_2(t) = 0.15t^2$.

C1. Copy the graph.

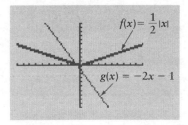

$f(x) = \frac{1}{2}|x|$

$g(x) = -2x - 1$

Use the superposition principle to generate a graph of each function.
a) $y = f(x) + g(x)$
b) $y = f(x) - g(x)$
c) $y = g(x) - f(x)$

C2. Let $f(x) = x + 5$, $g(x) = x^2 - 21 + x$, and $h(x) = \left(\frac{1}{2}\right)^x$.

Determine an algebraic and graphical model for each combined function. Identify the domain and range in each case.

a) $y = f(x) + g(x)$

b) $y = f(x) + g(x) + h(x)$

c) $y = f(x) - h(x)$

C3. Use Technology Use graphing technology to check your answers to question C2.

C4. Alexis can earn $7.50/h as a server, plus an additional $12.25/h in tips.

a) Graph Alexis's earnings from wages as a function of hours worked.

b) Graph Alexis's earnings from tips as a function of hours worked.

c) Develop an algebraic and a graphical model for Alexis's total earnings.

d) How much can Alexis earn if she works 32 h in one week?

C5. Let $u(x) = x^4$ and $v(x) = \sin x$. Work in radians.

a) What type of symmetry do you predict the combined function $y = u(x)v(x)$ will have? Explain your reasoning.

b) Use Technology Use graphing technology to check your prediction.

C6. Let $f(x) = x - 5$ and $g(x) = x^2 - 9x + 20$.

a) Determine an algebraic and a graphical model for $y = \dfrac{f(x)}{g(x)}$ and identify its domain and range.

b) Determine an algebraic and a graphical model for $y = \dfrac{g(x)}{f(x)}$ and identify its domain and range.

C7. Let $f(x) = x^2 + 5x + 1$ and $g(x) = 7x - 4$. Determine an equation for each composite function, graph the function, and give its domain and range.

a) $y = f(g(x))$

b) $y = g(f(x))$

c) $y = g(g(x))$

d) $y = g^{-1}(g(x))$

C8. Let $f(x) = 7 \sin\left(\frac{1}{2}x\right)$ and $g(x) = 2^x$.

a) Identify the region for which

i) $f(x) > g(x)$

ii) $g(x) > f(x)$

b) Illustrate this inequality graphically in two different ways.

C9. Let $f(x) = x^3 - 5x^2 - 35x$ and $g(x) = 9 - x^2$.

a) Graph these functions on the same set of axes.

b) Identify, by inspecting the graphs, the interval(s) for which $f(x) > g(x)$.

c) Check your answer to part b) using another method.

C10. A pendulum is released and allowed to swing back and forth according to the equation $x(t) = 8 \sin(3t) \times 0.80^t$, where x is the horizontal displacement from the rest position, in centimetres, as a function of time, t, in seconds.

a) Graph the function. What type of motion is this? Identify the domain and range in the context of this problem.

b) This combined function is the product of two component functions. Identify the component that is responsible for:

i) the periodic nature of the motion

ii) the exponential decay of the amplitude

c) At what horizontal distance from the rest position was the bob of the pendulum released?

d) At what point(s) is the rate of change zero? When does this occur with respect to the motion of the pendulum bob?

e) After what elapsed time will the pendulum's amplitude diminish to 30% of its initial value?

C11. The cost, C, and revenue, R, as functions of the number of burgers sold by Harry's Hamburgers, are shown on the graph.

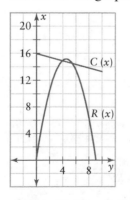

a) Identify the region(s) for which

i) $C > R$

ii) $R > C$

b) What can you conclude about this business venture?

c) What suggestions would you give to the restaurant in order to help it improve this situation?

C12. A company that produces sunscreen estimates that the cost of manufacturing x bottles of the product is given by $C(x) = 480 - 0.32x + 0.000\,5x^2$ and the revenue is given by $R(x) = 0.78x + 0.000\,3x^2$.

a) Graph $C(x)$ and $R(x)$ on the same set of axes.

b) Identify the break-even point and explain what its coordinates mean.

c) Develop an algebraic and a graphical model for the profit function, $P(x)$.

d) What is the maximum daily profit that the sunscreen company can earn?

C13. A skier is skiing down a 350-m hill at a constant speed of 2 m/s, through a series of moguls, or small hills. The constant slope of the hill is -3. Assuming that the moguls measure 3 m from crest to trough and are roughly 2 m apart, develop an algebraic and a graphical model of the height of the skier versus time.

C14. A skier's height, h, in metres, as a function of time, t, in seconds, can be modelled by the combined function $h(t) = -2t + 150 + 1.95 \sin(1.5t)$.

a) Graph this function.

b) Assuming that the skier stops the first time that her height reaches zero, find the domain and range relevant to the problem.

By the end of this chapter, I will be able to:

- Add or subtract two or more functions graphically using the superposition principal
- Add or subtract two or more functions algebraically
- Combine and simplify a product of functions algebraically
- Combine and simplify a quotient of functions algebraically, and identify any restrictions on the vairable
- Graph the sum, difference, product, or quotient of functions with and without graphing technology and identify the key characteristics of the graph
- Algebraically determine the composition of two or more functions
- Understand the effect of operating on a variable by a function followed by its inverse
- Solve inequalities of combined functions algebraically
- Solve inequalities of combined functions graphically, with and without technologty, using a variety of strategies
- Model contextual situations using combinations of functions
- Solve problems involving various combinations of functions

University Preparation 1: Extending Algebraic Skills

UP 1.1 Factoring Complex Equations

- Complex algebraic expressions can be factored by applying a combination of the factoring techniques that you are familiar with: common factoring, difference of squares, and trinomial factoring.

Example 1

Factor $9(x-1)^2 - 25(2x+3)^2$.

Solution

In the expression $9(x-1)^2 - 25(2x+3)^2$ let $m = x-1$ and $n = 2x+3$ to obtain $9m^2 - 25n^2$.

Factor $9m^2 - 25n^2$, using difference of squares.

$= (3m - 5n)(3m + 5n)$

Substitute for m and n.

$= [3(x-1) - 5(2x+3)][3(x-1) + 5(2x+3)]$

Expand.

$= [3x - 3 - 10x - 15][3x - 3 + 10x + 15]$

Simplify.

$= (-7x - 18)(13x + 12)$

Example 2

Factor $x^2 + 6xy + 9y^2 - a^2 + 12a - 36$.

Solution

$x^2 + 6xy + 9y^2 - a^2 + 12a - 36$

Group the trinomials.

$= (x^2 + 6xy + 9y^2) - (a^2 - 12a + 36)$

Factor each trinomial.

$= (x + 3y)^2 - (a - 6)^2$

Factor this difference of squares.

$= [(x + 3y) - (a - 6)][(x + 3y) + (a - 6)]$

Simplify.

$= (x + 3y - a + 6)(x + 3y + a - 6)$

A

1. Factor.

   a) $(x-2)^2 - 4$

   b) $n^2 - (n+1)^2$

   c) $(3x+y)^2 - 1$

   d) $(2x+3)^2 - 49x^2$

   e) $3(x+4)^2 - 75$

   f) $2(5-x)^2 - 72x^2$

   g) $(x-1) - (x-1)^2$

2. Factor.

   a) $(x-6)^2 - (2x+3)^2$

   b) $(x+2)^2 - (x-7)^2$

   c) $\frac{1}{9}(x+2)^2 - (7x-5)^2$

   d) $0.01(1-8x)^2 - (1+3x)^2$

B

3. Factor.

   a) $2(4x-1)^2 - 8(3-x)^2$

   b) $48(5-x)^4 - 3(x+1)^4$

   c) $32(a-b+2c)^2 - 128(a-b-2c)^2$

   d) $64(x+2y)^4 - 16(2x-y)^4$

4. Factor.

   a) $x^2 + 4x + 4 - y^2$

   b) $x^2 - 6x + 9 - 4y^2$

   c) $a^2 + 10a + 25 - 9b^2$

   ★**d)** $4m^2 - 4n^2 - 8np - 4p^2$

   e) $2p^2 + 8qr - 8r^2 - 2q^2$

   f) $x^4 - y^2 + 2yz - z^2$

   g) $x^2 - 2xy + y^2 - 9a^2$

5. Factor.

   a) $9a^2 + 18ab + 9b^2 - 4x^2 + 8xy - 4y^2$

   b) $16s^2 - 32st + 16t^2 - p^2 - 4pq - 4q^2$

   c) $25r^2 - 60rs + 36s^2 - 9g^2 + 12gh - 4h^2$

   ★**d)** $s^2 - 14st + 49t^2 - a^2 - 18ab - 81b^2$

C

6. Factor.

   a) $(x+1)^2 + 11(x+1) + 28$

   b) $(2x+3)^2 + 8(2x+3) - 9$

   ★**c)** $6(x^2-1)^2 + 23(x^2-1) + 7$

   d) $52(3-2x)^2 - 57(3-2x)(x+3) - 10(x+3)^2$

7. Factor.

   a) $x^{4n} - y^{6n}$

   b) $9x^{6n} - 12x^{3n}y^{2n} + 4y^{4n}$

   c) $16x^{4n+2} + 24x^{2n+1}y^{4n} + 9y^{8n}$

KEY CONCEPTS

- You have previously learned to solve quadratic equations by factoring or using the quadratic formula.
- These methods may be applied to solve certain complex equations by using substitution to convert them to quadratic equations.

Example 1

Solve $\dfrac{1}{x^6} + \dfrac{9}{x^3} + 8 = 0$.

Solution

Write the equation $\dfrac{1}{x^6} + \dfrac{9}{x^3} + 8 = 0$ in quadratic form as follows:

$\left(\dfrac{1}{x^3}\right)^2 + 9\left(\dfrac{1}{x^3}\right) + 8 = 0$

Let $w = \dfrac{1}{x^3}$.

$w^2 + 9w + 8 = 0$

Factor: $(w + 8)(x + 1) = 0$

$\qquad\qquad w = -8 \text{ or } w = -1$

Revert to x: $\dfrac{1}{x^3} = -8 \text{ or } \dfrac{1}{x^3} = -1$

Take the reciprocal of each side: $x^3 = -\dfrac{1}{8} \text{ or } x^3 = -1$

$$x = -\dfrac{1}{2} \text{ or } x = -1$$

Example 2

Determine the roots of the equation $x^2 + x + \dfrac{12}{x^2 + x} = 8$.

Solution

Let $n = x^2 + x$ ①.

Substitute ① in $(x^2 + x) + \dfrac{12}{(x^2 + x)} = 8$.

$$n + \dfrac{12}{n} = 8$$

Multiply each term by n: $n^2 + 12 = 8n$

$\qquad\qquad n^2 - 8n + 12 = 0 \qquad\quad$ Factor.

$\qquad\qquad (n - 6)(n - 2) = 0$

$\qquad\qquad\quad n = 6 \text{ or } n = 2$

Revert to x: $x^2 + x = 6 \text{ or } x^2 + x = 2$

Now solve each quadratic equation:

$x^2 + x = 6$	or	$x^2 + x = 2$
$x^2 + x - 6 = 0$		$x^2 + x - 2 = 0$
$(x + 3)(x - 2) = 0$		$(x + 2)(x - 1) = 0$
$x = -3 \text{ or } x = 2$		$x = -2 \text{ or } x = 1$

The roots are $x = -3, -2, 1, \text{ or } 2$.

A

1. a) Use the substitution $m = x^2$ to convert the quartic equation $x^4 - 17x^2 + 16 = 0$ into a quadratic equation.

b) Solve the new equation in part a).

2. Use the method of question 1 to find all the roots of $x^4 - 26x^2 + 25 = 0$.

3. a) Use the substitution $n = 2^x$ to convert the equation $2^{2x} - 6(2^x) + 8 = 0$.

b) Solve the new equation in part a).

B

4. i) State a suitable substitution that will convert each of the following to a quadratic equation.

ii) Use your substitution to find all the roots of each equation.

a) $x^4 - 5x^2 + 4 = 0$

b) $x^4 - 16 = 0$

c) $x^4 - 16x^2 + 60 = 0$

d) $x^4 - 36x^2 + 35 = 0$

e) $x^4 - 20x^2 + 64 = 0$

f) $x^4 - 29x^2 + 100 = 0$

g) $x^4 - 5x^2 + 6 = 0$

h) $x^4 - 3x^2 - 10 = 0$

5. i) State a suitable substitution that will convert each of the following to a quadratic equation.

ii) Use your substitution to find all the roots of each equation.

a) $5^{2x} - 6(5^x) + 5 = 0$

b) $3^{2x} - 30(3^x) + 81 = 0$

c) $2^{2x} - 12(2^x) + 32 = 0$

d) $2^{2x} - 18(2^x) + 32 = 0$

e) $2^{2x} - 10(2^x) + 16 = 0$

f) $3^{2x} - 12(3^x) + 27 = 0$

★g) $5^{2x} - 30(5^x) + 125 = 0$

6. Solve.

a) $4(4^{2x-1} + 1) = 5(4^x)$

b) $3(3^{2x}) + 1 = 10(3^x) - 2$

c) $x^2(x^2 - 1) + 2 = 9x^2 - 7$

7. Solve.

a) $(x - 5)^2 + 7(x - 5) + 10 = 0$

b) $(3x + 2)^2 = 5(3x + 2)$

c) $(x^2 + 2x)^2 + 4 = 11(x^2 + 2x) - 20$

d) $(x^2 - 3x)^2 - 5 = 2(x^2 - 3x) + 3$

★e) $(x^2 - 2x)^2 - 4 = 2(x^2 - 2x) - 1$

8. Solve.

a) $x^2 = -\dfrac{36}{x^2} + 13$ **b)** $\dfrac{3}{x^2} + \dfrac{7}{x} = -2$

c) $\dfrac{1}{x^2} + \dfrac{1}{x} = 12$ **d)** $\dfrac{1}{x^4} - \dfrac{9}{x^2} + 20 = 0$

e) $x^{-4} - 9x^{-2} + 8 = 0$

C

9. Solve and verify.

a) $\dfrac{1}{(x-2)^2} - \dfrac{12}{(x-2)} + 35 = 0$

b) $\dfrac{2}{(x+4)^2} + \dfrac{7}{(x+4)} = -3$

c) $(x^2 + x) + \dfrac{24}{(x^2 + x)} = 14$

10. Solve and verify.

a) $\left(x + \dfrac{6}{x}\right)^2 - 2\left(x + \dfrac{6}{x}\right) - 35 = 0$

b) $\left(x + \dfrac{4}{x}\right)^2 = 9\left(x + \dfrac{4}{x}\right) - 20$

c) $\left(x - \dfrac{1}{x}\right)^2 = 7\left(x - \dfrac{1}{x}\right) - 12$

11. a) State a suitable substitution to convert $\left(x^2 + \dfrac{1}{x^2}\right) = 10 - x - \dfrac{1}{x}$ into a quadratic equation.

b) Use your substitution from part a) to determine all the roots of the equation.

c) Verify your answer(s) in part b).

University Preparation 2: Absolute Value

UP 2.1 Solving Equations Involving Absolute Value

⟪ KEY CONCEPTS ⟫

On a number line, the numbers -5 and 5 are each located 5 units from 0, one to the left of 0 and the other to the right. Each number is said to have an absolute value of 5. Write them as $|-5| = 5$ and $|5| = 5$.

- $|x| = x, x \geq 0$, and $|x| = -x, x < 0$
- Absolute value equations are solved by considering case i) let $x \geq 0$ and case ii) let $x < 0$.
- In some situations, a solution to an absolute value equation may not satisfy the initial restriction, and so the value found is not valid.
- To check whether a value is a solution, substitute into the left side and right side of the original equation to see if it satisfies the given equation.

Definition of Absolute Value

i) $|x| = x, x \geq 0$

ii) $|x| = -x, x < 0$

Example 1

Evaluate.

a) $|4|$

b) $|-4|$

Solution

a) $|4| = 4$, since the absolute value of a positive number is the number itself.

b) $|-4| = 4$, since the absolute value of a negative number is a positive number.

Example 2

Solve for x.

a) $|x| = 3$

b) $|x - 1| = 3$

Solution

a) $|x| = 3$

Case i) $x \geq 0$; then, for these values of x, $|x| = x$ and, so, $x = 3$.

Case ii) $x < 0$; then, for these values of x, $|x| = -x$ and so $-x = 3$ or $x = -3$.

The solution is $x = -3$ or $x = 3$.

---

b) $|x - 1| = 3$

Case i) $x - 1 \geq 0$; i.e., $x \geq 1$.
The solution below is valid only for $x \geq 1$.

Then, $|x - 1| = x - 1$.

And so, $x - 1 = 3$

$\qquad\qquad x = 4$, which satisfies the restriction $x \geq 1$.

Case ii) $x - 1 < 0$; i.e., $x < 1$.
The solution below is valid only for $x < 1$.

Then, $|x - 1| = -(x - 1)$

So, $-(x - 1) = 3$

$\qquad -x + 1 = 3$

$\qquad\qquad -x = 2$

$\qquad\qquad x = -2$, which satisfies the restriction $x < 1$.
The solution is $x = 4$ and $x = -2$.

Example 3

Solve and check.
$|x - 2| = 3x$

Solution

Case i) $x - 2 \geq 0$, i.e., $x \geq 2$
The solution below is valid only for $x \geq 2$.
$|x - 2| = x - 2$
So, $x - 2 = 3x$
$\qquad -2 = 2x$
$\qquad\quad x = -1$, which is not a valid solution because it does not satisfy the restriction $x \geq 2$.

Case ii) $x - 2 < 0$, i.e., $x < 2$
The solution below is valid only for $x < 2$.
$|x - 2| = -(x - 2)$
So, $-(x - 2) = 3x$
$\qquad -x + 2 = 3x$
$\qquad\qquad 2 = 4x$
$\qquad\qquad x = 0.5$, which satisfies the restriction $x < 2$.
The solution is $x = 0.5$.

Check:
Substitute $x = 0.5$ in the left side and right side of the given equation, $|x - 2| = 3x$.
$\begin{aligned} \text{L.S.} &= |0.5 - 2| \\ &= |-1.5| \\ &= 1.5 \end{aligned}$

$\begin{aligned} \text{R.S.} &= 3(0.5) \\ &= 1.5 \\ &= \text{L.S.} \end{aligned}$

Therefore, $x = 0.5$ is, indeed, a solution.

A

1. Evaluate.
   a) $|6|$
   b) $|-8|$
   c) $|2 - 9|$
   d) $|3(2 - 6) + 1|$
   e) $\left|\dfrac{6 - 14}{-5 + 3}\right|$

2. Solve for x, if possible.
   a) $|x| = 2$
   b) $|x| = 9$
   c) $|4x| = 36$
   d) $|-3x| = 99$
   e) $2|8x - 12x| = 100$
   f) $|x| - 7 = 32$
   g) $9 - |x| = -26$
   h) $\dfrac{3}{4}|x| = 6$
   i) $-\dfrac{3}{4}|-8x| = 24$

B

3. Solve for x, if possible.
   a) $|x + 4| = 3$
   b) $|x - 3| = 6$
   c) $|x - 2| = 7$
   d) $|x + 1| = 5$
   e) $|x - 4| = -2$
   f) $|1 - x| = 8$

4. Solve for x, if possible.
   a) $|2x - 1| = 9$
   b) $|4x - 1| = 3$
   c) $4|x + 3| = 12$
   d) $|2 - 3x| = 11$
   e) $|3 - 2x| = -5$
   f) $-|4x + 2| = -3$
   g) $-|2x - 5| = 3$

5. Solve and check.
   a) $|x - 4| = 5x$
   b) $|x + 5| = -2x$
   c) $3x = |2 - x|$
   d) $|4 + 3x| = 7x$
   e) $4|4x - 3| = 32x$
   f) $\dfrac{1}{4}|3 - 2x| = \dfrac{3}{2}$

6. Solve for x, if possible.
   a) $|3x - 4| + |9x - 12| = 12x$
   b) $|3x - 4| + |7 - 2x| = 0$
   c) $|2x - 8| + |12 - 3x| = 0$
   d) $|x - 3| + |3 - x| = 0$
   ★e) $16x - 3|2x - 1| = |10x - 5|$
   f) $\left|\dfrac{x - 6}{3}\right| + 4x = 0$

C

7. Solve for x.
   a) $|x + 1| + 2 = 3|x + 1|$
   b) $7|x + 2| = 2|x + 2| + 15$
   c) $|2x| = |x + 5|$
   d) $|3x - 2| = |2x|$
   e) $6|x + 1| - 14 = 4|x + 1| + 6$

8. Solve for x.
   a) $|5x - 3| = |x + 1|$
   b) $|2x - 5| = |x - 1|$
   c) $|2 - 3x| = |5 + x|$
   d) $|x - 3| = |4x - 7|$
   ★e) $|3x - 7| = |2 - x|$

9. Solve for x, if possible.
   a) $|x + 2| + |2 - x| = 8$
   b) $|2x - 1| - |1 - 2x| = 4$

KEY CONCEPTS

- An inequality is an algebraic expression with one of the following symbols: $\leq$, $\geq$, $>$, or $<$.
- To solve absolute value inequalities, apply the definition of absolute value and use the principles of case i) $x \geq 0$ and case ii) $x < 0$.
- In general, for any constant, a, and any positive constant, c, an inequality of the form

    i) $|x + a| \leq c$ has the solution $-c - a \leq x \leq c - a$, and

    ii) $|x + a| \geq c$ has the solution $x \leq -c - a$ or $x \geq c - a$.

Example 1

Solve $|x - 6| \leq 3$.

Solution

Method 1: Using Cases

Case i) $x - 6 \geq 0$, i.e., $x \geq 6$ ①

Then, $|x - 6| = x - 6$

Solve $x - 6 \leq 3$

$$x \leq 9 \ ②$$

The solution must satisfy ① and ②, so $6 \leq x \leq 9$.

Case ii) $x - 6 < 0$, i.e., $x < 6$ ①

Then, $|x - 6| = -(x - 6)$

$$= -x + 6$$

Solve $\quad -x + 6 \leq 3$

$$-x \leq -3$$

Divide by -1; change $\leq$ to $\geq$.

$$x \geq 3 \ ②$$

The solution must satisfy ① and ②, so $3 \leq x < 6$.

From case i) and case ii), $6 \leq x \leq 9$ and $3 \leq x < 6$; the solution is $3 \leq x \leq 9$.

Method 2: Without Cases

For $|x - 6| \leq 3$, the equivalent inequality is $-3 \leq x - 6 \leq 3$.

$$-3 \leq x - 6 \text{ and } x - 6 \leq 3$$

$$3 \leq x \text{ and } x \leq 9$$

$$3 \leq x \leq 9$$

Strategy Tip: In general, for any constant, a, and any positive constant, c, inequalities of the form

i) $|x + a| \leq c$ may be solved by solving the equivalent inequality $-c \leq x + a \leq$, which results in $-c - a \leq x \leq c - a$.

ii) $|x + a| \geq c$ may be solved by solving the equivalent inequality $x + a \leq -c$ or $x + a \geq c$, which results in $x \leq -c - a$ or $x \geq c - a$.

Example 2

Solve $|3x - 4| \geq 2$; then, graph the solution on a number line.

Solution

The inequality $|3x - 4| \geq 2$ is of the form $|x + a| \geq c$.

Use strategy tip ii):

$3x - 4 \leq -2$ or $3x - 4 \geq 2$

$\qquad 3x \leq 2 \quad$ or $\qquad 3x \geq 6$

$\qquad x \leq \dfrac{2}{3} \quad$ or $\qquad x \geq 2 \quad$ The dots indicate the end points that are included in the solution.

0 $\frac{2}{3}$ 2

A

1. Solve.

   a) $|x| > 3$ **b)** $|x| < 2$

   c) $|x| \leq 5$ **d)** $|x| \geq -1$

   e) $|4x| \leq 7$ **f)** $|-3x| > 12$

   g) $|5x| + 7 < 21$ **h)** $3 - |x| > -4$

   i) $21 \geq |-4x| + 5$

2. Solve and graph the solution.

   a) $2|x| - 5 > 14$ **b)** $-\dfrac{3}{4}|x| \geq 6$

   c) $\left|-\dfrac{2}{3}x\right| + 4 < 13$ **d)** $|x| - 6 \leq 4$

   e) $1 - |-3x| \geq -20$ **f)** $6 + \left|\dfrac{5x}{-9}\right| > 3$

   g) $9|x| - |-5x| < 28$

B

3. Solve and graph the solution.

   a) $|x - 3| > 3$ **b)** $|x + 4| \leq 1$

   c) $|x - 1| < 7$ **d)** $|5 - x| \geq 0$

   e) $|x + 3| > 10$ **f)** $|8 - x| \leq 15$

   g) $|6 + x| > 9$ **h)** $|2 - x| \geq 2$

   i) $|x + 10| < 6$

4. Solve.

   a) $|2x + 1| > 3$ **b)** $|3 - 5x| \geq 8$

   c) $|7x - 2| < 1$ **d)** $|2x - 5| \leq 3$

   e) $|3x + 1| < 9$ **f)** $|7 - 4x| + 2 \geq 15$

   g) $8 - |2x + 3| < -3$ **h)** $5 + \dfrac{2}{3}|4 - 6x| \geq 7$

   i) $\left|\dfrac{3x + 1}{6}\right| - 2 > 9$ **j)** $\dfrac{2}{|x + 4|} \leq 5$

5. Solve.

   a) $|3x + 2| < 5x + 1$

   b) $|2x + 1| < 3x$

   c) $|6 - 3x| \leq x - 2$

   ★**d)** $|2 - 3x| > 3x - 6$

   e) $|x + 1| \geq x - 4$

   f) $\left|\dfrac{x - 2}{3}\right| > x + 1$

   g) $5 - |x + 2| \leq 6x$

C

6. Solve and check.

   a) $|3x - 1| \leq |2x + 18|$

   b) $|6x + 5| < |5x + 6|$

   ★**c)** $|x + 2| > 4 + |x|$

7. Solve and graph your solution.

   a) $|x| + |x - 1| < 5$

   b) $|x - 1| \geq |x + 2|$

   c) $2 - |3x + 6| < |-5x - 10| - 8$

8. Solve.

   a) $\left|\dfrac{x - 1}{x + 3}\right| < 1$

   b) $\left|\dfrac{2x - 3}{4x + 1}\right| \geq 2$

   c) $|2x - 4| + 3|x + 5| \leq 2|6 - 3x|$
   $\quad - |-5x - 25|$

University Preparation 3: Matrices

UP 3.1 Introduction to Matrices

> ## KEY CONCEPTS
>
> Numerical data is often displayed or organized in the form of a matrix. For instance, teachers often keep a record of class marks in the form of a matrix, with **rows** indicating students' names and marks and **columns** indicating the test title and marks.
>
> | | Test 1 | Test 2 | Test 3 |
> |------------|--------|--------|--------|
> | P. Adams | 98 | 88 | 93 |
> | R. Butler | 75 | 81 | 85 |
> | G. Casten | 86 | 89 | 79 |
> | K. Dustop | 62 | 74 | 83 |
>
> - A **matrix** is a rectangular array of numbers arranged in rows (horizontal) and columns (vertical). Each number in the array is called an **element** or **entry** of the matrix.
> - The **dimensions** or **order** of a matrix are the number of rows by the number of columns in the matrix. In general, an $m \times n$ (read m by n) matrix is a matrix with m rows and n columns.
> - In mathematics, it is conventional to use capital letters to denote matrices using square brackets around the elements.
>
> - Matrix A represents the test information shown above.
>
> $$A = \begin{bmatrix} 98 & 88 & 93 \\ 75 & 81 & 85 \\ 86 & 89 & 79 \\ 62 & 74 & 83 \end{bmatrix}$$ The dimensions of this matrix are 4×3. The entry in row 3, column 2 is 89. This entry, or element, can also be identified as a_{32}.
>
> - In general, if A is an $m \times n$ matrix, we write $A = [a_{ij}]_{m \times n}$, where i represents the row number and j the column number of element a in a matrix of m rows and n columns. Thus,
>
> $$A = \begin{bmatrix} a_{11} & a_{12} & \cdots & a_{1n} \\ a_{21} & a_{22} & \cdots & a_{2n} \\ \vdots & \vdots & a_{ij} & \vdots \\ a_{m1} & a_{m2} & \cdots & a_{mn} \end{bmatrix}$$
>
> - Two matrices have the **same size** if they each have the same dimensions, that is, the same number of rows and the same number of columns. Two matrices are **equal** if and only if they have the same dimensions and all their corresponding entries are equal.
>
> **Matrix Addition and Subtraction**
>
> - Matrices that have the same dimensions can be added or subtracted by adding or subtracting corresponding entries or elements.
>
> - The resulting matrix is the same size as the matrices that were added or subtracted.

Scalar Multiplication

- A matrix can be multiplied by a scalar k by multiplying each entry or element by the scalar k. The resulting matrix is the same size as the original matrix.

Properties of Matrix Addition and Scalar Multiplication

For matrices A, B, and C, all of which have the same dimensions, and scalars k and s, the following properties hold true:

1. $A + B = B + A$ (Commutative property)
2. $A + (B + C) = (A + B) + C$ (Associative property)
3. $s(kA) = (sk)A$ (Associative property)
4. $k(A + B) = kA + kB$ (Distributive property)
5. $(k + s)A = kA + sA$ (Distributive property)

Example 1

Given $A = \begin{bmatrix} -2 & 5 \\ 7 & 3 \end{bmatrix}$, $B = \begin{bmatrix} 1 & -4 \\ -6 & 11 \end{bmatrix}$, and $C = \begin{bmatrix} 0 & -3 \\ -1 & 10 \\ 8 & 4 \end{bmatrix}$, determine the following, if possible.

a) $A + 2B$

b) $-3(4C)$

c) $C - A$

Solution

a) $A + 2B = \begin{bmatrix} -2 & 5 \\ 7 & 3 \end{bmatrix} + 2\begin{bmatrix} 1 & -4 \\ -6 & 11 \end{bmatrix}$

$= \begin{bmatrix} -2 & 5 \\ 7 & 3 \end{bmatrix} + \begin{bmatrix} 2 & -8 \\ -12 & 22 \end{bmatrix}$

$= \begin{bmatrix} -2 + 2 & 5 - 8 \\ 7 - 12 & 3 + 22 \end{bmatrix}$

$= \begin{bmatrix} 0 & -3 \\ -5 & 25 \end{bmatrix}$

b) $-3(4C) = (-3 \times 4)C = -12C$

$= -12\begin{bmatrix} 0 & -3 \\ -1 & 10 \\ 8 & 4 \end{bmatrix}$

$= \begin{bmatrix} 0 & 36 \\ 12 & -120 \\ -96 & -48 \end{bmatrix}$

c) $C - A$

It is not possible to subtract A from C since matrix C is a 3×2 matrix and matrix A is a 2×2 matrix.

Matrix Multiplication

- Matrix multiplication—that is, the multiplication of one matrix by another—is based on column-by-row multiplication. If you have two matrices, A and B, you can multiply B by A only if the number of columns in A equals the number of rows in B. Therefore, if A is a 2×2 matrix and B is a 2×3 matrix, you can multiply B by A (AB) because B has two rows and A has two columns. However, you *cannot* multiply A by B (BA) because A has two rows and B has *three* columns. The new matrix will have dimensions 2×3, the same dimensions as the matrix being multiplied. This rule may be written as $A_{m \times n} \times B_{n \times p} = (AB)_{m \times p}$.

Example 2

Given $D = \begin{bmatrix} -2 & 5 \\ 7 & 3 \end{bmatrix}$, $E = \begin{bmatrix} 6 & -3 & 1 \\ 2 & -1 & -2 \end{bmatrix}$, and $F = \begin{bmatrix} 0 & -3 \\ -1 & 10 \\ 8 & 4 \end{bmatrix}$ determine the following, if possible.

a) DE

b) EF

c) DF

d) E^2

Solution

a) D is a 2×2 matrix and E is a 2×3 matrix. The number of rows of D equals the number of columns of E, so the product DE exists. The resulting matrix will be a 2×3 matrix.

$$DE = \begin{bmatrix} -2 & 5 \\ 7 & 3 \end{bmatrix}\begin{bmatrix} 6 & -3 & 1 \\ 2 & -1 & -2 \end{bmatrix}$$

$$= \begin{bmatrix} (-2)(6) + (5)(2) & (-2)(-3) + (5)(-1) & (-2)(1) + (5)(-2) \\ (7)(6) + (3)(2) & (7)(-3) + (3)(-1) & (7)(1) + (3)(-2) \end{bmatrix}$$

$$= \begin{bmatrix} -2 & 1 & -12 \\ 48 & -24 & 1 \end{bmatrix}$$

b) E is a 2×3 matrix and F is a 3×2 matrix. The number of rows of E equals the number of columns of F, so the product EF exists. The resulting matrix will be a 2×2 matrix.

$$EF = \begin{bmatrix} 6 & -3 & 1 \\ 2 & -1 & -2 \end{bmatrix}\begin{bmatrix} 0 & -3 \\ -1 & 10 \\ 8 & 4 \end{bmatrix}$$

$$= \begin{bmatrix} (6)(0) + (-3)(-1) + (1)(8) & (6)(-3) + (-3)(10) + (1)(4) \\ (2)(0) + (-1)(-1) + (-2)(8) & (2)(-3) + (-1)(10) + (-2)(4) \end{bmatrix}$$

$$= \begin{bmatrix} 11 & -44 \\ -15 & -24 \end{bmatrix}$$

c) D is a 2×2 matrix and F is a 3×2 matrix. The number of rows of D is not equal to the number of columns of F, so the product DF is not possible.

d) E^2 means $E \times E$. Since E is a 2×3 matrix, the number of rows of E is not equal to the number of columns of E, so the product E^2 is not possible.

A

1. Given $A = \begin{bmatrix} -4 & 3 & 8 \\ 5 & 1 & -2 \end{bmatrix}$, determine:

   a) the dimensions of A

   b) the value of the entries a_{12} and a_{23}

   c) $-A$ d) $2(3A)$

   e) $5A - 2A$

★2. Given $B = \begin{bmatrix} 9 & -6 & 10 \\ -1 & 2 & 7 \end{bmatrix}$ and $C = \begin{bmatrix} -3 & 1 \\ 0 & 4 \end{bmatrix}$,

   state whether each of the products below exists. If it does exist, state the dimensions of the resulting matrix. If it does not exist, explain why.

   a) BC b) CB

   c) B^2 d) C^2

B

3. Calculate each product in question 2 that does exist.

   Use the following matrices for questions 4 and 5.

   $P = \begin{bmatrix} 1 & 3 & -1 \\ 2 & -9 & 4 \\ 0 & 5 & -6 \end{bmatrix}$ $Q = \begin{bmatrix} 12 & 3 \\ 0 & -1 \\ -3 & 7 \end{bmatrix}$

   $R = \begin{bmatrix} -6 & 1 & 3 \\ 2 & 4 & -2 \end{bmatrix}$ $S = \begin{bmatrix} -8 & 2 & 0 \\ -5 & 7 & 1 \\ 3 & -1 & 11 \end{bmatrix}$

4. Perform the indicated operation, if it exists. If it does not exist, explain why.

   a) $P + S$ b) $3(S + P)$

   c) $R - Q$ d) $-\frac{2}{3}Q$

5. Perform the indicated operation, if it exists. If it does not exist, explain why.

   a) QR b) $QR - S$

   c) QP d) PQ

   e) $(PQ)R$ f) P^2

   g) $RS - P^2$ h) $PS - P^2$

   i) $SP - 3S$

6. Given that A, B, and C are 2×2 matrices, and k is a scalar, determine whether or not each of the following is true. Support your answer with an example.

   a) $AB = BA$

   b) $(AB)C = A(BC)$

   c) $k(AB) = (kA)B = A(kB)$

7. Determine the unknown values in the following:

   $\begin{bmatrix} a + 2 & b - 3 \\ 2c - 1 & 3 - 4d \end{bmatrix} = \begin{bmatrix} 2a - 3 & -b + 1 \\ 5 - c & -2d + 5 \end{bmatrix}$

8. Evaluate.

   a) $\begin{bmatrix} 6 & 12 \\ -11 & 5 \end{bmatrix}\left(\begin{bmatrix} -1 & 3 \\ 7 & 16 \end{bmatrix} - \begin{bmatrix} 4 & -5 \\ 20 & -2 \end{bmatrix}\right)$

   ★b) $[3 \quad -4]\begin{bmatrix} -1 & 1 & 2 \\ 8 & 3 & -5 \end{bmatrix}$

   $+ 4[2 \quad -1 \quad -2]\begin{bmatrix} 3 & 2 & 4 \\ -1 & 0 & 1 \\ 5 & 6 & -2 \end{bmatrix}$

C

9. Given $H = \begin{bmatrix} 2 & 5 \\ -3 & 7 \end{bmatrix}$, determine a matrix

   $I = \begin{bmatrix} a & b \\ c & d \end{bmatrix}$, such that $HI = IH$.

10. Determine the unknown values.

    a) $\begin{bmatrix} 2 & -3 \\ 5 & -1 \end{bmatrix}\begin{bmatrix} x \\ y \end{bmatrix} = \begin{bmatrix} -7 \\ 4 \end{bmatrix}$

    b) $\begin{bmatrix} x & 0 & 1 \\ 2 & -3 & 5 \\ 7 & y & 0 \end{bmatrix}\begin{bmatrix} 2 & 0 \\ 1 & 0 \\ -3 & 1 \end{bmatrix} + \begin{bmatrix} -1 & 2 \\ 3 & -2 \\ 1 & 4 \end{bmatrix}$

    $= \begin{bmatrix} y & z \\ -11 & 3 \\ x & 4 \end{bmatrix}$

11. Given $M = \begin{bmatrix} 2 & -1 \\ -6 & 3 \end{bmatrix}$, verify that $M^2 = 5M$.

12. Is the following true for all 2×2 matrices A and B? Justify your answer.

    $(A + B)(A - B) = A^2 - B^2$

KEY CONCEPTS

- One very useful application of matrices is to determine the solution to a system of linear equations. For instance, consider the following linear system of two lines in the Cartesian plane.

$2x - 3y = 7$
$5x + y = 9$

Solve this system of linear equations by using the method of elimination or the method of substitution. Another way to solve the system is to use **determinants**.

The **determinant** (det) of a 2×2 matrix $A = \begin{bmatrix} a_1 & b_1 \\ a_2 & b_2 \end{bmatrix}$ is

$\det A = \begin{vmatrix} a_1 & b_1 \\ a_2 & b_2 \end{vmatrix} = a_1 b_2 - b_1 a_2$, where $a_1 b_2 - b_1 a_2$ is a real number.

The determinant of a 3×3 matrix $B = \begin{bmatrix} a_1 & b_1 & c_1 \\ a_2 & b_2 & c_2 \\ a_3 & b_3 & c_3 \end{bmatrix}$ is

$\det B = \begin{vmatrix} a_1 & b_1 & c_1 \\ a_2 & b_2 & c_2 \\ a_3 & b_3 & c_3 \end{vmatrix} = a_1 \begin{vmatrix} b_2 & c_2 \\ b_3 & c_3 \end{vmatrix} - b_1 \begin{vmatrix} a_2 & c_2 \\ a_3 & c_3 \end{vmatrix} + c_1 \begin{vmatrix} a_2 & b_2 \\ a_3 & b_3 \end{vmatrix}.$

Example 1

Find the determinant of each matrix below.

a) $A = \begin{bmatrix} 7 & -2 \\ 5 & 12 \end{bmatrix}$
b) $B = \begin{bmatrix} -3 & 1 & 6 \\ 4 & -5 & 2 \\ 3 & 8 & 7 \end{bmatrix}$

Solution

a) $A = \begin{bmatrix} 7 & -2 \\ 5 & 12 \end{bmatrix}$

$\det A = \begin{vmatrix} 7 & -2 \\ 5 & 12 \end{vmatrix}$
$= 7(12) - (-2)(5)$
$= 94$

b) $B = \begin{bmatrix} -3 & 1 & 6 \\ 4 & -5 & 2 \\ 3 & 8 & 7 \end{bmatrix}$

$\det B = \begin{vmatrix} -3 & 1 & 6 \\ 4 & -5 & 2 \\ 3 & 8 & 7 \end{vmatrix}$

$= (-3)\begin{vmatrix} -5 & 2 \\ 8 & 7 \end{vmatrix} - (1)\begin{vmatrix} 4 & 2 \\ 3 & 7 \end{vmatrix} + (6)\begin{vmatrix} 4 & -5 \\ 3 & 8 \end{vmatrix}$

$= -3[(-5)(7) - 2(8)] - [4(7) - 2(3)] +$
$\qquad 6[4(8) - (-5)(3)]$

$= -3(-51) - (22) + 6(47)$

$= 413$

- When two lines **intersect in a point,** the corresponding linear system is said to have a **unique solution.** Determinants are useful because not only can they be used to determine if a linear system has a unique solution, but they can also be used to find the point of intersection.

Example 2

Determine whether each linear system below has a unique solution. Use Cramer's rule to find the unique solution, if it exists.

a) $4x - 5y = 2$ **b)** $2x - 3y = 5$

$\quad\ 3x + 2y = 6$ $-4x + 6y = 7$

Solution

a) $4x - 5y = 2$

$\quad\ 3x + 2y = 6$

$\quad D = \begin{vmatrix} 4 & -5 \\ 3 & 2 \end{vmatrix}$

$\qquad = 8 + 15$

$\qquad = 23$

Since $D \neq 0$, the linear system has a unique solution.

The solution is

$x = \dfrac{D_1}{D} = \dfrac{\begin{vmatrix} 2 & -5 \\ 6 & 2 \end{vmatrix}}{23}$

$\qquad = \dfrac{34}{23}$

$y = \dfrac{D_2}{D} = \dfrac{\begin{vmatrix} 4 & 2 \\ 3 & 6 \end{vmatrix}}{23}$

$\qquad = \dfrac{18}{23}$

The point of intersection is $(x, y) = \left(\dfrac{34}{23}, \dfrac{18}{23} \right)$.

b) $2x - 3y = 5$

$\quad -4x + 6y = 7$

$\quad D = \begin{vmatrix} 2 & -3 \\ -4 & 6 \end{vmatrix}$

$\qquad = 12 - 12$

$\qquad = 0$

Since $D = 0$, the linear system does not have a unique solution.

A

1. The values of the determinants D, D_1, and D_2 of a linear system are given. State if the system has a unique solution. If it does, state the solution.

   a) $D = 4$, $D_1 = 9$, $D_2 = -17$

   b) $D = 0$, $D_1 = -23$, $D_2 = 15$

   c) $D = -9$, $D_1 = 22$, $D_2 = 36$

2. Describe the similarities and differences between a matrix and a determinant. Use examples to support your answer.

B

3. Evaluate the determinant for each of the following matrices.

   a) $\begin{vmatrix} 5 & -3 \\ 1 & 9 \end{vmatrix}$

   b) $\begin{vmatrix} 7 & -1 \\ -6 & 4 \end{vmatrix}$

   c) $\begin{vmatrix} 3 & 1 & 6 \\ -4 & 2 & -1 \\ 5 & 8 & -3 \end{vmatrix}$

   d) $\begin{vmatrix} -\frac{1}{2} & 4 & 5 \\ 1 & -3 & 2 \\ 0 & 8 & -4 \end{vmatrix}$

   ★e) $5\begin{vmatrix} 9 & 10 \\ -7 & 4 \end{vmatrix} - \frac{2}{3}\begin{vmatrix} 6 & 27 \\ 18 & -15 \end{vmatrix}$

4. Determine whether each linear system below has a unique solution. If it does, use Cramer's rule to find the solution.

   a) $5x - 2y = 3$
      $4x + 3y = 8$

   b) $-x + 3y = 1$
      $3x - 9y = 4$

   c) $8x - 5y = -4$
      $2x - 3y = 2$

   d) $-4x - 2y = 6$
      $10x + 5y = -15$

   e) $1.5x + 3y = -8$
      $4.5x - 2y = 7$

★5. Determine the value(s) of x such that

$\begin{vmatrix} 1 & 1-x \\ x-4 & 2 \end{vmatrix} = 0.$

6. Use determinants to find the values of a and b, such that the point $(4, -3)$ is the unique solution to the linear system below.
   $ax + 2y = -2$
   $3x + by = -9$

C

7. A system of three equations in three variables x, y, and z has a unique solution if, and only if, the 3×3 determinant $D \neq 0$. In this case, the unique solution is
   $x = \dfrac{D_1}{D}, y = \dfrac{D_2}{D},$ and $z = \dfrac{D_3}{D},$
   where D_i is the determinant obtained from D by replacing the ith column with the constants on the right-hand side of the linear system. Determine whether each linear system that follows has a unique solution.

   a) $4x - y + 2z = 3$
      $-x + 3y + z = 1$
      $5x + 2y - z = -7$

   b) $x + y + 2z = -2$
      $3x - y + 14z = 6$
      $x + 2y = -5$

   c) $2x + y + z = -4$
      $3y - 2z = 2$
      $3x + y + 2z = -7$

8. Use Cramer's rule to find a quadratic function, $f(x)$, such that $f(1) = 5$, $f(2) = 6$, and $f(-2) = 26$.

University Preparation 4: CONICS

UP 4.1 Introduction

KEY CONCEPTS

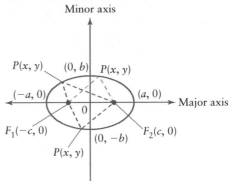

- An ellipse is defined as the set of all points for which the **sum** of the distances to two fixed points, F_1 and F_2, (called **foci**, plural of focus) is constant, that is, $PF_1 + PF_2 = k$.
- The general equation of an ellipse with centre $(0, 0)$ and foci $F_1(-c, 0)$ and $F_2(c, 0)$ on the x-axis may be developed from the basic definition. Note that $c^2 = a^2 - b^2$.

  The distance from point $P(x, y)$ to $F_1(-c, 0)$ is
  $$PF_1 = \sqrt{(x + c)^2 + (y - 0)^2}.$$
  The distance from point $P(x, y)$ to $F_2(c, 0)$ is
  $$PF_2 = \sqrt{(x - c)^2 + (y - 0)^2}.$$
  $$PF_1 + PF_2 = k$$
  $$\sqrt{(x + c)^2 + (y - 0)^2} + \sqrt{(x - c)^2 + (y - 0)^2} = k$$
  Rewrite the above equality as
  $$\sqrt{x^2 + 2xc + c^2 + y^2} = k - \sqrt{x^2 - 2xc + c^2 + y^2} \quad ①$$

  By squaring both sides, simplifying, and substituting $c^2 = a^2 - b^2$, equation ① simplifies to $b^2x^2 + a^2y^2 = a^2b^2$.

  Divide each side by a^2b^2 to obtain $\dfrac{x^2}{a^2} + \dfrac{y^2}{b^2} = 1$, where $a > b$.

- This represents an ellipse with foci and vertices on the x-axis. Since $a > b$, it is wider along the x-axis than along the y-axis, so the **major axis** is the x-axis and the **minor axis** is the y-axis.

- The equation of an ellipse with foci and vertices on the y-axis may be developed in a similar way to the above, and is $\dfrac{x^2}{b^2} + \dfrac{y^2}{a^2} = 1$, where $a > b$.
- This ellipse is wider along the y-axis than along the x-axis, so the y-axis is the major axis and the x-axis is the minor axis.

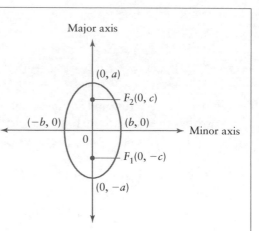

Ellipse: Key Characteristics		
	$\dfrac{x^2}{a^2} + \dfrac{y^2}{b^2} = 1, a > b$	$\dfrac{x^2}{b^2} + \dfrac{y^2}{a^2} = 1, a > b$
Centre	$(0, 0)$	$(0, 0)$
Vertices	$(\pm a, 0)$	$(0, \pm a)$
Intercepts	$y = \pm b$	$x = \pm b$
Major axis and length	x-axis, length is $2a$	y-axis, length is $2a$
Minor axis and length	y-axis, $2b$	x-axis, $2b$
Foci	$(\pm c, 0)$ where $c^2 = a^2 - b^2$	$(0, \pm c)$ where $c^2 = a^2 - b^2$
Distance between foci	$2c$	$2c$

Example 1

Identify the key characteristics of each ellipse: $\dfrac{x^2}{100} + \dfrac{y^2}{16} = 1$, $\dfrac{x^2}{4} + \dfrac{y^2}{36} = 1$

Solution

	$\dfrac{x^2}{100} + \dfrac{y^2}{16} = 1$	$\dfrac{x^2}{4} + \dfrac{y^2}{36} = 1$
Centre	$(0, 0)$	$(0, 0)$
Vertices	$(\pm 10, 0)$	$(0, \pm 6)$
Intercepts	$y = \pm 4$	$x = \pm 2$
Major axis and length	x-axis, length is $2(10) = 20$	y-axis, length is $2(6) = 12$
Minor axis and length	y-axis, length is $2(4) = 8$	x-axis, length is $2(2) = 4$
Foci	$c^2 = 100 - 16$ $= 84$ $c = 2\sqrt{21}$ The foci are: $(\pm 2\sqrt{21}, 0)$	$c^2 = 36 - 4$ $= 32$ $c = 4\sqrt{2}$ The foci are: $(0, \pm 4\sqrt{2})$
Distance between foci	$4\sqrt{21}$	$8\sqrt{2}$

Example 2

Determine an equation of an ellipse with foci at $(-4, 0)$ and $(4, 0)$ and a constant sum of focal radii 10.

Solution

Let $P(x, y)$ be any point on the ellipse.

$PF_1 + PF_2 = 10$

$\sqrt{(x + 4)^2 + y^2} + \sqrt{(x - 4)^2 + y^2} = 10$

Write the equation so that there is a radical on each side.

$\sqrt{x^2 - 8x + 16 + y^2} = 10 - \sqrt{x^2 + 8x + 16 + y^2}$

Square both sides.

$x^2 - 8x + 16 + y^2 = 100 - 20\sqrt{x^2 + 8x + 16 + y^2} + x^2 + 8x + 16 + y^2$

Simplify.

$5\sqrt{x^2 + 8x + 16 + y^2} = 4x + 25$

Square both sides again.

$25x^2 + 200x + 400 + 25y^2 = 16x^2 + 200x + 625$

Simplify.

$9x^2 + 25y^2 = 225$

Divide each side by 225.

The equation of the ellipse is $\dfrac{x^2}{25} + \dfrac{y^2}{9} = 1$.

A

1. For each of the sets of information given below, state the equation of an ellipse with centre $(0, 0)$.

   a) The vertices are $(\pm 7, 0)$; y-intercepts are ± 5.

   b) The y-axis is the major axis with length 16; the x-axis is the minor axis with length 6.

   c) $a^2 = 100$, $c^2 = 64$, and the major axis is the x-axis.

2. Sketch a graph of each ellipse in question 1 and identify the key characteristics.

B

3. i) Determine the foci of each ellipse below.

   ii) For each ellipse, state which is the major axis and which is the minor axis.

   a) $\dfrac{x^2}{16} + \dfrac{y^2}{64} = 1$

   b) $\dfrac{x^2}{100} + \dfrac{y^2}{81} = 1$

   c) $\dfrac{x^2}{4} + \dfrac{y^2}{49} = 1$

   d) $\dfrac{x^2}{25} + \dfrac{y^2}{36} = 1$

   e) $4x^2 + 25y^2 = 100$

   f) $16x^2 + 4y^2 = 100$

4. Complete this chart for each ellipse, with centre $(0, 0)$.

	$\dfrac{x^2}{121} + \dfrac{y^2}{64} = 1$	$\dfrac{x^2}{16} + \dfrac{y^2}{81} = 1$	$\dfrac{x^2}{144} + \dfrac{y^2}{169} = 1$	$\dfrac{x^2}{18} + \dfrac{y^2}{44} = 1$
Vertices				
Intercepts				
Major axis and length				
Minor axis and length				
Foci				
Distance between foci				

5. a) Find an equation of each ellipse described below, with centre $(0, 0)$.

   i) The length of the major axis is 10; the length of the minor axis is 8.

   ii) The length of the minor axis is 6; one vertex is $(-5, 0)$.

   iii) One intercept is $(5, 0)$; one vertex is $(0, -7)$.

   b) For each of the above, is there another possible equation that satisfies the given conditions? Justify your answer.

★6. a) Determine the equation of an ellipse with foci at (−8, 0) and (8, 0) and constant sum of focal radii 20.

b) Identify the key characteristics of the ellipse you found in part a).

c) Sketch a graph of the ellipse.

7. a) Determine an equation of an ellipse with foci at (0, −7) and (0, 7) and constant sum of focal radii 18.

b) Identify the key characteristics of the ellipse you found in part a).

c) Sketch a graph of the ellipse.

★8. A pool has the shape of an ellipse. The major axis has length 10 m and the minor axis has length 8 m.

a) Write an equation of the ellipse.

b) Find the width of the pool at a point on the major axis that is 2 m from the centre.

C

9. Ellipses can be long and narrow or nearly circular. The **eccentricity**, e, of an ellipse is a measure of the amount of **elongation** of an ellipse. The value of e is determined by the formula $e = \frac{c}{a}$, where $0 < e < 1$. The closer the value of e is to 1, the more elongated the ellipse. Determine the eccentricity of each ellipse in question 4.

10. Find an equation of an ellipse with centre (0, 0), vertices (± 6, 0), and eccentricity $\frac{2}{3}$.

11. An equation of an ellipse with centre (h, k), and major axis the x-axis, is $\frac{(x-h)^2}{a^2} + \frac{(y-k)^2}{b^2} = 1$.

a) Determine the key characteristics of the ellipse $\frac{(x-2)^2}{4} + \frac{(y+3)^2}{9} = 1$.

b) Sketch a graph of this ellipse.

KEY CONCEPTS

- A hyperbola is defined as the set of all points for which the **difference** of the distances to two fixed points, F_1 and F_2, is constant, that is, $|PF_1 - PF_2| = k$.

- The general equation of a hyperbola with centre $(0, 0)$ and foci $F_1(-c, 0)$ and $F_2(c, 0)$ on the x-axis may be developed from the basic definition in a fashion similar to the one used to develop the equation of an ellipse. Note that $c^2 = a^2 + b^2$.

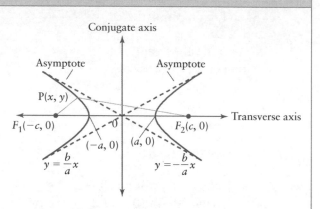

The distance from point $P(x, y)$ to $F_1(-c, 0)$ is $PF_1 = \sqrt{(x + c)^2 + (y - 0)^2}$.

The distance from point $P(x, y)$ to $F_2(c, 0)$ is $PF_2 = \sqrt{(x - c)^2 + (y - 0)^2}$.

The sum of the distances is constant, i.e., $|PF_1 - PF_2| = k$ and so $\sqrt{(x + c)^2 + (y - 0)^2} - \sqrt{(x - c)^2 + (y - 0)^2} = k$.

Rewrite the above equality as $\sqrt{x^2 + 2xc + c^2 + y^2} = k + \sqrt{x^2 - 2xc + c^2 + y^2}$ ①

Further algebraic operations and simplification reduce equation ① to $\dfrac{x^2}{a^2} - \dfrac{y^2}{b^2} = 1$.

- This represents a hyperbola with foci and vertices on the x-axis, which is called the **transverse axis**. The y-axis is the **conjugate axis**. The hyperbola with centre $(0, 0)$ has two branches that intersect only one axis. The axis that is intersected is called the **transverse axis**, and the other axis (which is not intersected) is called the **conjugate axis**.

- This hyperbola has **asymptotes** with equations $y = \pm\dfrac{b}{a}x$ and no y-intercepts. The **asymptotes** of a hyperbola are two imaginary lines that the branches of this curve become closer and closer to but do not intersect. They determine the shape of the hyperbola. The equations of the asymptotes are based on the values of a and b.

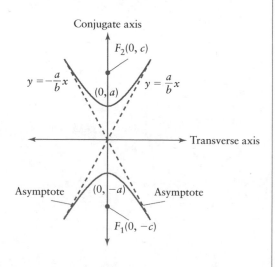

- The equation of a hyperbola with foci and vertices on the y-axis is $\dfrac{x^2}{b^2} - \dfrac{y^2}{a^2} = -1$. In this case, the y-axis is the transverse axis and the x-axis is the conjugate axis. This hyperbola has asymptotes with equations $y = \pm\dfrac{a}{b}x$ and no x-intercepts.

Hyperbola: Key Characteristics		
	$\dfrac{x^2}{a^2} - \dfrac{y^2}{b^2} = 1$	$\dfrac{x^2}{b^2} - \dfrac{y^2}{a^2} = -1$
Centre	$(0, 0)$	$(0, 0)$
Vertices	$(\pm a, 0)$	$(0, \pm a)$
Transverse axis and length	x-axis, $2a$	y-axis, $2a$
Conjugate axis and length	y-axis, $2b$	x-axis, $2b$
Foci	$(\pm c, 0)$ where $c^2 = a^2 + b^2$	$(0, \pm c)$ where $c^2 = a^2 + b^2$
Distance between foci	$2c$	$2c$
Asymptotes	$y = \pm\dfrac{b}{a}x$	$y = \pm\dfrac{a}{b}x$

Example 1

Identify the key characteristics of each hyperbola with centre $(0, 0)$: $\dfrac{x^2}{25} - \dfrac{y^2}{9} = 1$, $\dfrac{x^2}{4} - \dfrac{y^2}{36} = -1$

Solution

	$\dfrac{x^2}{25} - \dfrac{y^2}{9} = 1$	$\dfrac{x^2}{4} - \dfrac{y^2}{36} = -1$
Vertices	$(\pm 5, 0)$	$(0, \pm 6)$
Transverse axis and length	x-axis, $2(5) = 10$	y-axis, $2(6) = 12$
Conjugate axis and length	y-axis, $2(3) = 6$	x-axis, $2(2) = 4$
Foci	$c^2 = 25 + 9$ $= 34$ $c = \sqrt{34}$ $\left(\pm\sqrt{34}, 0\right)$	$c^2 = 36 + 4$ $= 40$ $c = 2\sqrt{10}$ $\left(0, \pm 2\sqrt{10}\right)$
Distance between foci	$2\sqrt{34}$	$4\sqrt{10}$
Asymptotes	$y = \pm\dfrac{3}{5}x$	$y = \pm 3x$

Example 2

Determine an equation of a hyperbola with foci at $(-5, 0)$ and $(5, 0)$ and constant difference of focal radii 8.

Solution

Let $P(x, y)$ be any point on the ellipse.

$|PF_1 - PF_2| = 8$.

$\sqrt{(x + 5)^2 + y^2} - \sqrt{(x - 5)^2 + y^2} = 8$

Write the equation so that there is a radical on each side.

$-\sqrt{x^2 - 10x + 25 + y^2} = 8 - \sqrt{x^2 + 10x + 25 + y^2}$

Square both sides.

$x^2 - 10x + 25 + y^2 = 64 - 16\sqrt{x^2 + 10x + 25 + y^2} + x^2 + 10x + 25 + y^2$

Simplify.

$4\sqrt{x^2 + 10x + 25 + y^2} = 5x + 16$

Square both sides again.

$16x^2 + 160x + 400 + 16y^2 = 25x^2 + 160x + 256$

Simplify.

$9x^2 - 16y^2 = 144$

Divide each side by 144.

The equation of the hyperbola is $\dfrac{x^2}{16} - \dfrac{y^2}{9} = 1$.

A

1. For each hyperbola below, state the transverse axis and the conjugate axis, and their lengths.

   a) $\dfrac{x^2}{16} - \dfrac{y^2}{64} = -1$

   b) $\dfrac{x^2}{100} - \dfrac{y^2}{81} = 1$

   c) $\dfrac{x^2}{4} - \dfrac{y^2}{49} = 1$

   d) $\dfrac{x^2}{25} - \dfrac{y^2}{36} = -1$

   e) $4x^2 - 25y^2 = -100$

   f) $16x^2 - 4y^2 = 100$

2. Sketch a graph of each hyperbola in question 1.

B

3. A hyperbola has centre $(0, 0)$ and transverse axis on the y-axis. Write the equation of the hyperbola if:

   a) $a = 4$, $b = 7$

   b) $a = 3$, $b = 6$

   c) $a = 8$, $b = 5$

   d) the transverse axis has length 8 units and the conjugate axis has length 18 units

   e) one vertex is $(0, -3)$ and one asymptote is $y = -2x$.

4. A hyperbola has centre $(0, 0)$ and transverse axis on the x-axis. Write the equation of the hyperbola if:

   a) $a = 10, b = 3$

   b) $a = 8, b = 6$

   c) $a = 9, b = 11$

   d) the transverse axis has length 14 units and the conjugate axis has length 10 units

   e) one vertex is $(-4, 0)$ and one focus is $(-5, 0)$

5. State the key characteristics of each hyperbola you graphed in question 2.

6. Complete this chart for each hyperbola with centre $(0, 0)$.

	$\frac{x^2}{81} - \frac{y^2}{64}$ $= 1$	$\frac{x^2}{4} - \frac{y^2}{36}$ $= -1$	$\frac{x^2}{144} - \frac{y^2}{121}$ $= 1$	$\frac{x^2}{9} - \frac{y^2}{25}$ $= -1$
Vertices				
Transverse axis and length				
Conjugate axis and length				
Foci				
Distance between foci				
Asymptotes				

★**7. a)** Determine an equation of a hyperbola with foci at $(-6, 0)$ and $(6, 0)$ and constant difference of focal radii 10.

   b) Identify the key characteristics of the hyperbola you found in part a).

   c) Sketch a graph of the hyperbola.

8. a) Determine an equation of a hyperbola with foci at $(0, -7)$ and $(0, 7)$ and constant difference of focal radii 8.

   b) Identify the key characteristics of the hyperbola you found in part a).

   c) Sketch a graph of the hyperbola.

★**9.** Determine the equation of a hyperbola with center $(0, 0)$ that has one vertex at $(\sqrt{6}, 0)$ and passes through the point $(9, 5)$.

C

10. The **eccentricity**, e, of a hyperbola is defined the same way as for an ellipse, $e = \frac{c}{a}$. Determine the eccentricity of each ellipse in question 6 to two decimal places.

11. Find an equation of a hyperbola with centre $(0, 0)$, where the transverse axis is the x-axis with length 8 and the eccentricity is 1.5.

12. The equation of a hyperbola with centre (h, k) and transverse axis on the x-axis is $\frac{(x-h)^2}{a^2} - \frac{(y-k)^2}{b^2} = 1$. Determine the key characteristics of the hyperbola $\frac{(x-2)^2}{4} - \frac{(y+3)^2}{9} = 1$. Sketch a graph of this hyperbola.

13. Write the equation $7x^2 - 2y^2 - 14x + 12y = 101$ in the form $\frac{(x-h)^2}{a^2} - \frac{(y-k)^2}{b^2} = 1$ and sketch the graph, indicating the key characteristics.

1. For each of these polynomial functions,
   i) $f(x) = x^6 - 2x^5 - x^4 + 3x^3 - x^2 - x + 1$
   ii) $g(x) = 5(x-4)^3 (x-2)(x+11)^2 (x^2-4)$

   a) determine the degree

   b) describe the end behaviour

   c) list the real zeros of the polynomial and the order of each zero

2. Find a polynomial of degree 3 such that $f(-1) = 0, f(1) = 0$, and $f(0) = 5$.

3. Determine an equation for each of the following functions. Give reasons for your choices.

   a)

   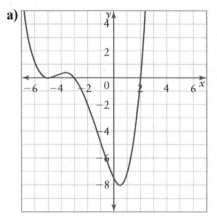

   b)

   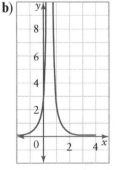

   c)

   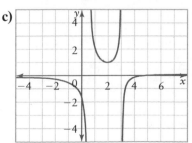

4. Solve the inequality $x^4 - 11x^2 + 18 \geq 0$.

5. **Use Technology** A national security review studied the number of murders that took place over a ten-year period.

Time in Years, t	Number of Murders, n (per 100 000 population)
0	9.110 4
1	9.217 2
2	9.456 4
3	9.799 8
4	10.294
5	11.058
6	12.289
7	14.225
8	17.301
9	21.844
10	28.376

   a) Graph the data on a graphing calculator.

   b) Use the graph to predict the degree of the polynomial function that models this data.

   c) i) Determine which finite differences will be constant for this polynomial function.

   ii) What is the value of the constant finite differences?

   iii) What is the value of the leading coefficient? Explain how you know.

   d) Use the regression feature on the graphing calculator to determine an equation for a function that models this situation.

   e) How can you use the equation to determine the number of times the function crosses the x-axis?

   f) If the study began in 1990, when was the rate 8 people per 100 000?

6. The value of Laura's college fund is the sum of the three investments that she has made over the last five years. To estimate the total value of those investments, Laura used the equation $T(x) = 100x^5 + 56x^3 + 250x$, where T is the total current value of the stocks, and x represents the interest rate plus 1 $(r + 1)$.

   a) What is the current value of her investments at an average annual rate of 6.25%?

   b) Determine the average rate of change of the total as the interest rate increases from 6.25% to 7%.

   c) What is the instantaneous rate of change at the average annual rate? What does this value tell Laura?

7. The scenery for a high school drama includes a house with a painted window. Special gloss paint covers the area representing the window to make it look like real glass. If the expensive gloss paint covers only 2000 cm^2 and the window must be 15 cm taller than it is wide, how large should the scenery painters make the window?

8. Use the Integral or Rational Root Theorem to determine a zero of each of these polynomials. Then, solve for the other real roots.

   a) $3x^3 - 4x^2 - 36x + 16 = 0$

   b) $21x^4 - 42x^3 - 45x^2 + 102x - 24 = 0$

9. For each of the following functions,

   i) $y = \dfrac{1}{2 - x}$

   ii) $y = \dfrac{4x - 3}{2x + 1}$

   iii) $f(x) = \dfrac{x + 3}{x^2 + 6x - 27}$

   a) determine the x- and y-intercepts

   b) determine the equations of any vertical, horizontal, or oblique asymptotes

   c) state the domain and range of the function

   d) sketch a graph of the function

10. Solve each of the following inequalities and illustrate each solution on a number line.

   a) $\dfrac{1}{x - 4} \geq -2$

   b) $\dfrac{1}{x^2 - 13x + 40} \leq 0$

11. An arc of 10-cm length has a central angle of $\dfrac{\pi}{5}$ radians. Determine the radius of the circle.

12. Find the area of a sector of a circle that has a central angle of $\dfrac{3\pi}{8}$ and a radius of 7 cm. Round your answer to the nearest tenth.

13. Determine exact values of the six trigonometric ratios for each of the following angles:

   a) $\dfrac{11\pi}{6}$

   b) $\dfrac{2\pi}{3}$

   c) $\dfrac{5\pi}{4}$

   d) π

14. Given that $\sin \dfrac{5\pi}{11} \doteq 0.9898$, determine the following, to four decimal places, without using a calculator. Justify your answers.

   a) $\cos \dfrac{21\pi}{11}$

   b) $\cos \dfrac{\pi}{22}$

15. Write an equation for a sine function with an amplitude of 3, a period of 4π, and a phase shift of $+\dfrac{\pi}{3}$.

16. Prove the following identities:

a) $\cos^2 x + 2 \sin^2 x - 1 = \sin^2 x$

b) $\sin(x + y) = \dfrac{\tan x + \tan y}{\sec x \sec y}$

c) $\sec^2 x - 1 = \tan^2 x$

17. If θ is an angle in the second quadrant where $\sec \theta = -\dfrac{2}{\sqrt{3}}$, the angle ϕ is in the first quadrant, and $\tan \phi = \dfrac{1}{\sqrt{3}}$, determine an exact value for each of the following:

a) $\sin 2\theta$

b) $\cos 2\phi$

c) $\sin(\theta + \phi)$

d) $\cos(\theta - \phi)$

18. Write an equation for a cosine function, reflected in the x axis, with an amplitude of $\dfrac{1}{2}$, a period of $\dfrac{\pi}{2}$, a phase shift of $\dfrac{-\pi}{6}$, and a horizontal translation of $+3$.

19. a) Sketch a graph of the function $y = \csc x$.

b) Predict the shape of each function, and then check by graphing.

   i) $y = 4 \csc x$

   ii) $y = \csc 3x$

   iii) $y = \csc x + 5$

   iv) $y = \csc (x - 2)$

20. Consider the function
$$y = -2 \cos \left[4\left(x - \dfrac{\pi}{6}\right) \right] + 1.$$

a) What is the amplitude?

b) What is the period?

c) Describe the phase shift.

d) Describe the vertical translation.

e) Sketch a graph of the function over two cycles.

21. Solve the following equations on the interval $x \in [0, 2\pi]$.

a) $\sin^2 x - \sin x = 2$

b) $2 \cos^2 x - 3 \cos x + 1 = 0$

c) $2 \sec x + \tan x = 3$

22. The following table shows the number of hours of daylight per day on various days of the year in Thunder Bay, Ontario.

Day of the Year	Hours of Daylight
16	8.72
75	11.82
136	15.18
197	15.83
259	12.68
320	9.18

a) Make a scatter plot of the data.

b) Write a sine function to model the data.

c) Graph your model on the same set of axes as in part a). Comment on the fit.

d) Check your model using a sinusoidal regression. How does the regression equation compare with the model?

e) Find the percent of days in the year with less than 10 h of daylight. Round your answer to the nearest percent.

23. a) Copy the following table and complete the values for the function $y = 3^x$.

x	y
-2	
-1	
0	
$\dfrac{1}{2}$	
1	
2	
3	

b) Graph the function.

c) Sketch a graph of the inverse of $y = 3^x$.

24. Evaluate each logarithm.

a) $\log_2 2^3$

b) $\log_2 \sqrt[5]{16}$

c) $\log 40 + \log 2.5$

d) $2 \log_3 12 - 2 \log_3 4$

e) $\log_5 \sqrt{225} - \log_5 \sqrt{9}$

25. Solve for x. Round each answer to two decimal places, if necessary.

a) $3^x = 21$

b) $x = \log_3 27$

26. The value of a vehicle depreciates by 20% each year. The value, V, in dollars, as a function of time, t, in years, can be modelled by the function $V(t) = 35\,000(0.80)^t$.

a) What is the initial value of the vehicle?

b) How long, to the nearest tenth of a year, will it take for the vehicle to depreciate to half its initial value?

27. The decibel rating of a sound is $\beta = \log\dfrac{I}{I_0}$, where I is the intensity, in watts per square metre, and I_0 is the minimum intensity of sound audible to the average person, or 1.0×10^{-12} W/m².

a) Find the decibel rating of a pneumatic drill with an intensity rating of 6.98×10^{-4} W/m².

b) The sound of a student whispering in class has a decimal rating of 26 dB. What is the intensity of the whisper?

28. Use Technology Solve. Check your answers using graphing technology.

a) $64^{2x-3} = 16^{x+5}$

b) $9^{4x-1} = 27^{2x}$

c) $\dfrac{27^x}{9^{2x-1}} = 3^{x+4}$

29. Solve for x. Round each answer to two decimal places.

a) $4^x = 7$

b) $7.3^x = 1200$

c) $15^{x-2} = 7$

d) $2^{-x+7} = 9$

e) $375^{3x+5} = 25^{x-7}$

f) $5^{3x} = 0.75^{x-8}$

30. Various radioactive substances are used in medical tests.

a) In thyroid deficiency tests, a 50-mg sample of radioactive material decays to 38.5 mg in 72 h. What is the half-life of the material to the nearest hour?

b) In bone density tests, a 200-mg sample of radioactive material decays to 120 mg in 2 h. Determine the half-life of the substance to the nearest tenth of an hour.

31. Simplify. State any restrictions on the variable(s).

a) $\log(x^2 - x - 12) - \log(x + 3)$

b) $3 \log 4x + \log x^5 - 2 \log x$

c) $\log\left(2 + \dfrac{3y}{x} + \dfrac{4y^2}{x^2}\right) - 2 \log x$

32. Use Technology Solve. Identify and reject any extraneous roots. Check your solutions using graphing technology.

a) $\log(x + 1) + \log(x - 2) = 1$

b) $\log(x^2 - 1) - \log(x + 1) = 1 + \log 2$

c) $2 \log(x + 1) - \log(5x + 1) + \log(x - 1) = \log 2$

33. The population of a city is 48 000 and is increasing by 9% annually.

a) Write an equation to show the population as a function of time, t, in years.

b) How long, to the nearest tenth of a year, will it take for the population to triple?

c) After how many years will the population reach 67 000?

34. Let $f(x) = 3^x + 1$, $g(x) = 3x^2 + 9x$, and $h(x) = 3x$. Determine an algebraic and a graphical model for each function. Identify the domain and range of each.

a) $y = f(x) + g(x)$

b) $y = f(x) + g(x) - h(x)$

c) $y = g(x)h(x)$

d) $y = \dfrac{g(x)}{h(x)}$

35. An Internet service provider has modelled its projected number of business subscribers as $B(t) = 85t + 3700$, and the projected average number of Internet connections per business subscriber as $C(t) = 0.009t^2 + 1.8$, where t is the time, in weeks, over the next year. The projected total number of business Internet connections is then $N(t) = B(t) \times C(t)$.

a) Determine the growth rate of the number of business connections after t weeks.

b) Determine the growth rate of the number of business connections after 15 weeks.

36. Consider $f(x) = 2x - 1$ and $g(x) = \sin x$, where x is in radians.

a) Describe and sketch a graph of $f(x)$. Is this function even, odd, or neither?

b) Describe and sketch a graph of $g(x)$. Is this function even, odd, or neither?

c) Predict the shape of $y = f(x)g(x)$. Sketch the graph of your prediction.

d) Use Technology Check your work by graphing the three functions in parts a) to c) using graphing technology.

e) Give the domain and range of $y = f(x)g(x)$.

37. Let $f(x) = x^3 - 6x^2 - x + 30$ and $g(x) = 16 - x^2$.

a) Graph these functions on the same set of axes.

b) Identify, by inspecting the graphs, the interval or intervals for which $f(x) > g(x)$.

c) Check your answer to part b) using another method.

38. Let $f(x) = \sqrt{2x - 6}$ and $g(x) = \dfrac{2}{x^2}$. Write a simplified algebraic model for each composite function. State the domain and range of each.

a) $y = f(g(x))$

b) $y = g(f(x))$

39. The season ticket sales for a football team depend on the number of wins that the team has in the previous year according to the formula $N(w) = 10\,000\left(\dfrac{10 + w}{10}\right)^2$, where the number of season tickets sold is N and the number of wins in the previous season is w. The number of wins that the team has in the previous year is currently given by $w(t) = -\dfrac{1}{2}(t - 4)^2 + 12$, where t is the year, with $t = 0$ in 2009.

a) Calculate the number of season tickets sold in 2009.

b) Graph $y = w(t)$. If the season has 14 games, describe what the model predicts concerning the winning success of the team.

c) What domain restrictions must be placed on $w(t)$? Explain.

d) The team's stadium holds 50 000 fans. Does the model predict a need for expansion? Justify your answer.

e) The team plans to sign several older star free agents for next year. How might this affect $w(t)$?

f) The team has just drafted four rookies who are projected to be stars in 4 years. How might this affect $w(t)$?

Answers
Advanced Functions 12 Study Guide and University Handbook
Chapter 1

1.1 Power Functions
1. **a)** 2 **b)** 3 **c)** 10 **d)** 1 **e)** 3 **f)** 4 **g)** 6 **h)** 1
2. **a)** line **b)** point **c)** line **d)** point **e)** point
   f) line **g)** line **h)** point
   Even-degree power functions have line symmetry in the *y*-axis. Odd-degree power functions have point symmetry about the origin.
3. **a)** quadrant 2 to 1, even exponent, positive leading coefficient
   b) quadrant 2 to 4, odd exponent, negative leading coefficient
   c) quadrant 2 to 1, even exponent, positive leading coefficient
   d) quadrant 2 to 4, odd exponent, negative leading coefficient
   e) quadrant 2 to 4, odd exponent, negative leading coefficient
   f) quadrant 2 to 1, even exponent, positive leading coefficient
   g) quadrant 3 to 4, even exponent, negative leading coefficient
   h) quadrant 3 to 1, odd exponent, positive leading coefficient
4. **a)** yes **b)** no **c)** no **d)** no **e)** yes **f)** yes **g)** no
5. Answers may vary. For example:
   a) $y = x^3$ **b)** $y = 2x^3$ **c)** $y = -x$ **d)** $y = -x^2$
6. **a)** no **b)** yes **c)** yes **d)** no
7. **a)**
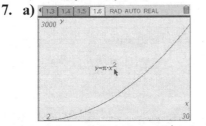

   b) The domain is $\{r \in \mathbb{R} \mid 0 \le r \le 30\}$
   The range is approximately $\{A \in \mathbb{R} \mid 0 \le A \le 2827.4\}$
   c) Similarities: The functions $A(r) = \pi r^2$ and $y = x^2$ are both quadratic, with positive leading coefficients. Both graphs pass through the origin $(0, 0)$ and have one end that extends upward in quadrant 1.

   Differences: The graph of $A(r)$ has a restricted domain. Since the two functions are both quadratic power

functions that have different leading coefficient, all points on each graph, other than $(0, 0)$, are different.

8. **a)**
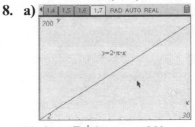

   b) $\{r \in \mathbb{R} \mid 0 \le r \le 30\}$;
   $\{C \in \mathbb{R} \mid 0 \le C \le 188.5\}$
   c) Similarities: linear; positive leading coefficient; passes through the origin; one end extends upward in quadrant 1. Differences: $C(r)$ has restricted domain; all points, other than $(0, 0)$, are different.

9. **a)**
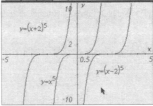

   quadrant 3 to 1; degree 5; leading coefficient 1; same shape; same domain and range; $g(x)$ and $h(x)$ are horizontal translations of $f(x)$

   b)
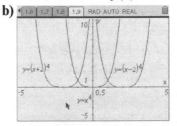

   quadrant 2 to 1; degree 4; leading coefficient 1; same shape; same domain and range; $g(x)$ and $h(x)$ are horizontal translations of $f(x)$
   c) They have the same end behaviour and shape. The function $y = (x + b)^n$ is a horizontal translation of $y = x^n$. If $b > 0$, there is a horizontal translation to the left. If $b < 0$, the horizontal translation is to the right.
   d) Answers will vary.

10. a)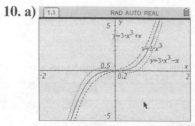

b) Similarities: domain $\{x \in \mathbb{R}\}$, range $\{y \in \mathbb{R}\}$, degree 3, positive leading coefficient 3, end behaviour: quadrant 3 to 1, point symmetry about the origin, y-intercept 0

Differences: $f(x) = 3x^3$ and $h(x) = 3x^3 + x$ and both have one x-intercept: 0; $g(x) = 3x^3 - x$ has three x-intercepts: $0, \pm\dfrac{1}{\sqrt{3}}$.

11. a)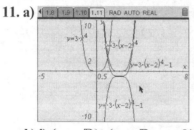

b) i) $\{x \in \mathbb{R}\}$; $\{y \in \mathbb{R}, y \geq 0\}$; line symmetry in the y-axis; quadrant 2 to 1

ii) $\{x \in \mathbb{R}\}$; $\{y \in \mathbb{R}, y \geq 0\}$; line symmetry in $x = 2$; quadrant 2 to 1

iii) $\{x \in \mathbb{R}\}$; $\{y \in \mathbb{R}, y \geq -1\}$; line symmetry in $x = 2$; quadrant 2 to 1

iv) $\{x \in \mathbb{R}\}$; $\{y \in \mathbb{R}, y \leq -1\}$; line symmetry in $x = 2$; quadrant 3 to 4

12. a)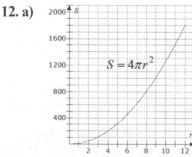

b) domain $\{x \in \mathbb{R}, 0 \leq r \leq 12\}$
range $\{s \in \mathbb{R}, 0 \leq s \leq 1809.6\}$

c) Similarities: both are quadratic functions, end behaviour to quadrant 1, positive leading coefficients

Differences: $s(r) = 4\pi r^2$ has restricted domain, $s(r) = 4\pi r^2$ is obtained by

applying a vertical stretch by a factor of 4π of the graph of $y = x^2$, therefore other than $(0, 0)$ all points are different.

13. a) $y = -\dfrac{1}{2}(x + 1)^5 - 4$ to $y = x^5$ Reflection in the x-axis, vertical by factor $\dfrac{1}{2}$, translation 1 unit to left and 4 units down

b) $y = -\dfrac{1}{2}(x + 1)^3 - 4$ to $y = x^3$
Reflection in the x-axis, vertical by factor $\dfrac{1}{2}$, translation 1 unit to left and 4 units down

c)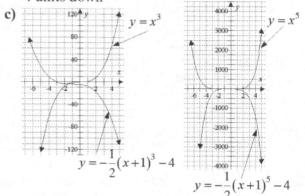

14. a)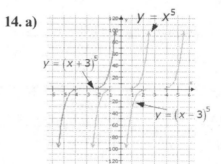

b) Similarities: quadrant 3 to 1, degree 5, leading coefficient 1, same domain and range, $y = (x + 3)^5$ and $y = (x - 3)^5$ are horizontal translations of $y = x^5$

Differences: different point symmetry. The graph of $y = (x + 3)^5$ is obtained by translating the graph of $y = x^3$ three units left, whereas the graph of $y = (x - 3)^5$ is obtained by translating the graph of $y - x^3$ three units right.

15. a)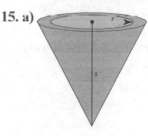

The volume of this conical reservoir can be described with the function $V(r) = \frac{1}{3}\pi r^2 s$, where r is the radius in metres and s is the depth of water in metres. The maximum diameter of the cone is 10 m; therefore, the maximum radius is 5 m. The maximum depth of water in the cone is also 5 m. As the reservoir fills with water, the radius and the depth of water increase at the same rate. Therefore, we can substitute r for s in the function for volume. The result is a function with only one variable r: $V(r) = \frac{1}{3}\pi r^3$.

b)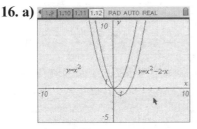

c) The domain is $r \in [0, 5]$. The range is approximately $V \in [0, 130.9]$.

16. a)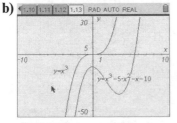

degree 2
Similarities: domain $\{x \in \mathbb{R}\}$, end behaviour: quadrant 2 to 1, positive leading coefficient
Differences: $f(x) = x^2$: range $\{y \in \mathbb{R}, y \geq 0\}$, line symmetry in the y-axis
$g(x) = x^2 - 2x$: range $\{y \in \mathbb{R}, y \geq -1\}$, line symmetry in $x = 1$

b)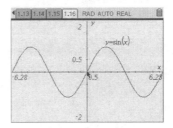

degree 3

Similarities: domain $\{x \in \mathbb{R}\}$, range $\{y \in \mathbb{R}\}$, end behaviour: quadrant 3 to 1, positive leading coefficient
Differences: different point symmetry, x-intercepts, y-intercepts

c)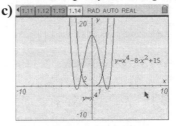

degree 4
Similarities: domain $\{x \in \mathbb{R}\}$, end behaviour: quadrant 2 to 1, positive leading coefficient, line symmetry in the y-axis
Differences: range, x-intercepts, y-intercepts

d)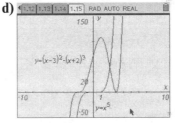

degree 5
Similarities: domain $\{x \in \mathbb{R}\}$, range $\{y \in \mathbb{R}\}$, end behaviour: quadrant 3 to 1, positive leading coefficient
Differences: x-intercepts, y-intercepts, $f(x) = x^5$ has point symmetry about origin, $g(x) = (x - 3)^2 (x + 2)^3$ has no symmetry

17. Answers may vary. For example:

$y = \sin x$ is a trigonometric function, not a polynomial function.

1.2 Characteristics of Polynomial Functions

1. **a)** degree 1, leading coefficient −3
   b) degree 2, leading coefficient 1
   c) degree 5, leading coefficient −2
   d) degree 4, leading coefficient 6
   e) degree 3, leading coefficient 5.25

2. **a)** 5 **b)** 3 **c)** 4 **d)** 4

3. Graph a): **a)** positive **b)** quadrant 3 to 1
   c) no symmetry **d)** local maximums 2,
   local minimums 2; no minimum or
   maximum points
   Graph b): **a)** negative **b)** quadrant 2 to 4
   c) no point symmetry about origin
   d) local maximum 1, local minimum 1; no
   minimum or maximum points
   Graph c): **a)** positive **b)** quadrant 2 to 1
   c) no symmetry **d)** local maximum 1, local
   minimum 2; minimum point 1, no maximum
   point
   Graph d): **a)** negative **b)** quadrant 3 to 4
   c) no symmetry **d)** local maximum 2, local
   minimum 1; no minimum point, maximum
   point 1

4. **a) i)** quadrant 2 to 1 **ii)** fourth **iii)** 24
   b) i) quadrant 2 to 4 **ii)** first **iii)** −7
   c) i) quadrant 2 to 4 **ii)** seventh **iii)** −15120
   d) i) quadrant 3 to 4 **ii)** second **iii)** −12
   e) i) quadrant 3 to 4 **ii)** fourth **iii)** −12
   f) i) quadrant 3 to 1 **ii)** third **iii)** 162

5. a) and iii); b) and iv); c) and ii); d) and i)

6. Construct a finite difference table. Determine
   the finite differences until they are constant.

a)

x	y	1st Differences	2nd Differences	3rd Differences	4th Differences
−3	140				
−2	37	37 − 140 = −103			
−1	8	8 − 37 = −29	−29 − (−103) = 74		
0	5	5 − 8 = −3	−3 − (−29) = 26	2 − 6 − 74 = −48	
1	4	4 − 5 = −1	−1 − (3) = 2	2 − 26 = −24	−24 − (−48) = 24
2	5	5 − 4 = 1	1 − (−1) = 2	2 − 2 = 0	0 − (−24) = 24
3	32	32 − 5 = 27	27 − 1 = 26	26 − 2 = 24	24 − 0 = 24

i) Since the 4th differences are constant,
the table of values represents a quartic
function.
ii) Since the 4th differences are positive, the
leading coefficient is positive.
iii) The value of the leading coefficient is
the value of a such that
$24 = a[n \times (n − 1) \times \ldots \times 2 \times 1]$.
Substitute $n = 4$:
$24 = a(4 \times 3 \times 2 \times 1)$
$24 = 24a$
$a = 1$

b)

x	y	1st Differences	2nd Differences	3rd Differences
−3	0			
−2	−4	−4 − 0 = −4		
−1	0	0 − (−4) = 4	4 − (−4) = 8	
0	6	6 − 0 = 6	6 − 4 = 2	2 − 8 = −6
1	8	8 − 6 = 2	2 − 6 = −4	−2 = −6
2	0	0 − 8 = −8	−8 − 2 = −10	−10 − (−4) = −6
3	−24	−24 − 0 = −24	−24 − (−8) = −16	−16 − (−10) = −6

i) Since the 3rd differences are constant, the
table of values represents a cubic function.
ii) Since the 3rd differences are negative, the
leading coefficient is negative.
iii) The value of the leading coefficient is the
value of a such that
$−6 = a[n \times (n − 1) \times \ldots \times 2 \times 1]$.
Substitute $n = 3$:
$−6 = a(3 \times 2 \times 1)$
$−6 = 6a$
$a = −1$

c)

x	y	1st Differences	2nd Differences
−3	36		
−2	16	16 − 36 = −20	
−1	4	4 − 16 = −12	−12 − (−20) = 8
0	0	0 − 4 = −4	−4 − (−12) = 8
1	4	4 − 0 = 4	4 − (−4) = 8
2	16	16 − 4 = 12	12 − 4 = 8
3	36	36 − 16 = 20	20 − 12 = 8

i) Since the 2nd differences are constant,
the table of values represents a quadratic
function.

ii) Since the 2nd differences are positive, the leading coefficient is positive.

iii) The value of the leading coefficient is the value of a such that
$8 = a[n \times (n-1) \times \ldots \times 2 \times 1]$.
Substitute $n = 2$:
$8 = a(2 \times 1)$
$8 = 2a$
$a = 4$

7. a) The function $P(x)$ is a polynomial of degree 4; therefore, it is a quartic function.

b) Since the degree of this polynomial is 4, then the 4th finite differences are constant. The value of the constant finite difference is $a[n \times (n-1) \times \ldots \times 2 \times 1]$, where a is the leading coefficient and n is the degree. Substitute $n = 4$ and $a = 0.65$:
Constant finite difference $=$
$0.65(4 \times 3 \times 2 \times 1) = 15.6$

c) The function is quartic with positive leading coefficient. The graph extends from quadrant 2 to quadrant 1.

d) Since x represents the number, in hundreds, of flying discs sold, x cannot be a negative number. Therefore, the domain is $\{x \in \mathbb{R}, x \geq 0\}$.

e) The x-intercepts of the graph represent the break-even point.

f) $P(x) = 0.65x^4 - 3.5x^2 - 12$
$P(5) = 0.65(5)^4 - 3.5(5)^2 - 12$
$= 306.75$
The profit from the sale is \$306,750.

8 a) degree 4; leading coefficient is negative; end behaviour: quadrant 3 to 4

b)

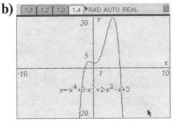

c) -24

9. Unrestricted domain and range because they extend from quadrant 2 to 4 or quadrant 3 to 1; no maximum points, no minimum points; at least one x-intercept, at least one y-intercept

10. TI-*n*spire graphing calculator was used to solve this problem.

a) Open Lists and Spreadsheets application and enter the data into a list.

Open Data and Statistics application and add *speed* variable to the x-axis and *stopdistance* variable to the y-axis.

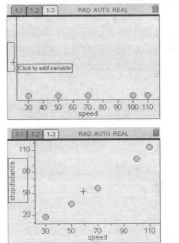

b) Click on Menu button; choose 3: Actions; choose 5: Regression; choose 4: Show Quadratic. The result is a quadratic model of the data:
$y = 0.005683x^2 + 0.45115x + 0.680237$

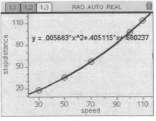

Linear function does not seem like a good fit:

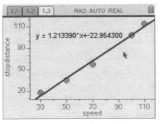

Cubic function adds a cubic term with leading coefficient so small that it does not make a big difference compared with the quadratic function:

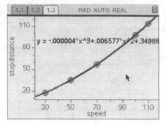

11. Polynomial functions used to draw graphs will vary. For example: **a)** $y = x^5$
b) $y = (x-3)^3 (x+1)^2$ **c)** $y = x(x-1)(x+1)(x-2)(x+2)$ **d)** $y = (x-1)^5$

12. Odd degree n: minimum 1 x-intercept, maximum n x-intercepts
Even degree n: minimum 0 x-intercepts, maximum n x-intercepts

13. **a)** The surface area of the silo (not including the top and bottom) can be represented as:
$A(r) = $ (circumference of the base) $\times$ (height)
$A(r) = (2\pi r) \times (h)$
where r is the radius and h is the height of the silo
Since $\frac{r}{h} = \frac{1}{6}$, then $h = 6r$
Substitute $6r$ for h:
$A(r) = (2\pi r) \times (6r)$
$A(r) = 12\pi r^2$
b) $V(r) = $ (area of the base) $\times$ (height)
$V(r) = (\pi r^2) \times (h)$
Substitute $6r$ for h:
$V(r) = (\pi r^2) \times (6r)$
$V(r) = 6\pi r^3$
c) $A(r) = 12\pi r^2$: domain $\{r \in R, r > 0\}$, range $\{A \in R, A > 0\}$, ends in quadrant 1
$V(r) = 6\pi r^3$: domain $\{r \in R, r > 0\}$, range $\{V \in R, V > 0\}$, ends in quadrant 1

1.3 Equations and Graphs of Polynomial Functions

1. **a) i)** 3, positive **ii)** quadrant 3 to 1
iii) 0, 2, −3
b) i) 4, negative **ii)** quadrant 3 to 4
iii) 2, 4 (order 2), 6

c) i) 4, positive **ii)** quadrant 2 to 1
iii) $\frac{1}{2}$, −3 (order 3)
d) i) 4, negative **ii)** quadrant 3 to 4
iii) 4, −1 (order 2), 2

2. **a) i)** −7, −0.5, 3.5 **ii)** positive: $-7 < x < -0.5$, $x > 3.5$; negative: $x < -7$, $-0.5 < x < 3.5$ **iii)** no roots of order 2 or order 3
b) i) −6 (order 2), 5 (order 2) **ii)** positive: no intervals; negative: $x < -6$, $-6 < x < 5$, $x > 5$ **iii)** order 2: yes, order 3: no
c) i) 0 (order 3), 4 **ii)** positive: $0 < x < 4$; negative: $x < 0$, $x > 4$ **iii)** order 2: no, order 3: yes

3. **a) i)** 0 (order 1), 3 (order 3) **ii)** $\frac{1}{5}$ (order 1), −2 (order 1), 1 (order 1) **iii)** −4 (order 2), $\frac{3}{4}$ (order 2)
b) i) neither **ii)** neither **iii)** neither **iv)** neither
c) i)

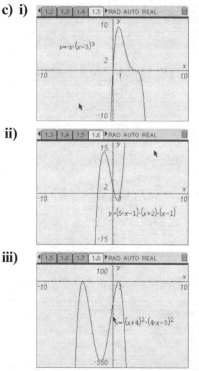

4. **a) i)** Since the exponent of each term is even, $y = -x^4 + 3x^2$ is an even function.
ii) Since the function is even, it has line symmetry about the y-axis.
b) i) Since the exponent of each term is odd, $y = -6x + 5x^3$ is an odd function.
ii) Since the function is odd, it has point symmetry about the origin.

c) i) Some exponents in $y = x^4 - x^2 + 4x + 2$ are even and some are odd, so the function is neither even nor odd.
ii) Since the function is neither even nor odd, there is no line symmetry about the y-axis, and no point symmetry about the origin.

5. Answers will vary. For example:
a) $y = (x - 4)^2 (x + 3)$; neither

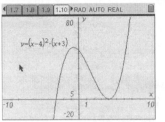

b) $y = (x - 2)^3 (x - 5)$; neither

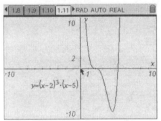

c) ; $y = (2x - 1)(4x - 3)(x + 1)$; neither

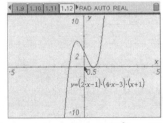

d) $y = -(x + 2)(x - 1)^2$; neither

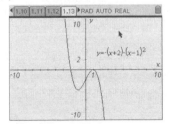

6. a) line symmetry **b)** neither
7. a) $f(x) = -x(x + 3)(x + 1)(x - 2)$
   b) $f(x) = x^2 (x + 1)(x - 2)(x - 5)^3$

8. Answers may vary. For example:
a) $y = x(x + 6)(x - 5)$

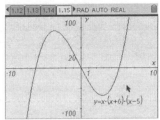

b) $y = -x^2 (x + 6)(x - 5)$

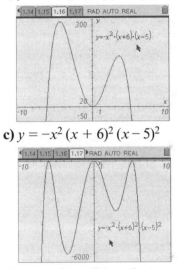

c) $y = -x^2 (x + 6)^2 (x - 5)^2$

d) $y = -x(x + 6)(x - 5)$

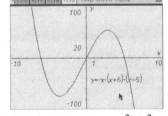

9. a) $f(x) = (30 - 13x - x^2)(x^2 - 10x + 25)$
   $f(x) = (2 - x)(15 + x)(x - 5)(x - 5)$
   $x = 2$ or $x = -15$ or $x = 5$ (*order* 2)

Verify the answers using a graphing calculator:

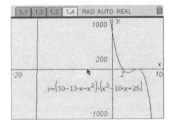

b) $g(x) = (x^3 - 4x^2 + 4x)(2x^2 - 7x + 3)$

$g(x) = x(x^2 - 4x + 4)(2x^2 - 7x + 3)$

$g(x) = x(x - 2)^2 (2x - 1)(x - 3)$

$x = 0$ or $x = 2$ (*order* 2) or $x = \frac{1}{2}$ or $x = 13$

Verify the answers using a graphing calculator:

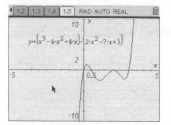

c) $h(x) = (x^2 - 8x + 15)(27 - 3x^2)$

$h(x) = 3(x - 5)(x - 3)(9 - x^2)$

$= -3(x - 5)(x - 3)^2 (x + 3)$

$x = 5$ or $x = 3$ (*order* 2) or $x = -3$

Verify using a graphing calculator:

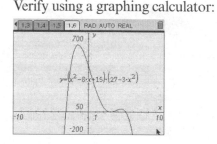

10. Answers may vary. For example:

$y = -x^4 - 1$

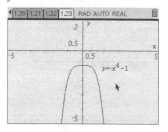

11. a) $y = \frac{35}{36} (x + 2)^3 (x - 3)^2$; neither

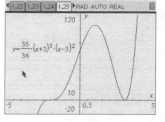

b) $y = -3(x + 2)^2 (x - 1)^2$; neither

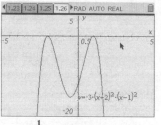

c) $y = -\frac{1}{2} (x + 3)(x + 2)^2 (x - 2)^2$; neither

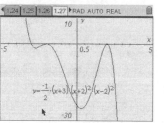

12. Answers may vary. For example:

$y = 7x^2(x - 1)(x - 2.2)^2 (x - 3)$

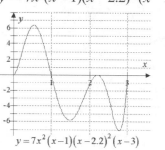

1.4 Transformations

1. a) $a = 5, k = 1, d = 1, c = 0$; vertical stretch by a factor of 5 and a reflection in the *x*-axis; translation 1 unit to the right

b) $a = 3, k = 1, d = 0, c = 5$; vertical stretch by a factor of 3; translation 5 units up

c) $a = -1, k = 3, d = \frac{2}{3}, c = 0$; reflection in the *x*-axis; horizontal compression by a factor of $\frac{1}{3}$ translation $\frac{2}{3}$ units to the right

d) $a = \frac{1}{3}, k = 1, d = 2, c = 0$; vertical compression by a factor of $\frac{1}{3}$; translation 2 units to the right

e) $a = \frac{3}{5}, k = 6, d = 1, c = -4$; vertical compression by a factor of $\frac{3}{5}$; horizontal compression by a factor of $\frac{1}{6}$; translation 1 unit right and 4 units down

f) $a = 7, k = -1, d = 0, c = 1$; vertical stretch by a factor of 7; reflection in the *y*-axis; translation 1 unit up

2. a) $\{x \in \mathbb{R}\}, \{y \in \mathbb{R}\}$ **b)** $\{x \in \mathbb{R}\}, \{y \in \mathbb{R}, y \geq 5\}$ **c)** $\{x \in \mathbb{R}\}, \{y \in \mathbb{R}, y \leq 0\}$
d) $\{x \in \mathbb{R}\}, \{y \in \mathbb{R}, y \geq 0\}$ **e)** $\{x \in \mathbb{R}\}, \{y \in \mathbb{R}\}$ **f)** $\{x \in \mathbb{R}\}, \{y \in \mathbb{R}\}$

3.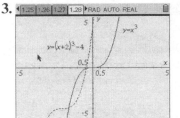

4. a) and i); b) and iii); c) and ii); d) and iv)

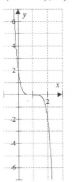

5. a) $y = 5(-x)^4$; vertical stretch by a factor of 5; reflection in the y-axis

b) $y = -2(x + 1)^3$; vertical stretch by a factor of 2 and a reflection in the x-axis; translation 1 unit to the left

c) $y = 5[-(x + 1)]^4 + 3$; vertical stretch by a factor of 5; reflection in the y-axis; translation 1 unit to the left and 3 units up

6. a) i)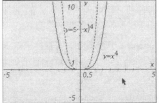

ii)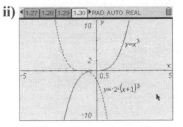

iii)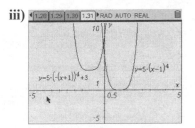

b) i) $y = x^4$: $\{x \in \mathbb{R}\}, \{y \in \mathbb{R}, y \geq 0\}$; vertex: $(0, 0)$, axis of symmetry: $x = 0$
$y = 5(-x)^4$: $\{x \in \mathbb{R}\}, \{y \in \mathbb{R}, y \geq 0\}$; vertex $(0, 0)$, axis of symmetry: $x = 0$

ii) $y = x^3$: $\{x \in \mathbb{R}\}, \{y \in \mathbb{R}\}$
$y = -2(x + 1)^3$: $\{x \in \mathbb{R}\}, \{y \in \mathbb{R}\}$

iii) $y = 5(x - 1)^4$: $\{x \in \mathbb{R}\}, \{y \in \mathbb{R}, y \geq 0\}$; vertex: $(1, 0)$, axis of symmetry: $x = 1$
$y = 5[-(x + 1)]^4 + 3$: $\{x \in \mathbb{R}\}, \{y \in \mathbb{R}, y \geq 3\}$, vertex: $(-1, 3)$, axis of symmetry: $x = -1$

7. a) i)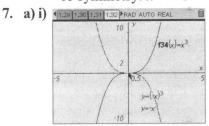

ii)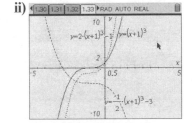

iii)

iv)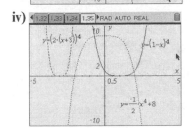

b)

Value of c in $y = a[k(x-d)]^n + c$	Transformation of the Graph of $y = x^n$
$c > 0$	Translation c units up
$c < 0$	Translation $|c|$ units down
Value of d in $y = a[k(x-d)]^n + c$	
$d > 0$	Translation d units right
$d < 0$	Translation $|d|$ units left
Value of a in $y = a[k(x-d)]^n + c$	
$a > 1$	Vertical stretch by a factor of a
$0 < a < 1$	Vertical compression by a factor of a
$-1 < a < 0$	Vertical compression by a factor of $|a|$ and a reflection in the x-axis
$a < -1$	Vertical stretch by a factor of $|a|$ and a reflection in the x-axis
Value of k in $y = a[k(x-d)]^n + c$	**Transformation of the Graph of $y = x^n$**
$k > 1$	Horizontal compression by $|a|$ factor of $\frac{1}{k}$
$0 < k < 1$	Horizontal stretch by a factor of $\frac{1}{k}$
$-1 < k < 0$	Horizontal stretch by a factor of $\left|\frac{1}{k}\right|$ and a reflection in the y-axis
$k < -1$	Horizontal compression by a factor of $\left|\frac{1}{k}\right|$ and a reflection in the y-axis

8. a) $a = \frac{1}{3}, k = -2, d = -4, c = -10$

b) The function $y = x^4$ is vertically compressed by a factor of $\frac{1}{3}$, horizontally compressed by a factor of $\frac{1}{2}$ and a reflection in the y-axis, translated left | 4 units, translated down 10 units.

c) domain: $\{x \in \mathbb{R}\}$, range: $\{y \in \mathbb{R}, y \geq -10\}$, vertex: $(-4, -10)$, axis of symmetry: $x = -4$

d) Apply transformation represented by a first, then k, then d and c, or apply k first, then a, then c and d.

9. a) i) $c = 4, d = 2; y = (x-2)^3 + 4$
ii) domain: $\{x \in \mathbb{R}\}$, range: $\{y \in \mathbb{R}\}$

b) i) $k = \frac{1}{5}, d = 3; y = [\frac{1}{5}(x-3)]^4$
ii) domain: $\{x \in \mathbb{R}\}$, range: $\{y \in \mathbb{R}, y \geq 0\}$, vertex: $(3, 0)$, axis of symmetry: $x = 3$

c) i) $a = 2, k = -1, c = -2, d = -4;$
$y = 2[-(x + 4)]^5 - 2$

ii) domain: $\{x \in \mathbb{R}\}$, range: $\{y \in \mathbb{R}\}$

d) i) $a = -1, k = -\frac{1}{3}, c = 3, d = -1;$
$y = -[-\frac{1}{3}(x + 1)]^6 + 3$

ii) domain: $\{x \in \mathbb{R}\}$, range: $\{y \in \mathbb{R}, y \leq 3\}$, vertex: $(-1, 3)$, axis of symmetry: $x = -1$

10. a) i) vertical stretch by factor 3, reflection in x-axis, translation 2 units right and 4 down
ii) $y = -3(x - 2)^2 - 4$
iii)

$y = -3(x - 2)^2 - 4$

iv) $\{x \in \mathbb{R}\}$, $\{y \in \mathbb{R} | y \leq -4\}$

b) i) vertical stretch by factor 2, horizontal compression by factor $\frac{1}{2}$, translation 3 units to left
ii) $y = 2(2x + 6)^4$
iii)

$y = 2(2x + 6)^4$

iv) $\{x \in \mathbb{R}\}$, $\{y \in \mathbb{R}, y \leq 0\}$

c) i) vertical compression by factor $\frac{1}{2}$, reflection in x-axis, horizontal stretch by factor 2, translation 1 unit to right and 5 down
ii) $y = \frac{-1}{2}\left(\frac{1}{2}(x - 1)\right)^3 - 5$
iii)

$y = -\frac{1}{2}\left(\frac{1}{2}(x - 1)\right)^3 - 5$

iv) $\{x \in \mathbb{R}\}, \{y \in \mathbb{R}\}$

11. a) horizontal shift three to the left and one down

b)

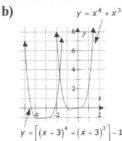

$y = x^4 + x^3$

$y = \left[(x+3)^4 + (x+3)^3\right] - 1$

c) For $y = x^4 + x^3$, the x-intercepts are $0, -1$
For $y = [(x+3)^4 + (x+3)^3] - 1$,
the x-intercepts are $-4.4, -2.2$

d) For $y = x^4 + x^3$, domain $= \{x|x\in\}$,
range $= \{y|y\in\mathbb{R}, y \geq -0.1\}$
For $y = [(x+3)^4 + (x+3)^3] - 1$,
domain $= \{x|x\in\}$,
range $= \{y|y\in\mathbb{R}, y \geq -1.1\}$

12. a) $y = [-3((x-2)-2)((x-2)+3)$
$((x-2)+5)^2] + 1$
$y = -3(x-4)(x+1)(x+3)^2 + 1$

b) $y = \frac{1}{3}[-3((-x)-4)((-x)+1)$
$((-x)+3)^2 + 1]$
$y = -(-x-4)(1-x)(3-x)^2 + \frac{1}{3}$

13. a) reflection in the x-axis; horizontal compression by a factor of $\frac{1}{2}$

b)

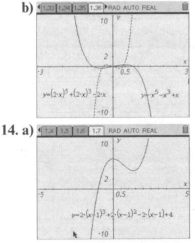

14. a)

b) $y = 2(x-1)^3 + 2(x-1)^2 - 2(x-1) + 4$
Vertical stretch by a factor of 2 and translation of 1 unit to the right were applied to the original function.
$y = 2(x)^3 + 2(x)^2 - 2(x) + 4$
$y = 2(x^3 + x^2 - x + 2)$
$y = x^3 + x^2 - x + 2$
Original function: $y = x^3 + x^2 - x + 2$

1.5 Slopes of Secants and Average Rates of Change

1. c), e), and f)

2. A: constant and negative, B: zero, C: constant and positive

3. A: -3, B: 0, C: $\frac{1}{3}$

4. a) -2 **b)** -3.8 **c)** -4 **d)** -2.7

5. 7.4

6. a) Average rate of change $=$
$\frac{\Delta Index}{\Delta Year} = \frac{128.8 - 120.5}{2004 - 2003} = 8.3$
Average rate of change $=$
$\frac{\Delta Index}{\Delta Year} = \frac{137.8 - 128.8}{2005 - 2004} = 9$
Average rate of change $=$
$\frac{\Delta Index}{\Delta Year} = \frac{144.2 - 137.8}{2006 - 2005} = 6.4$
Average rate of change $=$
$\frac{\Delta Index}{\Delta Year} = \frac{150.1 - 144.2}{2007 - 2006} = 5.9$

b) The greatest average rate of change was between 2004 and 2005. The least was between 2005 and 2006. The average rate of change of the new housing price index is positive but decreasing; the increase of prices of new houses is slowing down.

c) The average rate of change of the New Housing Price Index over the 4-year period, between 2003 and 2007, is 7.4. The average rate of change is positive; the prices of new houses are still increasing during that period. From part b) we see that the increase of prices is slowing down. This implies that the housing market in the St. Catharines-Niagara area is still doing well.

7. a) Average rate of change
$= \frac{\Delta Water Amount}{\Delta Time}$
$= \frac{\left[150000 - 7500(10) + (10)^2\right] - \left[150000 - 7500(5) + (5)^2\right]}{10 - 5}$
$= \frac{75100 - 112525}{5}$
$= -7485$ gallons per minute

b) Average rate of change
$= \frac{\Delta Water Amount}{\Delta Time}$
$= \frac{\left[150000 - 7500(10) + (10)^2\right] - \left[150000 - 7500(9) + (9)^2\right]}{10 - 9}$
$= \frac{75100 - 82581}{1}$
$= -7481$ gallons per minute

c) Average rate of change

$$= \frac{\Delta\, Water\, Amount}{\Delta\, Time}$$

$$= \frac{[150000 - 7500(10) + (10)^2] - [150000 - 7500(9.99) + (9.99)^2]}{10 - 9.99}$$

$$= \frac{75100 - 75174.8001}{0.01}$$

$$= -7480.01 \text{ gallons per minute}$$

$$\cong -7480 \text{ gallons per minute}$$

The estimated rate of change at which the water runs out after exactly 10 minutes is −7480 gallons per minute.

8. a) i) 14.1 **ii)** 13.5 **iii)** 13.4 **iv)** 12.9 **v)** 12.6
b) 12.6 **c)** same

9. a) i) constant and positive **ii)** constant and negative **iii)** zero for first 4 months and then constant and positive
b) i) $\frac{1}{4}$ **ii)** $-\frac{5}{12}$ **iii)** $\frac{11}{12}$

10. a) Marshall: 5.75 m/s; Teagan: 5.25 m/s
b) Marshall: 9.8 m/s; Teagan: 2.5 m/s

11. a) i) Average rate of change

$$= \frac{\Delta cost}{\Delta time}$$

$$= \frac{(4500 + 1530)(4) - 0.04(4)^3) - (4500 + 1530(0) - 0.04(0)^3)}{4 - 0}$$

$$= \$1529.36 \text{ per year}$$

ii) $\frac{(4500 + 1530(7) - 0.004(7)^3) - (4500 + 1530(4) - 0.004(4)^3)}{7 - 4}$
$$= \$1526.28 \text{ per year}$$

iii) $= \frac{(4500 + 1530(9) - 0.004(9)^3) - (4500 + 1530(7) - 0.004(7)^3)}{9 - 7}$
$$= 1522.28 \text{ per year}$$

b) The production became more efficient over time as average cost decreased.

12. a) i) Average rate of change

$$= \frac{\Delta height}{\Delta time}$$

$$= \frac{(120 - 4.9(4)^2) - (120 - 4.9(1)^2)}{4 - 1}$$

$$= -24.5 \text{ m/s}$$

ii) $= \frac{(120 - 4.9(6)^2) - (120 - 4.9(4)^2)}{6 - 4}$

$$= -49 \text{ m/s}$$

iii) $= \frac{(120 - 4.9(7)^2) - (120 - 4.9(6)^2)}{7 - 6}$

$$= -63.7 \text{ m/s}$$

b) The average rate of change represents the average speed of the ball.
c) The ball is falling faster as times passes.

13. a) i) Average rate of change

$$= \frac{\Delta population}{\Delta years}$$

$$= \frac{15\ 596 - 13\ 500}{1996 - 1991}$$

$$= 419.2 \text{ people per year}$$

ii) $\frac{16\ 039 - 15\ 596}{2001 - 1996}$

$$= 88.6 \text{ people per year}$$

iii) $\frac{17\ 290 - 16\ 039}{2006 - 2001}$

$$= 250.2 \text{ people per year}$$

iv) $\frac{17\ 290 - 13\ 500}{2006 - 1991}$

$$= 252.7 \text{ people per year}$$

b) Answers may vary.

14. a) approximately 0.18°C/h
b) between hours 12 and 14
c) Answers may vary. Sample answer: between hours 2 and 4 and between 4 and 6

15. a) The average rate of change is the change of distance with respect to a change in speed, i.e., the time it takes for a vehicle to stop.

b) i) Average rate of change $= \frac{\Delta Distance}{\Delta Speed}$

Since distance is measured in metres and speed in km/h, divide the distance by 1000 in order to change the distance into km.

$$= \frac{(d(30) - d(20))/1000}{30 - 20}$$

$$= \frac{([0.01(30)^2 - 0.25(30) + 10] - [0.01(20)^2 - 0.25(20) + 10])/1000}{10}$$

$$= \frac{(11.5 - 9)/1000}{10}$$

$$= 0.00025 \text{ hours}$$

ii) Average rate of change $= \frac{\Delta Distance}{\Delta Speed}$

Since distance is measured in m and speed in km/h, divide the distance by 1000 to change the distance to km.

$$= \frac{(d(50) - d(40))/1000}{50 - 40}$$

$$= \frac{([0.01(50)^2 - 0.25(50) + 10] - [0.01(40)^2 - 0.25(40) + 10])/1000}{10}$$

$$= \frac{(22.5 - 16)/1000}{10}$$

$$= 0.00065 \text{ hours}$$

iii) Average rate of change $= \dfrac{\Delta \text{Distance}}{\Delta \text{Speed}}$

Since distance is measured in m and speed in km/h, divide the distance by 1000 to change the distance to km.

$= \dfrac{(d(70) - d(60))/1000}{70 - 60}$

$= \dfrac{([0.01(70)^2 - 0.25(70) + 10] - [0.01(60)^2 - 0.25(60) + 10])/1000}{10}$

$= \dfrac{(41.5 - 31)/1000}{10}$

$= 0.00105$ hours

iv) Average rate of change $= \dfrac{\Delta \text{Distance}}{\Delta \text{Speed}}$

Since distance is measured in m and speed in km/h, divide the distance by 1000 to change the distance to km.

$= \dfrac{(d(90) - d(80))/1000}{90 - 80}$

$= \dfrac{([0.01(90)^2 - 0.25(90) + 10] - [0.01(80)^2 - 0.25(80) + 10])/1000}{10}$

$= \dfrac{(68.5 - 54)/1000}{10}$

$= 0.00145$ hours

c) As the speed increases, the average rate of change is positive and increasing.

d)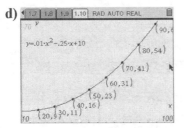

16. a) negative, zero, negative

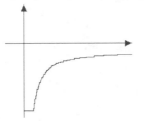

b) positive and increasing

c) positive and decreasing

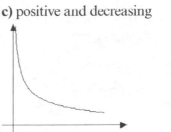

d) changes periodically from negative to zero to positive, etc.

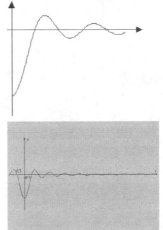

1.6 Slopes of Tangents and Instantaneous Rates of Change

1. a) i) negative **ii)** -1 **b) i)** zero **ii)** 0

c) i) positive **ii)** $\cong 1.8$

2. a) 2, 6, 18, 54, 162, 486 **b)** -0.02, -0.028, -0.034, -0.04, -0.044, -0.05

3. Method 1: Points on the Tangent Line

Estimate the slope of a tangent at the point $(4, 7)$ on the graph by sketching an approximate tangent line through that point and then selecting a second point on that line. Select the point $(7, 4)$.

$m = \dfrac{4 - 7}{7 - 4} = \dfrac{-3}{3} = -1$

The instantaneous rate of change at the point $(4, 7)$ on the graph is -1.

Method 2: Graph and Two Points

Estimate the instantaneous rate of change from the graph by finding the slope of a secant passing through the given point $(4, 7)$ and another point close to $(4, 7)$ on the curve. Select the point $(6, 4)$.

$m = \dfrac{4 - 7}{6 - 4} = -\dfrac{3}{2} = -1.5$

4. a) -0.65 mm/s **b) i)** -0.93 mm/s
ii) -0.70 mm/s **iii)** -0.48 mm/s **iv)** -0.26 mm/s

c)

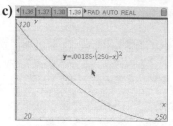

The slope of the graph is negative and increasing.

5. a)

Interval	ΔP	Δt	$\dfrac{\Delta P}{\Delta t}$
$9 \le t \le 10$	$[0.2(10)^2 + 500] - [0.2(9)^2 + 500]$ $= 520 - 516.2$ $= 3.8$	$10 - 9 = 1$	$\dfrac{3.8}{1} = 3.8$
$9.9 \le t \le 10$	$[0.2(10)^2 + 500] - [0.2(9.9)^2 + 500]$ $= 520 - 519.602$ $= 0.398$	$10 - 9.9 = 0.1$	$\dfrac{0.398}{1} = 3.98$
$9.99 \le t \le 10$	$[0.2(10)^2 + 500] - [0.2(9.99)^2 + 500]$ $= 520 - 519.96002$ $= 0.03998$	$10 - 9.99 = 0.01$	$\dfrac{0.03998}{0.01} = 3.998$
$10 \le t \le 10.1$	$[0.2(10.1)^2 + 500] - [0.2(10)^2 + 500]$ $= 520.402 - 520$ $= 0.402$	$10.1 - 10 = 0.1$	$\dfrac{0.402}{0.1} = 4.02$
$10 \le t \le 10.01$	$[0.2(10.01)^2 + 500] - [0.2(10)^2 + 500]$ $= 520.04002 - 520$ $= 0.04002$	$10.01 - 10 = 0.01$	$\dfrac{0.04002}{0.01} = 4.002$
$10 \le t \le 10.001$	$[0.2(10.001)^2 + 500] - [0.2(10)^2 + 500]$ $= 520.0040002 - 520$ $= 0.0040002$	$10.001 - 10 = 0.001$	$\dfrac{0.0040002}{0.001} = 4.0002$

b) Time intervals before and after 10 years decrease in size.

c) As the size of time intervals decreases, the average rate of change approaches 4. Therefore, the instantaneous rate of change at 10 years is approximately 4. This value represents increase in population at 10 years.

6. a) 1101 **b)** Answers will vary. For example: -9805, 1132 **c)** On average, the number of births per year is increasing.

7. a) The warmest day occurred on day 7, since the thickness of the ice was the smallest.

b) Rate of change $= m_{1,2} = \dfrac{7.6 - 8.9}{2 - 1}$
$= \dfrac{-1.3}{1} = -1.3$

c) Instantaneous rate of change $= \dfrac{\Delta T}{\Delta d}$
$= \dfrac{T(1) - T(0.999)}{1 - 0.999}$
$= \dfrac{[0.1(0.999)^3 + 1.2(0.999)^2 - 5.4(0.999) + 12] - [-0.1(1)^3 + 1.2(1)^2 - 5.4(1) + 12]}{0.001}$
$= \dfrac{7.7033009 - 7.7}{0.001}$
$= 3.3009$ cm/day $\cong 3.3$ cm/day

d) Average rate of change
$= \dfrac{T(1 + h) - T(1)}{(1 + h) - 1} = \dfrac{T(1 + h) - T(1)}{h}$

e) i) Average rate of change
$= \dfrac{T(1 + 0.1) - T(1)}{(1 + 0.1) - 1} = \dfrac{T(1.1) - T(1)}{0.1}$
$= \dfrac{[-0.1(1)^3 + 1.2(1)^2 - 5.4(1) + 12] - [0.1(1.1)^3 + 1.2(1.1)^2 - 5.4(1.1) + 12]}{0.1}$
$= \dfrac{7.7 - 7.3789}{0.1} = 3.2$ cm/day

ii) Average rate of change
$= \dfrac{T(1 + 0.01) - T(1)}{(1 + 0.01) - 1} = \dfrac{T(1.01) - T(1)}{0.01}$
$= \dfrac{[-0.1(1)^3 + 1.2(1)^2 - 5.4(1) + 12] - [-0.1(1.01)^3 + 1.2(1.01)^2 - 5.4(1.01) + 12]}{0.01}$
$= \dfrac{7.7 - 7.6670899}{0.01}$
$= 3.29101$ cm/day $\cong 3.3$ cm/day

iii) Average rate of change

$$= \frac{T(1 + 0.001) - T(1)}{(1 + 0.001) - 1} = \frac{T(1.001) - T(1)}{0.001}$$

$$= \frac{[-0.1(1)^3 + 1.2(1)^2 - 5.4(1) + 12] - [0.1(1.001)^3 + 1.2(1.001)^2 - 5.4(1.001) + 12]}{0.001}$$

$$= \frac{7.7 - 7.6967009}{0.001}$$

$$= 3.2991 \text{ cm/day} \cong 3.3 \text{ cm/day}$$

f) The instantaneous rate of change of the thickness after one day is approximately 3.3 cm/day.

8. -8; tangent line: $y = -8x - 48$

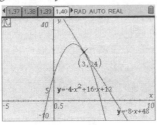

9. a) 250

b) Dollars per system sold

c) This tells us that the rate of change in profit is increasing at a rate of $250/unit when 1000 systems are sold.

10. a) 10 m/s   **b)** -2 m/s

c)

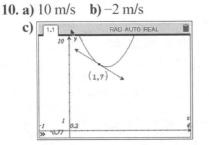

d) The particle is moving away from the origin between 1 and 4 s. It was moving towards the origin at 1 s.

11. a) Average rate of change $= \dfrac{P(10 + h) - P(10)}{(10 + h) - 10}$

$$= \frac{[-2(10 + h)^3 + 55(10 + h)^2 + 15(10 + h) + 22000] - [-2(10)^3 + 55(10)^2 + 15(10) + 22000]}{h}$$

b) i) 482 people/year

ii) 440 people/year

c) 515 people/year

d)

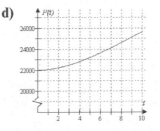

e) Answers may vary. For example: Yes because the population is growing.

f) No, the population is shrinking in 30 years.

12. a)

Rachel is running on a track. At the beginning she is running away from the start/finish position, and then she changes direction and runs back toward the start/finish line.

b)

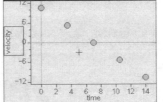

c) At time $t = 0$ s, Rachel is at the start line at position $s = 0$ m. At $t = 3.5$ s she is running away from the start position. At $t = 7$ s she is at the farthest position $s = 36.75$ m, where she changes direction and starts running back toward the finish line. At $t = 14$ s she is back at the finish line with position $s = 0$ m.

13. a)

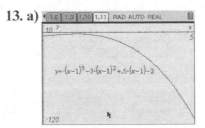

The depth of the fish is increasing.

b)

Interval	Δd	Δt	$\dfrac{\Delta d}{\Delta t}$
$3 \le t \le 4$	$[-(4-1)^3 - 3(4-1)^2$ $+ 0.5(4-1) - 2] -$ $[-(3-1)^3 - 3(3-1)^2$ $+ 0.5(3-1) - 2]$ $= [-(3)^3 - 3(3)^2 +$ $0.5(3) - 2] - [-(2)^3$ $- 3(2)^2 + 0.5(2) - 2]$ $= (-54.5) - (-21)$ $= -33.5$	$4 - 3$ $= 1$	$\dfrac{-33.5}{1}$ $= -33.5$
$3.5 \le t \le 4$	$[-(4-1)^3 - 3(4-1)^2$ $+ 0.5(4-1) - 2] -$ $[-(3.5-1)^3 - 3(3.5$ $-1)^2 + 0.5(3.5-1)$ $- 2]$ $= [-(3)^3 - 3(3)^2 +$ $0.5(3) - 2] - [-(2.5)^3$ $- 3(2.5)^2 + 0.5(2.5)$ $- 2]$ $= (-54.5) - (-35.125)$ $= -19.375$	$4 - 3.5$ $= 0.5$	$\dfrac{-19.375}{0.5}$ $= -38.75$
$3.9 \le t \le 4$	$[-(4-1)^3 - 3(4-1)^2$ $+ 0.5(4-1) - 2]$ $- [-(3.9-1)^3 - 3(3.9$ $-1)^2 + 0.5(3.9-1)$ $- 2]$ $= [-(3)^3 - 3(3)^2 +$ $0.5(3) - 2] - [-(2.9)^3$ $- 3(2.9)^2 + 0.5(2.9)$ $- 2]$ $= (-54.5) - (-50.169)$ $= -4.331$	$4 - 3.9$ $= 0.1$	$\dfrac{-4.331}{0.1}$ $= -43.31$
$3.99 \le t$ ≤ 4	$[-(4-1)^3 - 3(4-1)^2$ $+ 0.5(4-1) - 2] -$ $[-(3.99-1)^3 -$ $3(3.99-1)^2$ $+ 0.5(3.99-1) - 2]$ $= [-(3)^3 - 3(3)^2 +$ $0.5(3) - 2] - [-(2.99)^3$ $- 3(2.99)^2 +$ $0.5(2.99) - 2]$ $= (-54.5)$ $- (-54.056199)$ $= -0.443801$	$4 - 3.99$ $= 0.01$	$\dfrac{0.443801}{0.01}$ $= -44.3801$

c) As the time t approaches 4 s, the average rate of change approaches -44.4 m/s. The fish's velocity at $t = 4$ s is -44.4 m/s.

$d(4) = -(4-1)^3 - 3(4-1)^2 + 0.5(4-1) - 2$
$= -(3)^3 - 3(3)^2 + 0.5(3) - 2$
$= -54.5\ m$

At time $t = 4$ s, the fish is swimming at depth a of 54.5 m.

Chapter 1 Challenge Questions

C1. -4

C2. a)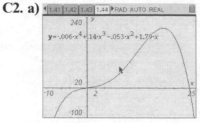

b) 0, 23.498; concentration of dye is zero at $t = 0$ s and $t \cong 23.5$ s **c)** 9.3

C3. a) 250 m, 2250 m, 9000 m

b) distance increases by 9 times

C4. -6, $y = -6x + 36$

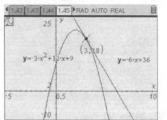

C5. 8.44 m by 10.44 m   **C6.** \$165/unit

C7. 25 times   **C8.** (3, 7)

C9. 4.45; $0 < x < 6.83$

Chapter 2

2.1 The Remainder Theorem

1. a) $\dfrac{3x^3 - 2x^2 - 8}{x + 5} = 3x^2 - 17x + 85 + \dfrac{-433}{x + 5}$

b) $x \ne -5$

c) $(3x^2 - 17x + 85)(x + 5) - 433$

2. a) $\dfrac{3x^4 + 2x^2 - 6x + 1}{x + 1} =$
$3x^3 - 3x^2 + 5x - 11 + \dfrac{12}{x + 1}$

b) $x \ne -1$

c) $(3x^3 - 3x^2 + 5x - 11)(x + 1) + 12$

3. a) $\dfrac{2x^2 - x + 5}{x + 3} = 2x - 7 + \dfrac{26}{x + 3}$, $x \ne -3$

b) $\dfrac{x^3 - x - 10}{x + 4} =$
$x^2 - 4x + 15 + \dfrac{-70}{x + 4}$, $x \ne -4$

c) $\dfrac{x^3 + x^2 - 4x + 4}{x - 2} =$
$x^2 + 3x + 2 + \dfrac{8}{x - 2}$, $x \ne 2$

d) $\dfrac{3x^4 + 2x^2 - 6x + 1}{x} =$

$3x^3 + 2x - 6 + \dfrac{1}{x}, x \neq 0$

e) $\dfrac{4x^3 - 10x^2 + 6x - 18}{2x - 5} =$

$2x^2 + 3 + \dfrac{-3}{2x - 5}, x \neq \dfrac{5}{2}$

f) $\dfrac{2x^3 - x^2 + 8x + 4}{2x - 1} = x^2 + 4 + \dfrac{8}{2x - 1}$

g) $\dfrac{x^5 - 10x^4 + 20x^3 - 5x - 95}{x + 10} =$

$x^4 - 20x^3 + 220x^2 - 2200x + 21995$

$+ \dfrac{-220045}{x + 10}$

4. a) -24 **b)** 7 **c)** -3 **d)** 0

5. $(y + 3) \times (2y + 3) \times (y - 4)$

6. a) 0 **b)** -15 **c)** 0 **d)** -15

7. a) 9 **b)** 0 **c)** -36 **d)** 8

8. a) 12 **b)** -10 **c)** 19 **d)** $\dfrac{8}{3}$

9. a) By the remainder theorem, when $P(x)$ is
divided by $x + 2$, the remainder is $P(-2)$.
Solve $P(-2) = 26$.
$(-2)^3 + k(-2)^2 - 4(-2) + 2 = 26$
$-8 + 4k + 8 + 2 = 26$
$4k = 24$
$k = 6$

b) $P(-1) = (-1)^3 + 6(-1)^2 - 4(-1) + 2$
$= -1 + 6 + 4 + 2$
$= 11$
$P(1) = (1)^3 + 6(1)^2 - 4(1) + 2$
$= 1 + 6 - 4 + 2$
$= 5$

10. a) 37 **b)** Answers may vary.

11. a) 3 **b)** $-11, 165$ **c)** 1 and $2\sqrt{2}$

12. a) 0 **b)** $-\dfrac{1}{2}$ **c)** 1 and $2\sqrt{2}$

13. Use the division statement
$p(x) = (x + 3)Q(x) + R$ to find $p(x)$.
$p(x) = (x + 3)(x^2 - 3x + 5) + 6$
$= x^3 - 3x^2 + 5x + 3x^2 - 9x + 15 + 6$
$= x^3 - 4x + 21$

14. $x^3 + 2x^2 - 15x + 10$

15. a) $Q(t) = 0.45t$
$R = 3.3t$
$\dfrac{N(t)}{t - 2} = Q(t) + \dfrac{R}{t - 2}, t \neq 2$

b) yes, as time increases, number of tickets
sold also increases

16. a) 0 **b)** $(x - 3)$ is a factor of the polynomial
c) $(x + 2)(2x + 5)(x - 3)$

17. $k = 7$ **18.** $a = 1, b = -2$

19. a) $c = 5$ **b)** Answers may vary.

20. $k = -5$

21. $4\dfrac{40}{81}$ **22.** $m = 3, n = 3$

23. Let $P(x) = -x^3 - vx^2 + 2x + w$
By the remainder theorem, when $P(x)$ is
divided by $x + 2$, the remainder is $P(-2)$.
Solve $P(-2) = 6$.
$-(-2)^3 - v(-2)^2 + 2(-2) + w = 6$
$8 - 4v - 4 + w = 6$
$-4v + w = 2$
By the remainder theorem, when $P(x)$ is
divided by $x - 3$, the remainder is $P(3)$.
Solve $P(3) = 119$.
$-(3)^3 - v(3)^2 + 2(3) + w = 119$
$-27 - 9v + 6 + w = 119$
$-9v + w = 140$
Solve the system of equations for v and w:
$-4v + w = 2$ // equation 1
$-9v + w = 140$ // equation 2
equation 1 − equation 2:
$5v = -138$
$v = -\dfrac{138}{5}$
Substitute $v = -\dfrac{138}{5}$ in equation 1 and solve
for w:
$-4\left(-\dfrac{138}{5}\right) + w = 2$
$\dfrac{552}{5} + w = 2$
$w = -\dfrac{542}{5}$

24. a) no **b)** no **c)** no **25.** $a = -5, b = 10$

2.2 The Factor Theorem

1. a) $(x + 4)$ **b)** $(x - 2)$ **c)** $(5x - 2)$
d) $(3x + 4)$

2. a) yes **b)** yes **c)** no

3. a)

-7	1	20	91
$+$		-7	-91
$\times$	1	13	0

b)

3	1	-9	27	-28
$+$		3	-18	27
$\times$	1	-6	9	-1

4. a) $\pm 1, \pm 2; (x - 1)(x^2 - 2x + 2)$
b) $\pm 1; (x + 1)(x^2 + x + 1)$
c) $\pm 1, \pm 3, \pm 5, \pm 15; (x + 3)(x^2 + 4x + 5)$

5. a) $(x + 2)(x - 2)(x - 1)$ **b)** $(x - 2)^2(x + 2)$
c) $(x + 1)(x + 1)(x + 1)$
d) $(x + 2)(x - 1)(x^2 + x + 1)$
e) $(x - 6)(3x^3 + 1)$ **f)** $(x - 1)(x + 1)(x^2 + 1)$

6. a) $\pm 1, \pm\frac{1}{2}, \pm 3, \pm\frac{3}{2}; (x - 1)(x - 3)(2x - 1)$

b) $\pm 1, \pm\frac{1}{2}, \pm\frac{1}{4}, \pm 3, \pm\frac{3}{2}, \pm\frac{3}{4};$
$(x + 1)(2x + 1)(2x - 3)$

c) $\pm 1, \pm\frac{1}{2}, \pm\frac{1}{4}, \pm 3, \pm\frac{3}{2}, \pm\frac{3}{4};$
$(x - 1), (2x - 3)(2x + 1)$

d) $\pm 1, \pm\frac{1}{3}; (x - 1)(x + 1)(3x - 1)$

7. a)

-7	1	-1	-56
$+$		-7	56
$\times$	1	-8	0

b)

3	1	-9	27	-28
$+$		3	-18	27
$\times$	1	-6	9	-1

c)

1	2	0	-2	-3
$+$		2	2	0
$\times$	2	2	0	-3

d)

-2	1	0	-8	0	16
$+$		-2	4	8	-16
$\times$	1	-2	-4	8	0

e)

$\frac{3}{2}$	2	-7	-10	26
$+$		3	-6	-24
$\times$	2	-4	-16	2

f)

$\frac{1}{3}$	9	0	2	-1
$+$		3	1	1
$\times$	9	3	3	0

8. a) $(x - 1)(2x^2 + x + 2)$ **b)** $(x + 4)(x + 1)$
$(2x - 1)$ **c)** cannot be factored
d) $(x + 3)(x - 3)(2x + 1)^2$ **e)** cannot be
factored **f)** $(x - 1)(2x - 1)(3x + 1)$
g) $(x - 4)(2x + 1)(x - 1)^2$

9. $k = 9$ **10.** $k = 3$

11. Let $p(x) = 2x^3 - (k + 1)x^2 + 6kx + 11$
Use the factor theorem to solve $p(1) = 0$.
$2(1)^3 - (k + 1)(1)^2 + 6k(1) + 11 = 0$
$2 - k - 1 + 6k + 11 = 0$
$5k = -12$
$k = -\frac{12}{5}$

12. a) Factor by grouping terms:
$p(x) = x^3 + 2x^2 - 9x - 18$
$= x^2(x + 2) - 9(x + 2)$
$= (x + 2)(x^2 - 9)$
$= (x + 2)(x - 3)(x + 3)$
So, $p(x) = x^3 + 2x^2 - 9x - 18$
$= (x + 2)(x - 3)(x + 3)$
b) $(x - 1)(2x + 1)(2x - 3)$
c) Let $p(x) = 6x^3 + x^2 - 31x + 10$.
Use the rational zero theorem:
Let b represent the factors of the constant
term 10, which are $\pm 1, \pm 2, \pm 5, \pm 10$.
Let a represent the factors of the leading
coefficient 6, which are $\pm 1, \pm 2, \pm 3, \pm 6$.
The possible values of $\frac{b}{a}$ are $\pm 1, \pm\frac{1}{2}, \pm\frac{1}{3},$
$\pm\frac{1}{6}, \pm 2, \pm\frac{2}{3}, \pm 5, \pm\frac{5}{2}, \pm\frac{5}{3}, \pm\frac{5}{6}, \pm 10, \pm\frac{10}{3}$
Test the values of $\frac{b}{a}$ for x to find the zeros.
Substitute $x = 2$ to test
$p(2) = 6(2)^3 + (2)^2 - 31(2) + 10$
$= 48 + 4 - 62 + 10 = 0$
$x = 2$ is a zero and $x - 2$ is a factor.
Use synthetic division method to
determine the other factors.

2	6	1	-31	10
$+$		12	26	-10
$\times$	6	13	-5	0

$6x^2 + 13x - 5$ can be factored further to
$6x^2 + 13x - 5 = (2x + 5)(3x - 1)$
So, $p(x) = 6x^3 + x^2 - 31x + 10$
$= (x - 2)(2x + 5)(3x - 1)$
d) $(2x + 3)(2x^2 - 3x + 7)$ **e)** $(x + 3)$
$(3x - 1)(x - 2)$ **f)** $(x + 1)^2(x + 3)(x - 4)$
g) $x(x + 2)(x^2 + x - 3)$

13. a) $(2x - 1)(4x^2 + 2x + 1)$ **b)** $64(2x - y)$
$(4x^2 + 2xy + y^2)$ **c)** $\left(x - \dfrac{1}{3}\right)\left(x^2 + \dfrac{1}{3}x + \dfrac{1}{9}\right)$
d) $(1 + 5x)(1 - 5x + 25x^2)$
e) $\dfrac{1}{8}\left(x + \dfrac{1}{2}\right)\left(x^2 - \dfrac{1}{2}x + \dfrac{1}{4}\right)$ **f)** $5(3x + 5y)$
$(9x^2 - 15xy + 25y^2)$

14. $Q(x) = 3x - 6; R = -5x^2 + 12x - 13$

15. a) $14(1)^{99} - 65(1)^{56} + 51 = 0$
b) $(1)^5 + 1 = 2$

16. $f(x) = 32x^4 - 128x^3 - 54x^2 + 243x - 108$
$f(1) = 32 - 128 - 54 + 243 - 108$
$\quad = -15 \quad$ therefore, $x - 1$ is not a factor
$f(2) = 32(2)^4 - 128(2)^3 - 54(2)^2 + 243(2)$
$\qquad - 108$
$\quad = -350 \quad x - 2$ is not a factor
$f(3) = 32(3)^4 - 128(3)^3 - 54(3)^2 + 243(3)$
$\qquad - 108$
$\quad = -729 \quad x - 3$ is not a factor
$f(4) = 32(4)^4 - 128(4)^3 - 54(4)^2 + 243(4)$
$\qquad - 108$
$\quad = 0 \quad x - 4$ is a factor
$f(-1) = 32 + 128 - 54 - 243 - 108$
$\quad = -245 \quad x + 1$ is not a factor
$f(-2) = 32(-2)^4 - 128(-2)^3 - 54(-2)^2$
$\qquad + 243(-2) - 108$
$\quad = 726 \quad x + 2$ is not a factor
$f(-3) = 32(-3)^4 - 128(-3)^3 - 54(-3)^2$
$\qquad + 243(-3) - 108$
$\quad = 4725 \quad x + 3$ is not a factor
$f(-4) = 32(-4)^4 - 128(-4)^3 - 54(-4)^2$
$\qquad + 243(-4) - 108$
$\quad = 14440 \quad x + 4$ is not a factor
Somewhere between $f(-1)$ and $f(-2)$
there must be a zero since the value of $f(x)$
changes from a negative for $x = -1$ to a
positive for $x = -2$. Using the remainder
theorem for a value between $x = -1$ and
$x = -2$, the remainder for $x = -\dfrac{3}{2}$:
$f(x) = 32x^4 - 128x^3 - 54x^2 + 243x - 108$
$f\left(-\dfrac{3}{2}\right) = 32\left(-\dfrac{3}{2}\right)^4 - 128\left(-\dfrac{3}{2}\right)^3$
$\qquad - 54\left(-\dfrac{3}{2}\right)^2 + 243\left(-\dfrac{3}{2}\right) - 108$
$\quad = 0 \quad 2x + 3$ is also factor

Dividing the polynomial by $(x - 4)(2x + 3)$
or $2x^2 - 5x - 12$:

$$
\begin{array}{r}
16x^2 - 24x + 9 \\
2x^2 - 5x - 12 \overline{\smash{\big)}\,32x^4 - 128x^3 - 54x^2 - 243x - 108} \\
\underline{-(32x^4 - 80x^3 - 192x^2)} \\
-48x^3 + 138x^2 - 243x \\
\underline{-(-48x^3 + 120x^2 + 288x)} \\
18x^2 - 45x - 108 \\
\underline{-(18x^2 - 45x - 108)} \\
0
\end{array}
$$

$32x^4 - 128x^3 - 54x^2 - 243x - 108$
$= (x - 4)(2x + 3)(16x^2 - 24x + 9)$
$= (x - 4)(2x + 3)(4x - 3)^2$

17. $a^n - a^n = 0$

18. $(a - a)^3 + (a - b)^3 + (b - a)^3 =$
$0 + (a - b)^3 - (a - b)^3 = 0$

2.3 Polynomial Equations

1. a) $x = 0, x = 1, x = -3$ **b)** $x = -2, x = -5$
c) $x = \dfrac{5}{2}, x = -3, x = \dfrac{1}{4}$ **d)** $x = \dfrac{7}{2}, x = \dfrac{4}{3},$
$x = -6$ **e)** $x = 3, x = -\dfrac{1}{2}, x = \dfrac{2}{15}$
f) $x = -8, x = 9, x = \dfrac{1}{3}$ **g)** $x = 2, x = \pm\dfrac{4}{5}$
2. a) $x = -4, x = -3, x = 0, x = 2$
b) $x = -1, x = 0, x = 1$ **c)** $x = -2, x = 4$
3. a) $x = 9, x = -9, x = -3$ **b)** $x = 5,$
$x = -3, x = 2$ **c)** $x = \dfrac{1}{3}, x = 2, x = -2,$
$x = -8$ **d)** $x = 3, x = -3, x = 1$ **e)** $x = -\dfrac{1}{2},$
$x = \dfrac{5}{2}, x = 2, x = -2$ **f)** $x = 10, x = -10$
g) $x = -1, x = \dfrac{4}{3}, x = -\dfrac{1}{2}, x = \dfrac{1}{3}$
4. a) $0, \pm\dfrac{7}{4}$ **b)** $0, -6$ **c)** $0, 9, 7$ **d)** $0, \pm 11$
e) $0, 3$ **f)** $\pm 2\sqrt{2}$ **g)** $\pm 3, \pm\sqrt{3}$
5. Since the zeros are -2 and 1, the factors for
a cubic function are $(x + 2)$ and $(x - 1)$.
Since there is a local minimum at $(1, 0)$,
$(x - 1)$ will be of order 2. An equation for a
cubic function is
$y = (x - 1)^2(x + 2)$.
6. $y = (x + 4)(x - 2)^2(x - 1)$
7. a) $x = 5, x = -2$ **b)** $x = -2, x = 2, x = 3$
c) $x = -4, x = 3, x = 4$ **d)** $x = -1, x = 2,$
$x = 3$ **e)** $x = -4, x = -3, x = -1$
f) $x = -3, x = -1, x = 4$ **g)** $x = -3,$
$x = -1, x = 2, x = 3$ **8.** same **9. a)** $x = -2,$
3 **b)** $x = -3, -1, 2, 3$ **c)** $x = -3, -2, 2$
d) $x = -3, -2, -1, 1, 2$

10. a) $x = 3.4$, $x = 0.6$ **b)** $x = 2$, $x = 0.4$, $x = -2.4$ **c)** $x = 2$, $x = 5.2$, $x = -0.2$ **d)** $x = -2$ **e)** $x = -2$ **f)** $x = -0.3$, $x = 2.9$

11. a) 3.9 bacteria/h, -38.1 bacteria/h **b)** growth rate never reaches 20 bacteria per hour during the first 100 hours of the experiment **c)** 14.5 h **d)** 26.8 h; decline in bacteria population **e)** 8.2 h

12. The box does not reach a volume of 9600 cm^3.

13. a)

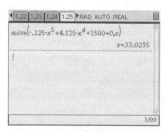

b) 1905 represents year 0. Substitute 0 for x in $f(x)$:
$$f(0) = -0.125(0)^5 + 4.125(0)^4 + 3500$$
$$= 3500$$
The population of wolves was 3500.

c) 1920 represents year 15. Substitute 15 for x in $f(x)$:
$$f(15) = -0.125(15)^5 + 4.125(15)^4 + 3500$$
$$= -94921.875 + 208828.125 + 3500$$
$$= 117406.25$$
$$\cong 117407$$
The population of wolves was 117 407.

d) Solve $f(x) = 0$
$$-0.125x^5 + 4.125x^4 + 3500 = 0$$
Use a graphing calculator to solve the equation. Use the solve() function to solve $-0.125x^5 + 4.125x^4 + 3500 = 0$

Or, use the graph from part a) to determine the zero of the function $y = -0.125x^5 + 4.125x^4 + 3500$

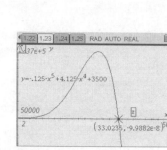

The wolf population became zero at approximately $x = 33$, in 1938.

14. $y = ax^3 + bx^2 + cx + d$
Point $(0, -1)$ *is on the graph. Substitute 0 for x and -1 for y.*
$$a(0)^3 + b(0)^2 + c(0) + d = -1; \boldsymbol{d = -1}$$
Point $(1, 0)$ is on the graph. Substitute 1 for x and 0 for y.
$$0 = a(1)^3 + b(1)^2 + c(1) + d$$
$$0 = a + b + c + d$$
Substitute -1 for d.
$$a + b + c - 1 = 0$$
$$a + b + c = 1 \qquad \text{// Equation 1}$$
Point $(-1, -4)$ is on the graph.
Substitute -1 for x and -4 for y.
$$a(-1)^3 + b(-1)^2 + c(-1) + d = -4$$
$$-a + b - c + d = -4$$
Substitute -1 for d.
$$-a + b - c - 1 = -4$$
$$-a + b - c = -3 \qquad \text{// Equation 2}$$
Point $(2, 5)$ is on the graph. Substitute 2 for x and 5 for y.
$$a(2)^3 + b(2)^2 + c(2) + d = 5$$
$$8a + 4b + 2c + d = 5$$
Substitute -1 for d.
$$8a + 4b + 2c - 1 = 5$$
$$8a + 4b + 2c = 6 \qquad \text{// Equation 3}$$
Solve the system of equations:
$$a + b + c = 1 \qquad \text{// Equation 1}$$
$$-a + b - c = -3 \qquad \text{// Equation 2}$$
$$8a + 4b + 2c = 6 \qquad \text{// Equation 3}$$
Equation 1 + Equation 2:
$$2b = -2; \boldsymbol{b = -1}$$
Substitute -1 for b in Equation 1:
$$a - 1 + c = 1; a + c = 2$$
Substitute -1 for b in Equation 3:
$$8a + 4(-1) + 2c = 6$$
$$8a + 2c = 10; 4a + c = 5$$
Solve the system of equations:
$$a + c = 2 \qquad \text{// Equation 4}$$
$$4a + c = 5 \qquad \text{// Equation 5}$$
Equation 5 − Equation 4:
$$3a = 3; a = 1$$

Substitute 1 for a in Equation 4:
$1 + c = 2; c = 1$
Substitute $a = 1, b = -1, c = 1, d = -1$ in
$y = ax^3 + bx^2 + cx + d$ to get the equation
of the cubic function whose graph passes
through the points $(1, 0)$, $(0, -1)$, $(-1, -4)$,
$(2, 5)$: $y = x^3 - x^2 + x - 1$

15. $(x + 4)(x + 3)(x + 1)(x - 1)(x - 3)$

16. a) $x = 0$, $x = \dfrac{1 \pm i\sqrt{19}}{2}$ **b)** $x = 0$, $x = \dfrac{9}{2}$

c) $x = 0$, $x = \pm 4$ **d)** $x = \pm i$, $x = \pm 3i$

e) $x = \pm\sqrt{2 + \sqrt{3}}$, $x = \pm\sqrt{2 - \sqrt{3}}$

2.4 Families of Polynomial Functions

1. a) $y = k(x - 5)(x - 8)$, $k \in R$
b) Answers may vary. Sample answer:
$y = (x - 5)(x - 8)$; $y = 2(x - 5)(x - 8)$
c) $y = -3(x - 5)(x - 8)$

2. a) $-2, 3, 8$
b) Answers may vary. Sample answer:
$y = (x + 2)(x - 3)(x - 8)$;
$y = 2(x + 2)(x - 3)(x - 8)$
c) $y = 4(x + 2)(x - 3)(x - 8)$

3. a) b) f) $y = k(x + 4)(x - 3)$
c) d) e) $y = k(2x - 1)(x - 5)$

4. a), e), and **h)** belong to one family; **b), d),**
and **g)** belong to another family; **c)** and **f)**
belong to a third family

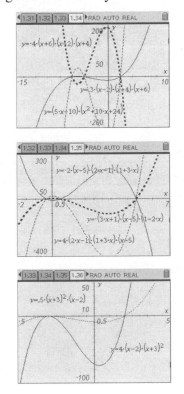

5. a) $y = k(x - 3)(x + 2)$ **b)** $y = kx(x - 1)$
$(x - 5)$ **c)** $y = k(x + 3)(x - 1)(x - 6)$
d) $y = kx(x + \sqrt{3})(x - \sqrt{3})(3x - 2)$

6. a) $y = k(x + 5)(x + 1)(x - 2)$
b) Answers may vary. Sample answer:
$y = (x + 5)(x + 1)(x - 2)$;
$y = 2(x + 5)(x + 1)(x - 2)$
c) $y = (x + 5)(x + 1)(x - 2)$

7. a) $y = k(x + 4)(x + 3)(x - 1)(x - 6)$
b) Answers may vary. Sample answer:
$y = (x + 4)(x + 3)(x - 1)(x - 6)$;
$y = \dfrac{1}{2}(x + 4)(x + 3)(x - 1)(x - 6)$
c) $y = \dfrac{1}{4}(x + 4)(x + 3)(x - 1)(x - 6)$

d)

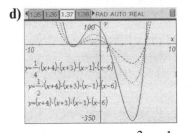

8. a) Since the zeros are $\dfrac{3}{2}, 0, \dfrac{1}{2}$, and 2, the
factors for the family of quartic functions
are $(2x + 3)$, x, $(2x - 1)$, and $(x - 2)$. An
equation for this family is $y = kx(2x + 3)$
$(2x - 1)(x - 2)$, where $k \in R$.
b) Use any two values for k to write two
members of the family.
For $k = 2$, $y = 2x(2x + 3)(2x - 1)(x - 2)$
For $k = -1$, $y = -x(2x + 3)(2x - 1)$
$(x - 2)$
c) Since the graph passes through $(-1, 4.5)$,
substitute $x = -1$ and $y = 4.5$ into
$y = kx(2x + 3)(2x - 1)(x - 2)$
$4.5 = k(-1)[2(-1) + 3][2(-1) - 1]$
$\qquad [(-1) - 2]$
$4.5 = k(-1)(1)(-3)(-3)$
$4.5 = -9k; k = \dfrac{-1}{2}$
The equation is
$y = \dfrac{-1}{2x}(2x + 3)(2x - 1)(x - 2)$
d)

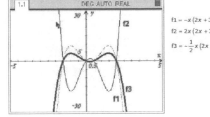

9. a) From the graph, the x-intercepts are $-4, -2, 2,$ and 3.

The corresponding factors are $(x + 4)$, $(x + 2)$, $(x - 2)$, and $(x - 3)$.

An equation for the family of polynomial functions with these zeros is

$y = k(x + 4)(x + 2)(x - 2)(x - 3)$

Select a point that the graph passes through, such as A(1, 90).

Substitute $x = 1$ and $y = 90$ into the equation to solve for k.

$90 = k(1 + 4)(1 + 2)(1 - 2)(1 - 3)$

$90 = k(5)(3)(-1)(-2)$

$90 = 30k;\ k = 3$

The equation is

$y = 3(x + 4)(x + 2)(x - 2)(x - 3).$

b) From the graph, the x-intercepts are $-\dfrac{5}{2}, 0$ (order 3), and 2.

The corresponding factors are $(2x + 5)$, $x^3, (x - 2)$.

An equation for the family of polynomial functions with these zeros is

$y = kx^3(2x + 5)(x - 2)$

Select a point that the graph passes through, such as A($-2, -32$).

Substitute $x = -2$ and $y = -32$ into the equation to solve for k.

$-32 = k(-2)^3[2(-2) + 5][(-2) - 2]$

$-32 = k(-8)(1)(-4)$

$-32 = 32k;\ k = -1$

The equation is $y = -x^3(2x + 5)(x - 2)$

10. a) $y = k(x^4 - 8x^3 - 2x^2 + 120x - 175)$

b) $y = 0.3(x^4 - 8x^3 - 2x^2 + 120x - 175)$

11. $y = (x + 4)^2(2x + 1)(x - 7)$

$y = (x + 4)(2x + 1)(x - 7)$

similarities: same domain, share three roots; differences: different range, degree, y-intercepts

12. a) Since the zeros are $1 \pm \sqrt{5}, -3,$ and $\dfrac{1}{3}$, the factors for the family of quartic functions are $(x - 1 - \sqrt{5}), (x - 1 + \sqrt{5}), (x + 3),$ and $(3x - 1)$. An equation for this family is $y = k(x - 1 - \sqrt{5})(x - 1 + \sqrt{5})(x + 3)(3x - 1)$, where $k \in R$

b) Since the graph passes through the point $(-2, -7)$, substitute $x = -2$ and $y = -7$ into the equation to solve for k.

$-7 = k[(-2)-1 - \sqrt{5}][(-2)-1 + \sqrt{5}]$
$((-2) + 3)(3(-2) - 1),$
$-7 = k(-3 - \sqrt{5})(-3 + \sqrt{5})(1)(-7)$
$-7 = k(4)(1)(-7)$
$-7 = -28k;\ k = \dfrac{1}{4}$

The equation is

$y = \dfrac{1}{4}(x - 1 - \sqrt{5})(x - 1 + \sqrt{5})$
$(x + 3)(3x - 1)$

13. Since the zeros are $1 \pm \sqrt{5}, -3,$ and $\dfrac{1}{3}$, the factors for the family of functions are $(x - 1 - \sqrt{5}), (x - 1 + \sqrt{5}), (x + 3),$ and $(3x - 1)$. To determine the equation for a family of functions with the same zeros, but with a higher degree, one or more of the zeros must be of order 2 or higher. An equation for this family is

$y = k(x - 1 - \sqrt{5})(x - 1 + \sqrt{5})$
$(x + 3)^2(3x - 1)^3$, where $k \in R$.

14. a) $y = k(x + 1.5)^2(x - 7)$ **b)** 3

c) $y = -0.5(x + 1.5)^2(x - 7)$

d) $y = 0.5(x - 1.5)^2(x + 7)$

e) $y = 0.5(x + 1.5)^2(x - 7)$

15. a) $(x - 2)$ is a factor **b)** Answers may vary. For example: As k increases, the height of the relative minimum to the right of $x = 0$ decreases and moves to the right and the relative maximum between $x = 0$ and $x - 2$ decreases and moves to the right. However, the y-intercept and the minimum at $x = 2$ remains constant. **c)** $k < -4$ or $k > 4$ **d)** Answers may vary. For example: $k = -2$

16. a) $y = k(x - 25)(x - 50)(x - 200)^2(x - 350)$

b) $y = k(0.5x - 25)(0.5x - 50)(0.5x - 200)^2$
$(0.5x - 350)$

2.5 Solve Inequalities Using Technology

1. a) $x > 1$ **b)** $x \le 2.5$ **c)** $2.5 < x < 6$

d) $0 \le x \le 3, x > 10$

2. a) $x < -2, -2 < x < 0, x > 0$ **b)** $x < -3$,
$-3 < x < 1, 1 < x < 2, x > 2$ **c)** $x < 1$,
$1 < x < 5, 5 < x < 6, 6 < x < 10, x > 10$
d) $x < -14, -14 < x < -12, -12 < x <$
$-0.5, -0.5 < x < 21, x > 21$

3. a) i) $0, 3$ **ii)** $0 < x < 3$ **iii)** $x < 0, x > 3$
b) i) $-2, 2$ **ii)** $x > 2$ **iii)** $x < -2, -2 < x < 2$
c) i) $-5, 2, 6$ **ii)** $-5 < x < 2, x > 6$
iii) $x < -5, 2 < x < 6$ **d) i)** $-1.5, 0$
ii) $x < -1.5, -1.5 < x < 0$ **iii)** $x > 0$

4. a) Answers may vary. For example:

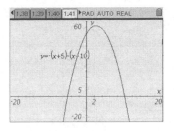

b) $-(x + 5)(x - 10) > 0$;
$-(x + 5)(x - 10) < 0$

5. a) Answers may vary. For example:

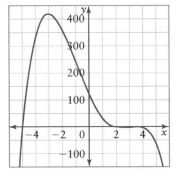

For the required quartic function, the function must exist below the x-axis for the intervals $x \leq -5$, $2 \leq x \leq 3$, and $x \geq 4$, and must exist above the x-axis for $-5 < x < 2$ and $3 < x < 4$. From this information, the x-intercepts are $x = -5, 2, 3,$ and 4. Therefore, the function must be $f(x) = -(x + 5)$ $(x - 2)(x - 3)(x - 4)$, with the negative required to have the needed behaviour in the intervals.

b) $f(x) \leq 0$, for $x \leq -5$, $2 \leq x \leq 3$ and $x \geq 4$
$f(x) > 0$, for $-5 < x < 2$ and $3 < x < 4$

6. a) $3 \leq x \leq 10$ **b)** $x < -12, x > -8$
c) $x \leq -2, 2 \leq x \leq 3$ **d)** $-4 \leq x \leq 3, x \geq 4$
e) $x < -1, 2 < x < 3$ **f)** $-4 \leq x \leq -3,$
$x \geq -1$ **g)** $-3 < x < -1, 2 < x < 3$

7. a) $-1.5 \leq x \leq 1, x \geq 2$ **b)** $x < -\sqrt{2}, \frac{1}{3} <$
$x < \sqrt{2}$ **c)** $1 - \sqrt{2} \leq x \leq 0.5, x \geq 1 + \sqrt{2}$
d) $x \leq -0.5, 1 \leq x \leq 1.5$ **e)** $-3 < x < 1.5, x$
> 2 **f)** $-3 \leq x \leq -1.5, x \geq 0.5$
g) $x < -2.5, 1 \_\_ 3 < x < 2$

8. a) $x < -0.32, x > 6.32$ **b)** $-8.67 < x < 0.17$
c) $-3.60 \leq x \leq -2.32, x \geq 1.92$
d) no solution **e)** $x < -1.34, -0.23 < x <$
6.57 **f)** $x > -1.24$ **g)** $-2.10 < x < 1.59$

9. a) Answers may vary. For example:
$y = -(x + 4.5)^3$

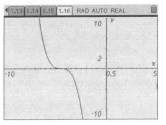

b) The family of functions $y = -k(x + 4.5)^3$ also satisfies this criterion.

10. a) $x > -2.2$ **c)** $x > 5$ **e)** $-3 \leq x \leq 4$
Use a graphing calculator to solve the three inequalities. Use the solve() function.

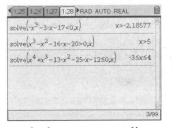

Or graph the corresponding polynomial functions. Find the zeros, and then find the values of x that satisfy the inequalities.

a)

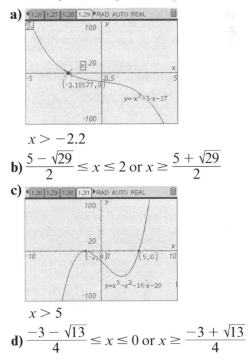

$x > -2.2$

b) $\dfrac{5 - \sqrt{29}}{2} \leq x \leq 2$ or $x \geq \dfrac{5 + \sqrt{29}}{2}$

c)

$x > 5$

d) $\dfrac{-3 - \sqrt{13}}{4} \leq x \leq 0$ or $x \geq \dfrac{-3 + \sqrt{13}}{4}$

e)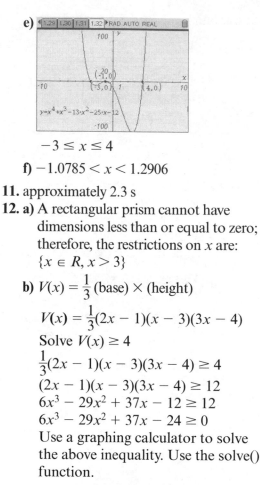

$-3 \le x \le 4$

f) $-1.0785 < x < 1.2906$

11. approximately 2.3 s

12. a) A rectangular prism cannot have dimensions less than or equal to zero; therefore, the restrictions on x are: $\{x \in R, x > 3\}$

b) $V(x) = \frac{1}{3}$ (base) $\times$ (height)

$V(x) = \frac{1}{3}(2x - 1)(x - 3)(3x - 4)$

Solve $V(x) \ge 4$

$\frac{1}{3}(2x - 1)(x - 3)(3x - 4) \ge 4$

$(2x - 1)(x - 3)(3x - 4) \ge 12$

$6x^3 - 29x^2 + 37x - 12 \ge 12$

$6x^3 - 29x^2 + 37x - 24 \ge 0$

Use a graphing calculator to solve the above inequality. Use the solve() function.

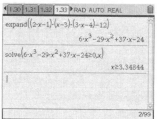

$x \ge 3.3$

Graph the corresponding polynomial function. Find the zeros, and then find the values of x that satisfy the inequality.

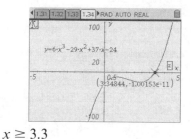

$x \ge 3.3$

13. a) $V(x) = \frac{2}{3}x^3$ **b)** $1 \le x \le 4.48$ and $\frac{2}{3} \le V(x) \le 60$

14. a) $(x + 2.5)(x - 3.5)(x - 5) > 0;$
$-(x + 2.5)(x - 3.5)(x - 5) < 0$

b) $(x + 2\sqrt{2})(x + \sqrt{2})(x - \sqrt{2}) < 0;$
$-(x + 2\sqrt{2})(x + \sqrt{2})(x - \sqrt{2}) > 0$

15. a) $x < -3, x > 2$ **b)** $x < -5$

c) $-4 < x < -1,$
$-\frac{3}{4} < x < \frac{2}{3}, 2 < x < 3$

16. Answers may vary. For example:

a) $(x + 3)(x - 2) > 0; (x + 3)^3(x - 2) > 0$

b) $(x + 5)^3 < 0; (x + 5)^5 < 0$

c) $(x + 4)(x + 1)(4x + 3)(3x - 2)(x - 2)$
$(x - 3) < 0; (x + 4)(x + 1)(4x + 3)$
$(3x - 2)(x - 2)(x - 3)^3 < 0$

17. Answers may vary. For example:
$y = x^2 + 1$ has two complex roots, $x = \pm i$
$x \in R$ is a solution to $x^2 + 1 > 0$.
There is no solution to $x^2 + 1 < 0$.

18. a) $x < 0.22, x > 2.28$ **b)** $x < -1.34,$
$-0.32 < x < 1.16$ **c)** $x < 0.92$

d) $x \le -2.66, -1.21 \le x \le 1.87$

e) $0.77 < x < 1.31$

19. a) $x > 2.7$ **b)** $x < 0.5$ **c)** $-3.4 \le x \le 0.5,$
$x \ge 2.9$ **d)** $1.3 \le x \le 2.8$

20. Answers will vary. For example:
$8x^4 - 68x^3 + 34x^2 + 425x - 525 > 0$

21. Use a similar graphing calculator to solve the inequality. Use the solve() function.

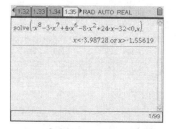

$x < -3.99$ or $x > -1.56$

Graph the corresponding polynomial function. Find the zeros, and then find the values of x that satisfy the inequality.

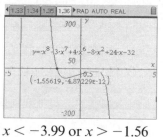

$x < -3.99$ or $x > -1.56$

22. $x \le -0.60, 0.54 \le x \le 3.$

23. Translate the model approximately 15 units up.

2.6 Solve Factorable Inequalities Algebraically

1. **a)** $x \leq 13$ **b)** $x \leq 6$ **c)** $x < -3$ **d)** $x \geq -11$
   e) $x < -1$ **f)** $x \leq \frac{1}{12}$

2. **a)** $-4 \leq x \leq 2$ **b)** $-3 \leq x \leq 2$
   c) $x < -\frac{2}{3}, x > \frac{3}{4}$ **d)** $\frac{1}{2} < x < \frac{5}{6}$

3. **a)** $-4 < x < -2, x > 1$ **b)** $x \leq -4, -2 \leq$
   $x \leq 1$ **c)** $x \leq -3, \frac{1}{2} \leq x \leq \frac{3}{5}$ **d)** $x \leq \frac{1}{4}$

4. **a)** $x \leq -4, x \geq 6$ **b)** $5 - \sqrt{46} \leq x \leq 5 + \sqrt{46}$
   c) $-\frac{3}{2} < x < \frac{1}{3}$ **d)** $\frac{-5 - \sqrt{97}}{4} \leq x \leq$
   $\frac{-5 + \sqrt{97}}{4}$ **e)** $-4 < x < -2, x > 4$
   f) $x \leq -4, -1 \leq x \leq 1$

5. **a)** $-4 \leq x \leq 1$ **b)** $x \leq -5, 0 \leq x \leq 4$
   c) $x < -1, x > 2$ **d)** $x \geq 3$ **e)** $x < -4,$
   $-\frac{4}{3} < x < 1$ **f)** no solution

6. **a)** $x \geq 2$; As the line of the inequality moves down from $y = 0$ to $y = -2$ to finally $y = -10$ the portions of the function $y = x^3 - 3x - 2$ that satisfy the inequality also shifts. For the inequality in a) the line $y = 0$ intersects the curve $y = x^3 - 3x - 2$ twice, the inequality in b) has the line $y = -2$ intersecting the curve $y = x^3 - 3x - 2$ three times and in c) the line $y = -10$ intersects the curve $y = x^3 - 3x - 2$ only once.
   b) $-\sqrt{3} \leq x \leq 0, x \geq \sqrt{3}$ **c)** $x \geq -2.49$

7. $A(x) = \text{length} \times \text{width}$
   Let width $= x$ and length $= x + 6$
   $A(x) = (x + 6)x = x^2 + 6x$
   Solve $A(x) \geq 630$
   $x^2 + 6x \geq 630$
   $x^2 + 6x - 630 \geq 0$
   Use quadratic formula to find the zeros of the polynomial $p(x) = x^2 + 6x - 630$
   $x = \frac{-b \pm \sqrt{b^2 - 4ac}}{2a}$
   $x = \frac{-6 \pm \sqrt{6^2 - 4(1)(-630)}}{2(1)}$
   $x = \frac{-6 \pm \sqrt{2556}}{2}$
   $x = \frac{-6 \pm 6\sqrt{71}}{2}$
   $x = -3 \pm 3\sqrt{71}$

The solution to the inequality is:
$x \leq -3 - 3\sqrt{71}$ or $x \geq -3 + 3\sqrt{71}$
Or approximately: $x \leq -28.3$ or $x \geq 22.3$
Since width or length of a rectangle cannot be negative, the possible widths of a rectangle are $x \geq -3 + 3\sqrt{71}$ cm or approximately $x \geq 22.3$ cm.

8. **a)** Factor the polynomial function.
   Let $p(x) = x^3 - x^2 - 34x - 56$
   Find a value $x = b$ such that $p(b) = 0$
   By the integral zero theorem, test factor of -56, that is $\pm 1, \pm 2, \pm 4, \pm 7,$ $\pm 8, \pm 14, \pm 28, \pm 56$
   Substitute $x = -2$ to test
   $p(-2) = (-2)^3 - (-2)^2 - 34(-2) - 56$
   $\quad\quad = -8 - 4 + 68 - 56 = 0$
   $x = -2$ is a zero and $x + 2$ is a factor.
   Use synthetic division method to determine the other factors.

-2	1	-1	-34	-56
$+$		-2	6	56
$\times$	1	-3	-28	0

$x^2 - 3x - 28$ can be further factored to $(x + 4)(x - 7)$
So $p(x) = x^3 - x^2 - 34x - 56$
$= (x + 2)(x + 4)(x - 7)$
Use intervals $x \leq -4, -4 \leq x \leq -2,$ $-2 \leq x \leq 7,$ and $x \geq 7$
Test arbitrary values of x for each interval.
The solution to the inequality $(x + 2)(x + 4)(x - 7) \geq 0$ is:
$-4 \leq x \leq -2$ or $x \geq 7$

b) $x < -2, -\frac{4}{3} < x < 1$
c) Factor the polynomial function.
Let $p(x) = 3x^3 + 4x^2 - 5x - 2$
Use the rational zero theorem to determine the values that should be tested.
Let b represent the factors of the constant term -2, which are $\pm 1, \pm 2$.
Let a represent the factors of the leading coefficient 3, which are $\pm 1, \pm 3$.
The possible values of $\frac{b}{a}$ are $\pm 1, \pm \frac{1}{3},$ $\pm 2, \pm \frac{2}{3}$.
Test the values of $\frac{b}{a}$ for x to find the zeros.
Substitute $x = 1$ to test

$p(1) = 3(1)^3 + 4(1)^2 - 5(1) - 2$
$= 3 + 4 - 5 - 2 = 0$
$x = 1$ is a zero and $x - 1$ is a factor.
Use synthetic division method to
determine the other factors.

1	3	4	−5	−2
+		3	7	2
×	3	7	2	0

$3x^2 + 7x + 2$ can be factored further
to $(x + 2)(3x + 1)$

So $p(x) = 3x^3 + 4x^2 - 5x - 2 =$
$(x - 1)(x + 2)(3x + 1)$

Use intervals $x < -2$, $-2 < x < -\frac{1}{3}$,
$-\frac{1}{3} < x < 1$, and $x > 1$.

Test arbitrary values of x for each
interval.
The solution to the inequality $(x - 1)$
$(x + 2)(3x + 1) > 0$ is:
$-2 < x < -\frac{1}{3}$ or $x > 1$
d) $x \leq -1$, $x \geq 1$
e) $x^4 - 13x^2 + 36 \leq 0$
Let $w = x^2$
Substitute w for x^2:
$w^2 - 13w + 36 \leq 0$
$(w - 4)(w - 9) \leq 0$
Substitute x^2 for w:
$(x^2 - 4)(x^2 - 9) \leq 0$
$(x - 2)(x + 2)(x - 3)(x + 3) \leq 0$
Use intervals $x \leq -3$, $-3 \leq x \leq -2$,
$-2 \leq x \leq 2$, $2 \leq x \leq 3$, $3 \geq x$
Test arbitrary values of x for each interval
The solution to the inequality $(x - 2)$
$(x + 2)(x - 3)(x + 3) \leq 0$ is:
$-3 \leq x \leq -2$ or $2 \leq x \leq 3$
f) $x = 1$
9. $0.75 \leq x \leq 3.25$
10. Let length $l = 12 + x$, width $w = 6 + x$,
and height $h = 2 + x$.
Surface area of a rectangular reflecting
pool is:
$SA(x) = 2lh + 2wh + lw$
$= 2(12 + x)(2 + x) + 2(6 + x)(2 + x)$
$+ (12 + x)(6 + x)$
$= 48 + 28x + 2x^2 + 24 + 16x + 2x^2$
$+ 72 + 18x + x^2$
$= 5x^2 + 62x + 144$

Solve $SA(x) \leq 440$
$5x^2 + 62x + 144 \leq 440$
$5x^2 + 62x + 144 - 440 \leq 0$
$5x^2 + 62x - 296 \leq 0$
Find zeros using quadratic formula
$x = \dfrac{-b \pm \sqrt{b^2 - 4ac}}{2a}$
$x = \dfrac{-62 \pm \sqrt{62^2 - 4(5)(-296)}}{2(5)}$
$x = \dfrac{-62 \pm \sqrt{9764}}{10}$
$x \cong 3.68$ or $x \cong -16.08$
Dimensions of a reflecting pool cannot be
less than or equal to zero; therefore,
$x \cong 3.68$ m.
The maximum dimensions of the larger
reflecting pool are approximately:
$l = 15.68$ m, $w = 9.68$ m, and $h = 5.68$ m
11. a) $0.3 \leq x \leq 4.5$, $x \geq 7.2$ **b)** domain:
$\{x \in R, 0 \leq x \leq 14\}$; range: $\{S \in R,$
$0 \leq S \leq 896\}$ **c)** The lemonade sales model
predicts over 600 000 sales toward the end
of summer, which is not very reasonable.
The model works only for the first two
weeks of summer.
12. a) $V(x) = (36 - x)(48 - x)(60 - x)$

b)
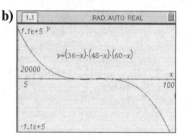

c) $(36 - x)(48 - x)(60 - x) = 62208$
d) $x \cong 7.17$ cm
13. $x < -2$, $-2 < x < -1$, $1 < x < 2$, $x > 2$;
$x \leq -1$, $x \geq 1$
14. The inequality has a real solution for all
$s \in R$ and all $t \in R$.
15. $x < -6.43$
16. $-3 \leq x \leq -1 - \sqrt{2}$, $-1 + \sqrt{2} \leq x \leq 1$

Chapter 2 Challenge Questions
C1. a) yes, only if $b = 0$, otherwise no
   b) yes **c)** yes, only if $b = 0$, otherwise no
   d) yes, only if $b = 0$, otherwise no
C2. $x \pm 4i$ **C3.** $10\sqrt{2} \times 5\sqrt{2}$
C4. a) $p(r_1) = 0$, $p(r_2) = 0$, $p(r_3) = 0$

b) $p(x) = a(x - r_1)(x - r_2)(x - r_3)$
$$= ax^3 - a(r_1 + r_2 + r_3)x^2 +$$
$$a(r_1 r_2 + r_2 r_3 + r_1 r_3)x - a(r_1 r_2 r_3)$$
$$= ax^3 + bx^2 + cx + d$$

c) $r_1 r_2 + r_2 r_3 + r_1 r_3 = \dfrac{c}{a}$

C5. a) $x^2 - 8x - 24 = 0$ **b)** $x^3 - 12x^2 + 36x = 0$

C6. $a = 28, b = \dfrac{57}{14}$

C7. a) two real positive zeros: $x = 2, x = -1.5,$
$\quad x = 0.25$

b) two real positive zeros: $x = -3, x = 0.5,$
$\quad x = 1$

C8. $x < -3, \dfrac{1}{2} < x < 5; x \neq \dfrac{1}{2}, x \neq -3$

C9. no solution

C10. a) $x \leq -2$ or $x \geq 3$ **b)** $-\dfrac{1}{2} < x < 2$

C11. a) $x < -4$ or $x > \dfrac{5}{3}$ **b)** $-\dfrac{2}{3} \leq x \leq 1$

Chapter 3
3.1 Reciprocal of a Linear Function

1. a) $x = 2, y = 0$ **b)** $x = -7, y = 0$ **c)** $x = 5,$
$\quad y = 0$ **d)** $x = 9, y = 0$ **e)** $x = \dfrac{4}{3}, y = 0$

f) $x = -\dfrac{1}{7}, y = 0$

2. a) $-\dfrac{1}{2}$ **b)** $\dfrac{3}{7}$ **c)** $\dfrac{4}{5}$ **d)** $\dfrac{2}{9}$ **e)** $\dfrac{1}{4}$ **f)** 5

3. a) $y = \dfrac{5}{x - 5}$ **b)** $y = \dfrac{-4}{x + 2}$ **c)** $y = \dfrac{1}{2x + 1}$

d) $y = \dfrac{-2}{x - 3}$

4. a)

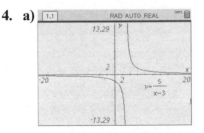

$\{x \in R, x \neq 3\}, \{y \in R, y \neq 0\},$
$x = 3, y = 0$

b)

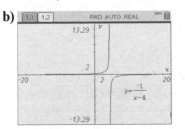

$\{x \in R, x \neq 4\}, \{y \in R, y \neq 0\},$
$x = 4, y = 0$

c)

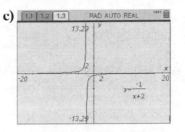

$\{x \in R, x \neq -2\}, \{y \in R, y \neq 0\},$
$x = -2, y = 0$

d)

$\{x \in R, x \neq -1\}, \{y \in R, y \neq 0\},$
$x = -1, y = 0$

e)

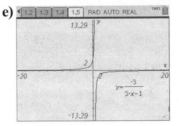

$\left\{x \in R, x \neq \dfrac{1}{2}\right\}, \{y \in R, y \neq 0\},$
$x = \dfrac{1}{2}, y = 0$

f)

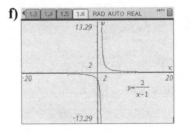

$\{x \in R, x \neq 1\}, \{y \in R, y \neq 0\},$
$x = 1, y = 0$

5. Answers may vary. Sample answer:

Vertical Asymptote	Comparison of Two Pairs of Points to the Left of Vertical Asymptote	Comparison of Two Pairs of Points to the Right of Vertical Asymptote
$x = \dfrac{1}{2}$	Points: $\left(-3, \dfrac{3}{7}\right), \left(-2, \dfrac{3}{5}\right)$	Points: $\left(3, -\dfrac{3}{5}\right), \left(4, -\dfrac{3}{7}\right)$
	Rate of change: $\dfrac{6}{35}$	Rate of change: $\dfrac{6}{35}$
	Points (closer to asymptote): $(-1, 1), (0, 3)$ Rate of change: 2	Points (closer to asymptote): $(1, -3), (2, -1)$ Rate of change: 2
Conclusion (Is rate of change increasing or decreasing?)	increasing	decreasing

6. a)

y-intercept: $y = -4$; $\left\{x \in R, x \neq \dfrac{1}{2}\right\}$,

$\{y \in R, y \neq 0\}$, $x = \dfrac{1}{2}$, $y = 0$

b)

y-intercept: $y = -\dfrac{1}{2}$; $\left\{x \in R, x \neq -\dfrac{4}{5}\right\}$,

$\{y \in R, y \neq 0\}$, $x = -\dfrac{4}{5}$, $y = 0$

c)

y-intercept: $y = \dfrac{1}{5}$; $\left\{x \in R, x \neq -\dfrac{5}{3}\right\}$,

$\{y \in R, y \neq 0\}$, $x = -\dfrac{5}{3}$, $y = 0$

d)

y-intercept: $y = -3$; $\left\{x \in R, x \neq \dfrac{1}{4}\right\}$,

$\{y \in R, y \neq 0\}$, $x = \dfrac{1}{4}$, $y = 0$

7. a) decreasing: $\left(-\infty, \dfrac{1}{2}\right)$, increasing: $\left(\dfrac{1}{2}, \infty\right)$

b) increasing: $\left(-\infty, -\dfrac{4}{5}\right)$, decreasing: $\left(-\dfrac{4}{5}, \infty\right)$

c) decreasing: $\left(-\infty, -\dfrac{5}{3}\right)$, increasing: $\left(-\dfrac{5}{3}, \infty\right)$

d) decreasing: $\left(-\infty, \dfrac{1}{4}\right)$, increasing: $\left(\dfrac{1}{4}, \infty\right)$

8. a) as $x \to \dfrac{1}{2}^-$, $f(x) \to -\infty$

as $x \to \dfrac{1}{2}^+$, $f(x) \to +\infty$

as $x \to +\infty$, $f(x) \to 0$ from above

as $x \to -\infty$, $f(x) \to 0$ from below

b) as $x \to -\dfrac{4}{5}^-$, $g(x) \to +\infty$

as $x \to -\dfrac{4}{5}^+$, $g(x) \to -\infty$

as $x \to +\infty$, $g(x) \to 0$ from below

as $x \to -\infty$, $g(x) \to 0$ from above

c) as $x \to -\dfrac{5}{3}^-$, $h(x) \to -\infty$

as $x \to -\dfrac{5}{3}^+$, $h(x) \to +\infty$

as $x \to +\infty$, $h(x) \to 0$ from above

as $x \to -\infty$, $h(x) \to 0$ from below

d) as $x \to \dfrac{1}{4}^-$, $k(x) \to -\infty$

as $x \to \dfrac{1}{4}^+$, $k(x) \to +\infty$

as $x \to +\infty$, $k(x) \to 0$ from above

as $x \to -\infty$, $k(x) \to 0$ from below

9. a) $y = \dfrac{2}{x + 4}$ **b)** $y = \dfrac{6}{3x - 1}$

10. a) 1.47 h, 1.25 h, 1.05 h

b) $t(v) = \dfrac{d}{v}$; d is distance in km, t is time in h, v is speed in km/h.

c)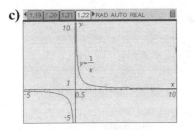

d) As speed increases, time decreases.
As speed decreases, time increases.

11. a) Answers may vary. Sample answers:

i)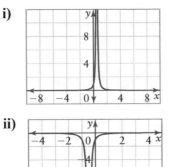

ii)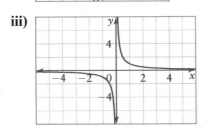

iii)

b) Answers may vary. Sample answers:

i) $y = \dfrac{1}{(2x - 1)^2}$ **ii)** $y = -\dfrac{1}{(2x + 1)^2}$

iii) $y = \dfrac{1}{x}$

12. a) $P(V) = \dfrac{20\,000}{V}$

b)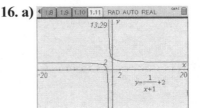

c) $\dfrac{800}{3}$ kPa

d) As the volume increases, the rate of change of the pressure decreases.

13. a) $0 < b < 1$, vertical compression by factor of b; $b > 1$, vertical stretch by factor of b

b) i)

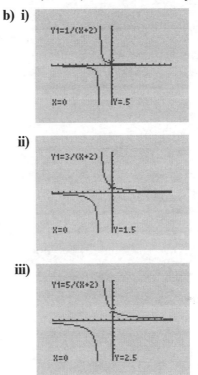

ii)

iii)

14. $\{x \in \mathbb{R}, x \neq k180°, k \in \mathbb{Z}\}$, $\{y \in \mathbb{R}, y \leq -1, y \geq 1\}$, vertical asymptotes: $x = k180°, k \in \mathbb{Z}$

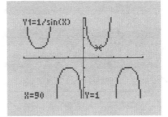

15. a) $\{x \in R, x \neq -1\}$, $\{y \in R, y \neq 2\}$, $x = -1, y = 2$

b) $\{x \in R, x \neq -1\}$, $\{y \in R, y \neq 2\}$, $x = -1, y = 2$

c) $\left\{x \in R, x \neq -\dfrac{1}{3}\right\}$, $\{y \in R, y \neq 0\}$, $x = -\dfrac{1}{3}, y = 0$

16. a)

b)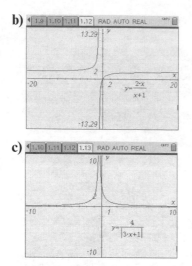

c)

17. 1 **18.** The reciprocal of a linear function $y = kx - c$ is a rational function of the form $y = \dfrac{1}{kx - c}$.

19. Similarities: domain $\{x \in R, x \neq 1\}$; range $\{y \in R, y \neq 0\}$; vertical asymptote: $x = 1$; horizontal asymptote: $y = 0$; no x-intercepts Differences:

	$f(x) = \dfrac{1}{1-x}$		$g(x) = \dfrac{1}{x-1}$	
Intervals	$x < 1$	$x > 1$	$x < 1$	$x > 1$
Sign of Function	+	−	−	+
Sign of Slope	+	+	−	−
Change in Slope	+	−	−	+
y-intercept	1		−1	

20. Similarities: range $\{y \in R, y \neq 0\}$; share one vertical asymptote: $x = -2$; horizontal asymptote: $y = 0$; no x-intercepts Differences:

	$f(x) = \dfrac{1}{x+2}$	$g(x) = \dfrac{1}{(x-2)(x+2)}$
Domain	$\{x \in R,$ $x \neq -2\}$	$\{x \in R, x \neq -2,$ $x \neq 2\}$
Vertical Asymptotes	$x = -2$	$x = -2, x = 2$
y-intercept	$\dfrac{1}{2}$	$-\dfrac{1}{4}$
Maximum	None	$\left(0, -\dfrac{1}{4}\right)$

21. $y = \dfrac{1}{(x+2)(x-4)}$

3.2 Reciprocal of a Quadratic Function

1. a) $x = 3, x = -4, \{x \in R, x \neq 3, x \neq -4\}$
b) $x = -3, \{x \in R, x \neq -3\}$
c) $x = -2, x = -6, \{x \in R, x \neq -2,$ $x \neq -6\}$
d) $x = -3, x = 3, \{x \in R, x \neq -3, x \neq 3\}$

2. a)

$x \rightarrow$	$f(x) \rightarrow$
1^-	$-\infty$
1^+	$+\infty$
-3^-	$+\infty$
-3^+	$-\infty$
$-\infty$	0 from above
$+\infty$	0 from above

b)

$x \rightarrow$	$f(x) \rightarrow$
$-\dfrac{1}{2}^-$	$+\infty$
$-\dfrac{1}{2}^+$	$-\infty$
2^-	$-\infty$
2^+	$+\infty$
$-\infty$	0 from above
$+\infty$	0 from above

3. a) i) 1 **ii)** none **iii)** $y = 0$ **iv)** $x = 1$ **b) i)** $-\dfrac{1}{6}$ **ii)** none **iii)** $y = 0$ **iv)** $x = -3, x = 2$
c) i) -1.67 **ii)** none **iii)** $y = 0$ **iv)** $x = \dfrac{1}{2},$ $x = 3$

4. a) $y = \dfrac{1}{(x-1)^2}$ **b)** $y = \dfrac{1}{(x+3)(x-2)}$
c) $y = -\dfrac{5}{(2x-1)(x-3)}$

5. a)

Intervals	$x < 1$	$x > 1$
Sign of Function	+	+
Sign of Slope	+	−
Change in Slope	+	+

b)

Intervals	$x < -3$	$-3 < x$ $< -\dfrac{1}{2}$	$x = -\dfrac{1}{2}$	$-\dfrac{1}{2} <$ $x < 2$	$x > 2$
Sign of Function	+	−	−	−	+
Sign of Slope	+	+	0	−	−
Change in Slope	+	−		−	+

c)

Intervals	$x < \frac{1}{2}$	$\frac{1}{2} < x < \frac{7}{4}$	$x = \frac{7}{4}$	$\frac{7}{4} < x < 3$	$x > 3$
Sign of Function	$-$	$+$	$+$	$+$	$-$
Sign of Slope	$-$	$-$	0	$+$	$+$
Change in Slope	$-$	$+$		$+$	$-$

6. a) i) $x = 7$, $x = -3$, $y = 0$

   ii) no x-intercepts, y-intercept: $-\dfrac{1}{21}$

   iii)

Intervals	$x < -3$	$-3 < x < 2$	$x = 2$	$2 < x < 7$	$x > 7$
Sign of Function	$+$	$-$	$-$	$-$	$+$
Sign of Slope	$+$	$+$	0	$-$	$-$
Change in Slope	$+$	$-$		$-$	$+$

   iv)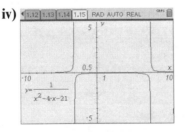

   v) $\{x \in R, x \neq 7, x \neq -3\}$, $\{y \in R, y \neq 0\}$

b) i) $x = 2$, $y = 0$ **ii)** no x-intercepts, y-intercept: $-\dfrac{1}{4}$

   iii)

Intervals	$x < 2$	$x > 2$
Sign of Function	$-$	$-$
Sign of Slope	$-$	$+$
Change in Slope	$-$	$-$

   iv)

   v) $\{x \in R, x \neq 2\}$, $\{y \in R, y \neq 0\}$

c) i) $x = -5$, $x = 5$, $y = 0$ **ii)** no x-intercepts, y-intercept: $-\dfrac{4}{25}$

   iii)

Intervals	$x < -5$	$-5 < x < 0$	$x = 0$	$0 < x < 5$	$5 > 2$
Sign of Function	$+$	$-$	$-$	$-$	$+$
Sign of Slope	$+$	$+$	0	$-$	$-$
Change in Slope	$+$	$-$		$-$	$+$

   iv)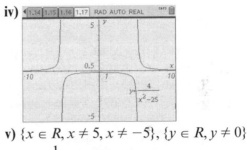

   v) $\{x \in R, x \neq 5, x \neq -5\}$, $\{y \in R, y \neq 0\}$

7. $y = \dfrac{1}{(x + 2)(x - 7)}$

8. a) i) Since the function approaches the x-axis as x approaches both positive and negative infinity, there is a horizontal asymptote at $y = 0$.

   ii) Since there is a horizontal asymptote at $y = 0$ that the function never crosses, there are no x intercepts. From the graph, the y- intercepts of $(0, 0.1)$ can be seen.

   iii) There is no restriction on x, so the domain is $x \in R$. The y values must be larger than zero, and can take on any values larger than zero, up to and including the y intercept of 0.1. Therefore, the range is $0 < y \leq 0.1$, $y \in R$

   iv)

Intervals	$x < 0$	$x = 0$	$x > 0$
Sign of Function	$+$	$+$	$+$
Sign of Slope	$+$	0	$-$

The function increases from negative infinity to the y-intercept and then decreases to positive infinity. Therefore, the interval of increase is $x < 0$ and the interval of decrease is $x > 0$.

b) There is no vertical asymptote because there is no value that x can take on that makes the function undefined.

c) Answers may vary. Sample answer:
$$y = \frac{1}{10(x^2 + 1)}$$

9. a) In the form $g(x) = \frac{1}{f(x)}, f(x) = 10(x^2 + 1)$.

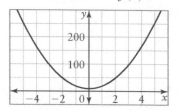

b) Answers may vary. Sample answer: From this graph, the domain for both $f(x)$ and $g(x)$ will be the same (that is, $x \in R$). They both do not have a vertical asymptote or x-intercepts. When $f(x)$ is increasing, $g(x)$ is decreasing and when $f(x)$ is decreasing, $g(x)$ is increasing.

10. a)

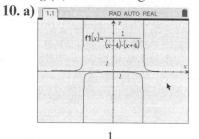

b) $y = \dfrac{1}{(x - 4)(x + 4)}$

11. a) $\{t \in R\}, \{P(t) \in R, 25 < P(t) \le 125\}$

b) $y = 25$, no vertical asymptotes

c)

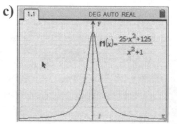

d)
$m_1 = -50$	$m_6 \cong -0.88$
$m_2 = -16$	$m_7 \cong -0.56$
$m_3 = -6$	$m_8 \cong -0.38$
$m_4 \cong -2.77$	$m_9 \cong -0.27$
$m_5 \cong -1.48$	

The rate of change is negative and therefore blood pressure is decreasing at $0 < t < 10$.

3.3 Rational Functions of the Form
$$f(x) = \frac{ax + b}{cx + d}$$

1. a) $x = 7$ **b)** $x = \frac{2}{3}$ **c)** $x = -4$ **d)** $x = -11$

2. a) $\{x \in R, x \ne 7\}$ **b)** $\left\{x \in R, x \ne \frac{2}{3}\right\}$
c) $\{x \in R, x \ne -4\}$ **d)** $\{x \in R, x \ne -11\}$

3. a) $y = 1$ **b)** $y = -5$ **c)** $y = -1$ **d)** $y = \frac{3}{4}$

4. a) $\{y \in R, y \ne 1\}$ **b)** $\{y \in R, y \ne -5\}$
c) $\{y \in R, y \ne -1\}$ **d)** $\left\{y \in R, y \ne \frac{3}{4}\right\}$

5. a)

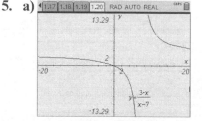

Intervals	$x < 0$	$0 < x < 7$	$x < 7$
Sign of Function	$+$	$-$	$+$
Sign of Slope	$-$	$-$	$-$
Change in Slope	$-$	$-$	$+$

b)

Intervals	$x < 0$	$0 < x < \frac{1}{5}$	$x < \frac{1}{5}$
Sign of Function	$-$	$+$	$-$
Sign of Slope	$+$	$+$	$+$
Change in Slope	$+$	$+$	$-$

c)

Intervals	$x < -2$	$-2 < x < \frac{1}{2}$	$x > \frac{1}{2}$
Sign of Function	+	–	+
Sign of Slope	+	+	+
Change in Slope	+	–	–

d)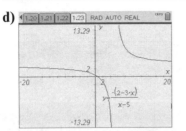

Intervals	$x < \frac{2}{3}$	$\frac{2}{3} < x < 5$	$x > 5$
Sign of Function	+	–	+
Sign of Slope	–	–	–
Change in Slope	–	–	+

6. a) i) 1 **ii)** $\frac{1}{2}$ **iii)** $y = 1$ **iv)** $x = 2$
  v) $\{x \in R, x \ne 2\}, \{y \in R, y \ne 1\}$
  b) i) 2 **ii)** $\frac{2}{3}$ **iii)** $y = -1$ **iv)** $x = -3$
  v) $\{x \in R, x \ne -3\}, \{y \in R, y \ne -1\}$
  c) i) $\frac{3}{2}$ **ii)** 1 **iii)** $y = 2$ **iv)** $x = 3$
  v) $\{x \in R, x \ne 3\}, \{y \in R, y \ne 2\}$

7. a) $y = \dfrac{x - 1}{x - 2}$ **b)** $y = -\dfrac{x - 2}{x + 3}$
  c) $y = \dfrac{2x - 3}{x - 3}$

8. a)

$y = 1, x = -3, \{x \in R, x \ne -3\},$
$\{y \in R, y \ne 1\}$

b)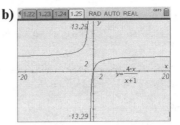

$y = 4, x = -1, \{x \in R, x \ne -1\},$
$\{y \in R, y \ne 4\}$

c)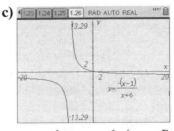

$y = -1, x = -6, \{x \in R, x \ne -6\},$
$\{y \in R, y \ne -1\}$

d)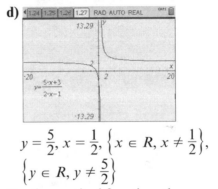

$y = \dfrac{5}{2}, x = \dfrac{1}{2}, \left\{x \in R, x \ne \dfrac{1}{2}\right\},$
$\left\{y \in R, y \ne \dfrac{5}{2}\right\}$

9. For the required function, the numerator must generate $x = 5$ when $y = 0$ is substituted. The numerator must be $x - 5$. The denominator must be equal to zero when $x = -\dfrac{8}{3}$, to give the vertical asymptote at this value, so the denominator must be $3x + 8$. The function must be: $f(x) = \dfrac{x - 5}{3x + 8}$. When $x = 0$, the y-intercept is the required value of $-\dfrac{5}{8}$, as well as the function having a horizontal asymptote at $y = \dfrac{1}{3}$.

10. a)
$$2x + 1 \overline{)6x - 3}$$
$$\underline{6x + 3}$$
$$-6$$

$f(x) = \dfrac{6x - 3}{2x + 1}$

$= 3 - \dfrac{6}{2x + 1}$

b) Answers may vary. Sample answer: For small values of x, the function $f(x)$ behaves according to $y = -\dfrac{6}{2x + 1}$, and as x increases to positive and negative infinity, the function behaves according to $y = 3$.

c)

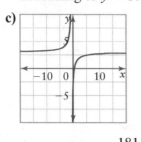

11. a) $f(x) = 11 + \dfrac{-181}{5x + 14}$

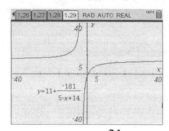

b) $g(x) = -3 + \dfrac{21}{9x + 4}$

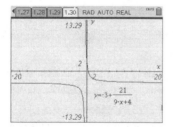

12. a) $\{x \in R, x \neq 0\}$ **b)** $x = 0,\ y = 7$

c)

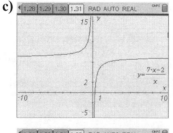

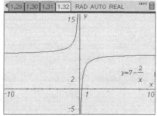

d) Answers may vary.

13. a) $x = -6$ **b)** $\{x \in R, x \neq -6\}$
c) $y = 3$ **d)** $\{y \in R, y \neq 3\}$
e)

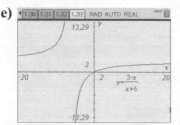

f)

Intervals	$x < -6$	$-6 < x < 0$	$x > 0$
Sign of Function	+	–	+
Sign of Slope	+	+	+
Change in Slope	+	–	–

g) i) $m_{-5} = 18$, $m_{15} = 0.04$, slope is positive and decreasing **ii)** $m_{-7} = 18$, $m_{-15} = 0.22$, slope is positive and increasing

14. a) \$147.90 **b)** $C(t) = \dfrac{1299 + 18t}{t}$

c)

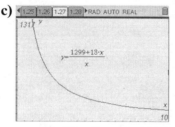

$t \in (0, 10)$, $C \in (0, 1317)$
d) vertical asymptote: $t = 0$; horizontal asymptote: $C = 0$ **e)** The longer the television lasts, the average annual costs approaches 0. **f)** no **g)** negative and increasing

15. a) $L(x) = 2x + \dfrac{500}{x}$, where L is length of rope in metres, x is width of enclosed area in metres.

b)

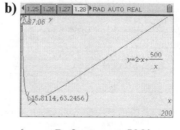

$\{x \in R, 0 < x < 500\}$

c) approximately 15.8 m by 31.6 m

16. vertical stretch by factor of 3. translation 5 units to the right; translation 8 units down

17. a)

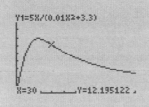

Y1=5X/(0.01X²+3.3)

X=30   Y=12.195122

b) The maximum concentration is about 13.8 mg/mL, which occurs at 18.2 min.

c) Increasing the "5" vertically stretches the graph. Decreasing the "5" vertically compresses the graph. Changing the sign of the "5" flips the graph about the x-axis. Increasing the "0.01" vertically compresses the graph and shifts the maximum to the left. Decreasing the "0.01" vertically stretches the graph and shifts the maximum to the right.

3.4 Solve Rational Equations and Inequalities

1. a) $x = 0$ **b)** $x = \dfrac{5}{6}$ **c)** $x = 5$ **d)** $x = -3, x = 6$

2. a) $x = -\dfrac{1}{13}$ **b)** $x = -1$ **c)** $x = \dfrac{4}{3}$ **d)** $x = \dfrac{4}{5}$

  e) $x = 3$ **f)** $x = 3$ **g)** $x = 0, x = \dfrac{-1 \pm \sqrt{97}}{2}$

3. a) -0.33 **b)** -1.27 **c)** $-0.04, 8.37$ **d)** $-1.78, -0.66, 0.76, 1.68$

4. a) $\left(-\infty, -\dfrac{1}{3}\right), (2, +\infty)$ **b)** $(-\infty, -4.5]$,

  $(-3, +\infty)$ **c)** $\left(-\infty, -\dfrac{3}{5}\right), \left[\dfrac{1}{2}, +\infty\right)$

  d) $(-\infty, -2), \left(-\dfrac{1}{2}, 1\right)$ **e)** $(-\infty, -2], (0, 4]$

  f) $(-3, 1), [5, +\infty)$ **g)** $(-1, 3), (3, +\infty)$

  h) $(-1 - \sqrt{3}, -2), (-1 + \sqrt{3}, 1)$

5. a) $[-4, 1), [1.5, 5)$ **b)** $(-\infty, 1), (2, 3)$

  c) $(-4, -1), [4, 5)$ **d)** $(-\infty, -6), (-4, 0), (12, +\infty)$ **e)** $(-\infty, -60], (-2, 2], (14, +\infty)$

  f) $(-1, -0.83), [0.5, 4.83)$

6. $y = \dfrac{x}{(x + 2)(2x - 1)}; x = -2, x = \dfrac{1}{2}$ are vertical asymptotes

7. $(-\infty, -9), (-1, 1)$

8. a) $x = 2, x = 6$ **b)** $x = \dfrac{23}{15}$ **c)** $x = \dfrac{5}{3}$

  d) $x = \dfrac{5}{13}$ **e)** $x \in R, x \neq 1$ **f)** $x = -\dfrac{1}{2}, x = 3$

9. a) $\dfrac{2}{3x} + \dfrac{5}{6x} > \dfrac{3}{4}$

  $\dfrac{4}{6x} + \dfrac{5}{6x} > \dfrac{3}{4}$

  $\dfrac{9}{6x} > \dfrac{3}{4}$

  $36 > 18x$

  $2 > x$

But $x = 0$ is a vertical asymptote, where the sign of the expression may change.
Test $x = -1$:

  $\dfrac{2}{3x} + \dfrac{5}{6x} > \dfrac{3}{4}$

  $\dfrac{2}{3(-1)} + \dfrac{5}{6(-1)} > \dfrac{3}{4}$

  $-\dfrac{2}{3} - \dfrac{5}{6} > \dfrac{3}{4}$

  $-\dfrac{9}{6} > \dfrac{3}{4}$

which is not a valid statement. So the solution is $0 < x < 2$.

b) $5 + \dfrac{1}{x} > \dfrac{16}{x}$

  $\dfrac{5x}{x} + \dfrac{1}{x} > \dfrac{16}{x}$

  $5x + 1 > 16$

  $5x > 15$

  $x > 3$

But at $x = 0$, there is a vertical asymptote where the expression could change signs.
Test $x = -1$:

  $5 + \dfrac{1}{-1} > \dfrac{16}{-1}$

  $5 - 1 > -16$

  $4 > -16$

which is a valid statement. Therefore, the solution is $x < 0$ or $x > 3$.

c) $1 + \dfrac{5}{x - 1} \leq \dfrac{7}{6}$

  $\dfrac{x - 1}{x - 1} + \dfrac{5}{x - 1} \leq \dfrac{7(x - 1)}{(x - 1)}$

  $x + 4 \leq 7x - 7$

  $11 \leq 6x$

  $\dfrac{11}{6} \leq x$

But at $x = 1$, there is a vertical asymptote where the expression could change signs.
Test $x = 36$:

$$1 + \frac{5}{36 - 1} \le \frac{7}{6}$$

$$1 + \frac{1}{7} \le \frac{7}{6}$$

$$\frac{8}{7} \le \frac{7}{6}$$

which is a valid statement. Therefore, the solution is $x < 1$ or $x \ge 31$.

d) $\dfrac{1}{2x + 1} + \dfrac{1}{x + 1} > \dfrac{8}{15}$

$$\frac{x + 1}{(2x + 1)(x + 1)} + \frac{2x + 1}{(2x + 1)(x + 1)}$$

$$> \frac{8(2x + 1)(x + 1)}{15(2x + 1)(x + 1)}$$

$$\frac{3x + 2}{(2x + 1)(x + 1)} > \frac{8(2x + 1)(x + 1)}{15(2x + 1)(x + 1)}$$

$$\frac{15(3x + 2)}{(2x + 1)(x + 1)} > \frac{8(2x + 1)(x + 1)}{(2x + 1)(x + 1)}$$

$$\frac{45x + 30}{(2x + 1)(x + 1)} > \frac{8(2x^2 + 3x + 1)}{(2x + 1)(x + 1)}$$

$$\frac{45x + 30}{(2x + 1)(x + 1)} > \frac{16x^2 + 24x + 8}{(2x + 1)(x + 1)}$$

$$0 > \frac{16x^2 - 21x - 22}{(2x + 1)(x + 1)}$$

The expression $16x^2 - 21x - 22$ is equal to zero when:

$$x = \frac{21 \pm \sqrt{(-21)^2 - 4(16)(-22)}}{2(16)}$$

$$= \frac{21 \pm \sqrt{1849}}{32}$$

$$= \frac{21 \pm 43}{32}$$

$$x = \frac{21 - 43}{32} \qquad x = \frac{21 + 43}{32}$$

$$x = -\frac{11}{16} \qquad x = 2$$

As well, there are vertical asymptotes at $x = -1$ and $x = -\dfrac{1}{2}$, which sets up the following intervals to test:

Interval	Test Value	Sign of Factors	Sign of Function
$x < -1$	$x = -2$	$\dfrac{(+)}{(-)(-)}$	$+$
$-1 < x < -\dfrac{11}{16}$	$x = -0.7$	$\dfrac{(+)}{(-)(+)}$	$-$

d) continued

Interval	Test Value	Sign of Factors	Sign of Function
$-\dfrac{11}{16} < x < -\dfrac{1}{2}$	$x = -0.6$	$\dfrac{(-)}{(-)(+)}$	$+$
$-\dfrac{1}{2} < x < 2$	$x = 0$	$\dfrac{(-)}{(+)(+)}$	$-$
$x > 2$	$x = 3$	$\dfrac{(+)}{(+)(+)}$	$+$

Therefore, the solution is $-1 < x < -\dfrac{11}{16}$ or $-\dfrac{1}{2} < x < 2$.

e) $\dfrac{x^2 + 3x + 2}{x^2 - 9} \ge 0$

$$\frac{(x + 2)(x + 1)}{(x - 3)(x + 3)} \ge 0$$

The zeros are at $x = -1$ and $x = -2$ and the vertical asymptotes are at $x = 3$ and $x = -3$, so the intervals to test are:

Interval	Test Value	Sign of Factors	Sign of Function
$x < -3$	$x = -4$	$\dfrac{(-)(-)}{(-)(-)}$	$+$
$- < x < -2$	$x = -.5$	$\dfrac{(-)(-)}{(-)(+)}$	$-$
$-2 < x < -1$	$x = -1.5$	$\dfrac{(+)(-)}{(-)(+)}$	$+$
$-1 < x < 3$	$x = 0$	$\dfrac{(+)(+)}{(-)(+)}$	$-$
$x > 3$	$x = 4$	$\dfrac{(+)(+)}{(+)(+)}$	$+$

Therefore, the solution is $-3 \le x \le -2$ or $-1 \le x \le 3$.

f) $\dfrac{(-2x - 10)(3 - x)}{(x^2 + 5)(x - 2)^2} < 0$

The zeros are at $x = -5$ and $x = 3$ and a vertical asymptote is at $x = 2$, so the intervals to test are:

Interval	Test Value	Sign of Factors	Sign of Function
$x < -5$	$x = -6$	$\dfrac{(+)(+)}{(+)(+)}$	$+$
$-5 < x < 2$	$x = 0$	$\dfrac{(-)(+)}{(+)(+)}$	$-$
$2 < x < 3$	$x = 2.5$	$\dfrac{(-)(+)}{(+)(+)}$	$-$
$x > 3$	$x = 4$	$\dfrac{(-)(-)}{(+)(+)}$	$+$

Therefore, the solution is $-5 < x < 2$ or $2 < x < 3$.

10. $\dfrac{x^2 - 2x + 5}{x^2 - 4x + 4} < 0; \dfrac{x^2 - 2x + 5}{(x-2)^2} < 0$

In this inequality, the denominator will always be positive. Therefore, the sign on the expression will be determined by the sign in the numerator. Solve for zeros in the numerator:

$b^2 - 4ac$

$= (-2)^2 - 4(1)(5)$

$= 4 - 20 = -16$

which means that there are no real roots. Therefore, the numerator will either always be positive or always be negative. Testing any value for x (say $x = 0$), we find the numerator will always be positive. Since both the numerator and denominator will always be greater than zero, the expression can never be less than zero, so there is no real solution to the inequality.

11. 1st inequality: $(-\infty, -3), (-1.83447, 4)$; 2nd inequality: $(-3, -1.83447), (4, +\infty)$

12. approximately 6.1 km/h

13. approximately 18.63 m

14. $\left(-\infty, -\dfrac{25}{3}\right), (5, +\infty)$

15. $x + \dfrac{x^2 - 5}{x^2 - 1} = \dfrac{x^2 + x + 2}{x + 1}$

$x + \dfrac{x^2 - 5}{(x-1)(x+1)} = \dfrac{x^2 + x + 2}{x + 1}$

$\dfrac{x(x-1)(x+1)}{(x-1)(x+1)} + \dfrac{x^2 - 5}{(x-1)(x+1)}$

$= \dfrac{(x^2 + x + 2)(x-1)}{(x+1)(x-1)}$

$\dfrac{x(x^2 - 1)}{(x-1)(x+1)} + \dfrac{x^2 - 5}{(x-1)(x+1)}$

$= \dfrac{x^3 + x^2 + 2x - x^2 - x - 2}{(x+1)(x-1)}$

$\dfrac{x^3 - x}{(x-1)(x+1)} + \dfrac{x^2 - 5}{(x-1)(x+1)}$

$= \dfrac{x^3 + x^2 + 2x - x^2 - x - 2}{(x+1)(x-1)}$

$\dfrac{x^3 - x}{(x-1)(x+1)} + \dfrac{x^2 - 5}{(x-1)(x+1)}$

$- \dfrac{x^3 + x^2 + 2x - x^2 - x - 2}{(x+1)(x-1)} = 0$

$\dfrac{x^3 - x + x^2 - 5 - x^3 - x^2 - 2x + x^2 + x + 2}{(x+1)(x-1)}$

$= 0$

$\dfrac{x^2 - 2x - 3}{(x+1)(x-1)} = 0$

$\dfrac{(x+1)(x-3)}{(x+1)(x-1)} = 0$

$\dfrac{x - 3}{x - 1} = 0$

$x = 3$

16. The equality has no solution because of the restriction on x (i. e. $x \neq 3$).

17. more than 7 years old

18. a) approximately $x = -1.60$, $x = 0.51$, $x = 1.33$ **b)** $(-3, -2.11)$, $[0.25, 1.86]$, $(2, +\infty)$

19. $\dfrac{-3}{x-3}$ and $\dfrac{-6}{x+3}$ **20.** 10

3.5 Making Connections with Rational Functions Equations

1. a) $T = 30 + 273 = 303$ K

$n = \dfrac{PV}{8.314T}$

$= \dfrac{(10130.0)(50)}{8.314(303)}$

$= 210.06$ moles

b) $V = \dfrac{8.314nT}{P}$

$= \dfrac{8.314(0.050)(400)}{(202.6)}$

$= 0.82$ L

c)

d) From the graph, it can be seen that there is a vertical asymptote at $V = 0$ and a horizontal asymptote at $P = 0$

e) Since the pressure and volume are inversely proportional to each other, as the volume increases, the pressure would decrease.

2. a)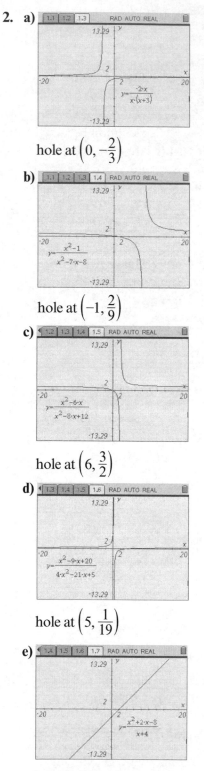

hole at $\left(0, -\frac{2}{3}\right)$

b)

$y = \frac{x^2 - 1}{x^2 - 7 \cdot x - 8}$

hole at $\left(-1, \frac{2}{9}\right)$

c)

$y = \frac{x^2 - 6 \cdot x}{x^2 - 8 \cdot x + 12}$

hole at $\left(6, \frac{3}{2}\right)$

d)

$y = \frac{x^2 - 9 \cdot x + 20}{4 \cdot x^2 - 21 \cdot x + 5}$

hole at $\left(5, \frac{1}{19}\right)$

e)

$y = \frac{x^2 + 2 \cdot x - 8}{x + 4}$

hole at $(-4, -6)$

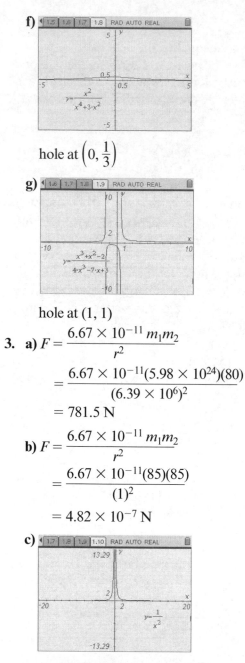

f)

$y = \frac{x^2}{x^4 + 3 \cdot x^2}$

hole at $\left(0, \frac{1}{3}\right)$

g)

$y = \frac{x^3 + x^2 - 2}{4 \cdot x^3 - 7 \cdot x + 3}$

hole at $(1, 1)$

3. a) $F = \dfrac{6.67 \times 10^{-11}\, m_1 m_2}{r^2}$

$= \dfrac{6.67 \times 10^{-11}(5.98 \times 10^{24})(80)}{(6.39 \times 10^6)^2}$

$= 781.5\ \text{N}$

b) $F = \dfrac{6.67 \times 10^{-11}\, m_1 m_2}{r^2}$

$= \dfrac{6.67 \times 10^{-11}(85)(85)}{(1)^2}$

$= 4.82 \times 10^{-7}\ \text{N}$

c)

$y = \frac{1}{x^2}$

$r \neq 0,\ F > 0$

d) Since the relation is an inverse square relation, as the distance increases, the force rapidly decreases.

e) As the mass of the objects decreases, the force of attraction between the objects also decreases. This is a direct proportionality.

4. a)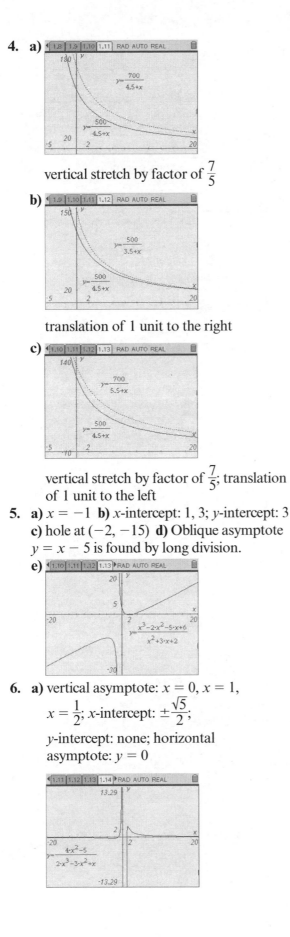

vertical stretch by factor of $\frac{7}{5}$

b)

translation of 1 unit to the right

c)

vertical stretch by factor of $\frac{7}{5}$; translation of 1 unit to the left

5. a) $x = -1$ **b)** x-intercept: 1, 3; y-intercept: 3
c) hole at $(-2, -15)$ **d)** Oblique asymptote $y = x - 5$ is found by long division.
e)

6. a) vertical asymptote: $x = 0$, $x = 1$,
$x = \frac{1}{2}$; x-intercept: $\pm\frac{\sqrt{5}}{2}$;
y-intercept: none; horizontal
asymptote: $y = 0$

b) vertical asymptote: $x = 2$; x-intercept:
-0.578; y-intercept: $-\frac{5}{2}$

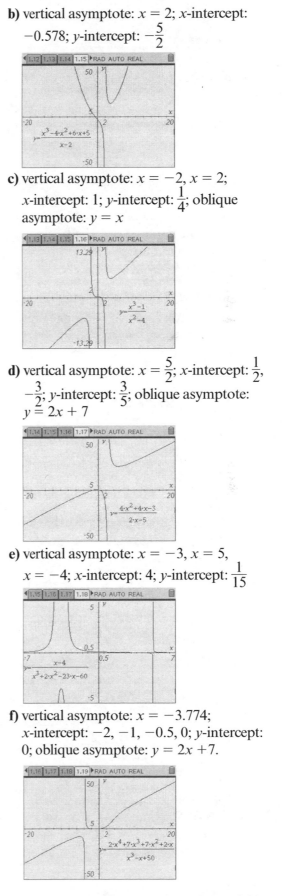

c) vertical asymptote: $x = -2$, $x = 2$;
x-intercept: 1; y-intercept: $\frac{1}{4}$; oblique
asymptote: $y = x$

d) vertical asymptote: $x = \frac{5}{2}$; x-intercept: $\frac{1}{2}$,
$-\frac{3}{2}$; y-intercept: $\frac{3}{5}$; oblique asymptote:
$y = 2x + 7$

e) vertical asymptote: $x = -3$, $x = 5$,
$x = -4$; x-intercept: 4; y-intercept: $\frac{1}{15}$

f) vertical asymptote: $x = -3.774$;
x-intercept: -2, -1, -0.5, 0; y-intercept:
0; oblique asymptote: $y = 2x + 7$.

7. a) $m = \dfrac{2K}{v^2}$

b)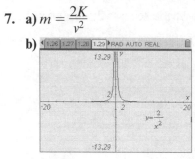

c) 1.5 kg

8. a) vertical asymptote: $x = -35$; horizontal asymptote: $C = 0.5$; as the number of litres of 0.5-molar solution is increasing, the concentration of the mixture approaches the 0.5

b) $C(x) = \dfrac{402.5}{x + 35} + 0.5$; vertical stretch by factor of 402.5; translation of 35 units to the left translation of 0.5 units up;

c) $C(x) = \dfrac{600 + 3x}{50 + x}$; **d)** 40 L

9. a) $SA = 2x^2 + \dfrac{2000}{x}$

b)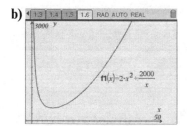

c) as side length approaches 0, the surface area approaches $+\infty$; **d)** at least 10.2 cm

10. a) as $t \to 15^-, I \to +\infty$;

b) vertical asymptote: $t = 15$

11. a) Since the relationship is an inverse proportionality, $t = \dfrac{k}{r}$, for time, t, in minutes and rate, r, in L/min.

b) Solving $t = \dfrac{k}{r}$ for k we obtain $k = rt$. Using last year's information of $r = 1000$ L/min and $t = 45$ min, we get $k = (1000)(45)$ or $k = 45\,000$, so $t = \dfrac{k}{r}$ becomes $t = \dfrac{45\,000}{r}$. This year, the pump has $r = 900$ L/min as a rate so $t = \dfrac{45\,000}{r}$ becomes $t = \dfrac{45\,000}{900}$ which means a total time of 50 minutes this year will be needed.

12.

$$
\begin{array}{r}
x^2 - 5 \\
x + 2 \overline{)\, x^3 - 2x^2 - 5x + 10} \\
\underline{x^3 - 2x^2} \\
0 - 5x + 10 \\
\underline{-5x - 10} \\
20
\end{array}
$$

Therefore, there is a parabolic asymptote at $y = x^2 - 5$.

13.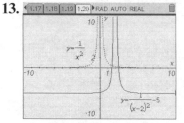

vertical asymptote: $x = 2$; horizontal asymptote: $y = -5$; $y = \dfrac{1}{(x - 2)^2} - 5$

14. $f^{-1}(x) = \dfrac{2}{x - 3}$; the inverse is a function; similarities: same shape differences:

	$f(x) = \dfrac{2}{x} + 3$	$f^{-1}(x) = \dfrac{2}{x} - 3$
Domain	$\{x \in R, x \neq 0\}$	$\{x \in R, x \neq 3\}$
Range	$\{y \in R, y \neq 3\}$	$\{y \in R, y \neq 0\}$
Vertical asymptotes	$x = 0$	$x = 3$
Horizontal asymptotes	$y = 3$	$y = 0$
x-intercepts	$-\dfrac{2}{3}$	none
y-intercepts	none	$-\dfrac{2}{3}$

15. a) 4 **b)** 64

Chapter 3 Challenge Questions

C1. a) $C(x) = \dfrac{330\,240 + 258x^2}{320x}$

b) $x = 368.62$ km/h or $x = 3.47$ km/h

c) 35.77 km/h

C2. a) $f(x) = \dfrac{x - 3}{x - 2}$ **b)** $f(x) = \dfrac{x - 3}{-x - 2}$ **c)** $f(x)$ has two vertical asymptotes because x in $|x|$ can be positive or negative.

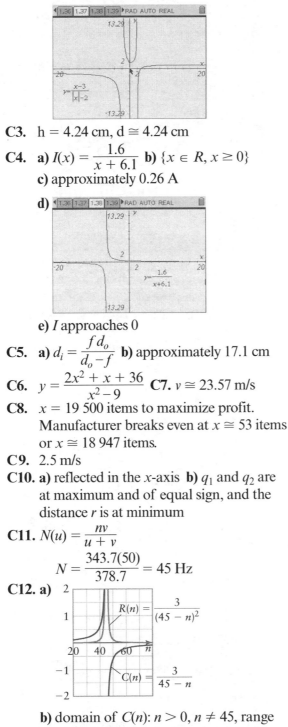

C3. h = 4.24 cm, d ≅ 4.24 cm

C4. a) $I(x) = \dfrac{1.6}{x + 6.1}$ b) $\{x \in R, x \geq 0\}$

c) approximately 0.26 A

d)

e) I approaches 0

C5. a) $d_i = \dfrac{f d_o}{d_o - f}$ b) approximately 17.1 cm

C6. $y = \dfrac{2x^2 + x + 36}{x^2 - 9}$ **C7.** $v \cong 23.57$ m/s

C8. $x = 19\,500$ items to maximize profit. Manufacturer breaks even at $x \cong 53$ items or $x \cong 18\,947$ items.

C9. 2.5 m/s

C10. a) reflected in the x-axis b) q_1 and q_2 are at maximum and of equal sign, and the distance r is at minimum

C11. $N(u) = \dfrac{nv}{u + v}$

$N = \dfrac{343.7(50)}{378.7} = 45$ Hz

C12. a)

b) domain of $C(n)$: $n > 0$, $n \neq 45$, range of $C(n)$: $C(n) > 0$; domain of $R(n)$: $n > 0$, $n \neq 45$, range of $R(n)$: $R(n) > 0$ c) slope = 0.0075 d) $R(25)$ = 0.0075

C13. a) $y = n$ b) vertical asymptotes $n = \pm 2$, x-intercept (0, 0), y-intercept (0, 0)
c) local minimum (3.46, 5.19) d) local maximum (−3.46, −5.19)

C14. The slope of the secant is $y = -2.5x$. The points on $g(x)$ that has a tangent with a slope of −2.5 is (0, 0) and (−4, −10).

Chapter 4
4.1 Radian Measure

1. a) $\dfrac{11\pi}{6}$ b) $\dfrac{\pi}{3}$ c) $\dfrac{5\pi}{12}$ d) $\dfrac{3\pi}{4}$ e) $\dfrac{5\pi}{4}$ f) $\dfrac{125\pi}{18}$

2. a) 180° b) 45° c) 150° d) 270° e) 315° f) 90° g) 213.75° h) 40°

3. a) 58.4° b) 100.3° c) 217.2° d) 343.8°

4. a) $\dfrac{\pi}{18}$ b) $\dfrac{16\pi}{45}$ c) $\dfrac{27\pi}{24}$ d) $\dfrac{19\pi}{12}$

5. 13.4 cm

6. $a = 14.6$ cm
$\theta = \dfrac{\pi}{4}$
$\theta = \dfrac{a}{r}$
$\dfrac{\pi}{4} = \dfrac{14.6}{r}$
$r = \dfrac{(4)(14.6)}{\pi}$ $r \cong 18.6$ cm

7. 163.4 cm²

8. a) 90°, $\dfrac{\pi}{2}$ b) 15°, $\dfrac{\pi}{12}$ c) 100°, $\dfrac{5\pi}{9}$ d) 25°, $\dfrac{5\pi}{36}$

9. a) $\dfrac{4\pi}{3}$ b) 60.4π c) $\dfrac{2\pi}{3}$ d) 2π

10. The radius of Earth r is 6336 km. The latitude of Philadelphia is 39° and the latitude of Ottawa is 45°.
$\theta = 45° - 39° = 6°$
Convert θ into radians
$\theta = 6\left(\dfrac{\pi}{180}\right) = \dfrac{\pi}{30}$
The distance between the two cities is the length of the arc a that subtends θ
$\theta = \dfrac{a}{r}$
$a = \theta r$ $a = \left(\dfrac{\pi}{30}\right)6336$ $a \cong 663.5$ km

11. $\dfrac{25\pi}{36}$ 12. 0.3375 rad

13. The length of the arc doubles and the area of the sector quadruples.

14. a) $r = 2.2$ m
$\theta = 180° - 45° = 135°$
The area of a sector is $A = \dfrac{\theta}{360}\pi r^2$, where θ is in degrees.
$A = \dfrac{\theta}{360}\pi r^2$
$A = \dfrac{135}{360}\pi (2.2)^2$
$A = 1.815\pi$ m² $A \cong 5.7$ m²
The total area of the sector is 5.7 m².

b) The radius r will increase by 0.5 m.

$r = 2.2 + 0.5 = 2.7$ m

$\theta = 135°$

$A = \dfrac{\theta}{360}\pi\, r^2$

$A = \dfrac{135}{360}\pi\, (2.7)^2 \quad A \cong 8.6\text{ m}^2$

The area of the yard in which the dog can move will increase from 5.7 m² to 8.6 m², which is about 50% more space.

15. a) 14062.5 rad **b)** 5π rad/s

16. a) $\dfrac{8\pi}{15}$ rad/s **b)** 1792π m

17. a) 4188.8 s or 69.8 min **b)** 11 km/s

18. a) $\dfrac{7\pi}{4}$ **b)** $\dfrac{7\pi}{6}$ **c)** $\dfrac{4\pi}{3}$ **d)** $\dfrac{\pi}{5}$ **e)** $\dfrac{\pi}{3}$ **f)** $\dfrac{16\pi}{15}$

19. 3.37 m/s²

20. a) $\dfrac{20\pi}{3}$ rad/s **b)** $\dfrac{80\pi^2}{3}$ m/s² **c)** 4π m

21. a) An airplane propeller rotates 20 times/s; therefore, the angular velocity is 20 rotations/s. Angular velocity = 20 rotations/s $\times$ 60 s = 1200 rotations/min. The propeller rotates through an angle of $20 \times 2\pi$, or 40π rad in 1 second. The angular velocity of an airplane propeller is 40π rad/s or 1200 rotations/min.

b) The propeller has diameter of 2 m. Therefore, the radius r is 1 m.

$v = r\dfrac{\theta}{t}$

$v = (1\text{m})(40\pi \text{ rad/s})$

$v = 40\pi$ m/s $\quad v \cong 125.7$ m/s

The linear velocity of the propeller is 40π m/s.

22. a) 16 rotations/day; 32π rad/day

b) $1\,322\,752\pi$ km/day

23. a) 4.05 rad/h

b) Angular velocity of 3.8 rad/h

$v = r\left(\dfrac{\theta}{t}\right)$

$2700 = (x + 6336)\,(3.8)$

$\dfrac{2700}{3.8} = x + 6336$

$x = \dfrac{2700}{3.8} - 6336$

$x = 769.3$ km

4.2 Trigonometric Ratios and Special Angles

1. a) i) 0.7071 **ii)** 5.6713 **iii)** 0.3256 **iv)** 0.5299

b) i) 0.7074 **ii)** 5.6626 **iii)** 0.3255 **iv)** 0.5300

c) The answers are almost the same because the angles in parts a) and b) are the same.

2. a) -0.7071 **b)** 0.9239 **c)** 0.5774 **d)** -0.5

3. a) 1.0125 **b)** 0.2867 **c)** -2.9238 **d)** 1.0642

4. a) 1.7878 **b)** 1.6507 **c)** -1.1676 **d)** -3.4364

5. a) -1.1547 **b)** 1.3764 **c)** 1.3054 **d)** 1.0353

6.

θ	sin	cos	tan
(a) $\dfrac{\pi}{3}$	$\dfrac{\sqrt{3}}{2}$	$\dfrac{1}{2}$	$\sqrt{3}$
(b) $\dfrac{5\pi}{4}$	$-\dfrac{1}{\sqrt{2}}$	$-\dfrac{1}{\sqrt{2}}$	1
(c) $\dfrac{7\pi}{6}$	$-\dfrac{1}{2}$	$-\dfrac{\sqrt{3}}{2}$	$\dfrac{1}{\sqrt{3}}$
(d) π	0	-1	0
(e) $\dfrac{5\pi}{6}$	$\dfrac{1}{2}$	$-\dfrac{\sqrt{3}}{2}$	$-\dfrac{1}{\sqrt{3}}$
(f) $\dfrac{7\pi}{4}$	$-\dfrac{1}{\sqrt{2}}$	$\dfrac{1}{\sqrt{2}}$	-1

7. Use the unit circle from Section 4.2 to determine the exact values of the trigonometric rations for each angle. The coordinates at the unit circle determine the exact values of the cosine and sine functions for the given angle of rotation.

a) The terminal arm of an angle $\dfrac{\pi}{6}$ is in the first quadrant; the coordinates of the point of intersection are $P\left(\dfrac{\sqrt{3}}{2}, \dfrac{1}{2}\right)$.

$\sin\dfrac{\pi}{6} = y,\ \sin\dfrac{\pi}{6} = \dfrac{1}{2}$

$\cos\dfrac{\pi}{6} = x,\ \cos\dfrac{\pi}{6} = \dfrac{\sqrt{3}}{2}$

$\tan\dfrac{\pi}{6} = \dfrac{y}{x},\ \tan\dfrac{\pi}{6} = \dfrac{\frac{1}{2}}{\frac{\sqrt{3}}{2}},\ \tan\dfrac{\pi}{6} = \dfrac{1}{\sqrt{3}}$

$\csc\dfrac{\pi}{6} = \dfrac{1}{y},\ \csc\dfrac{\pi}{6} = 2$

$\sec\dfrac{\pi}{6} = \dfrac{1}{x},\ \sec\dfrac{\pi}{6} = \dfrac{2}{\sqrt{3}}$

$\cot\dfrac{\pi}{6} = \dfrac{x}{y},\ \cot\dfrac{\pi}{6} = \sqrt{3}$

b) The terminal arm of an angle $\dfrac{5\pi}{3}$ is in the fourth quadrant; the coordinates of the point of intersection are $P\left(\dfrac{1}{2}, -\dfrac{\sqrt{3}}{2}\right)$.

$\sin\dfrac{5\pi}{3} = y,\ \sin\dfrac{5\pi}{3} = -\dfrac{\sqrt{3}}{2}$

$\cos\dfrac{5\pi}{3} = x,\ \cos\dfrac{5\pi}{3} = \dfrac{1}{2}$

$\tan\dfrac{5\pi}{3} = \dfrac{y}{x},\ \tan\dfrac{5\pi}{3} = \dfrac{-\frac{\sqrt{3}}{2}}{\frac{1}{2}},$

$\tan\dfrac{5\pi}{3} = -\sqrt{3}$

$\csc \dfrac{5\pi}{3} = \dfrac{1}{y}, \csc \dfrac{5\pi}{3} = -\dfrac{2}{\sqrt{3}}$

$\sec \dfrac{5\pi}{3} = \dfrac{1}{x}, \sec \dfrac{5\pi}{3} = 2$

$\cot \dfrac{5\pi}{3} = \dfrac{x}{y}, \cot \dfrac{5\pi}{3} = -\dfrac{1}{\sqrt{3}}$

c) The terminal arm of an angle $\dfrac{3\pi}{4}$ is in the second quadrant; the coordinates of the point of intersection are $P\left(-\dfrac{1}{\sqrt{2}}, \dfrac{1}{\sqrt{2}}\right)$.

$\sin \dfrac{3\pi}{4} = y, \sin \dfrac{3\pi}{4} = \dfrac{1}{\sqrt{2}}$

$\cos \dfrac{3\pi}{4} = x, \cos \dfrac{3\pi}{4} = -\dfrac{1}{\sqrt{2}}$

$\tan \dfrac{3\pi}{4} = \dfrac{y}{x}, \tan \dfrac{3\pi}{4} = \dfrac{\frac{1}{\sqrt{2}}}{-\frac{1}{\sqrt{2}}}, \tan \dfrac{3\pi}{4} = -1$

$\csc \dfrac{3\pi}{4} = \dfrac{1}{y}, \csc \dfrac{3\pi}{4} = \sqrt{2}$

$\sec \dfrac{3\pi}{4} = \dfrac{1}{x}, \sec \dfrac{3\pi}{4} = -\sqrt{2}$

$\cot \dfrac{3\pi}{4} = \dfrac{x}{y}, \cot \dfrac{3\pi}{4} = -1$

d) The terminal arm of an angle $\dfrac{5\pi}{6}$ is in the second quadrant; the coordinates of the point of intersection are $P\left(-\dfrac{\sqrt{3}}{2}, \dfrac{1}{2}\right)$.

$\sin \dfrac{5\pi}{6} = y, \sin \dfrac{5\pi}{6} = \dfrac{1}{2}$

$\cos \dfrac{5\pi}{6} = x, \cos \dfrac{5\pi}{6} = -\dfrac{\sqrt{3}}{2}$

$\tan \dfrac{5\pi}{6} = \dfrac{y}{x}, \tan \dfrac{5\pi}{6} = \dfrac{\frac{1}{2}}{-\frac{\sqrt{3}}{2}},$

$\tan \dfrac{5\pi}{6} = -\dfrac{1}{\sqrt{3}}$

$\csc \dfrac{5\pi}{6} = \dfrac{1}{y}, \csc \dfrac{5\pi}{6} = 2$

$\sec \dfrac{5\pi}{6} = \dfrac{1}{x}, \sec \dfrac{5\pi}{6} = -\dfrac{2}{\sqrt{3}}$

$\cot \dfrac{5\pi}{6} = \dfrac{x}{y}, \cot \dfrac{5\pi}{6} = -\sqrt{3}$

e) The terminal arm of an angle $\dfrac{11\pi}{6}$ is in the fourth quadrant; the coordinates of the point of intersection are $P\left(\dfrac{\sqrt{3}}{2}, -\dfrac{1}{2}\right)$.

$\sin \dfrac{11\pi}{6} = y, \sin \dfrac{11\pi}{6} = -\dfrac{1}{2}$

$\cos \dfrac{11\pi}{6} = x, \cos \dfrac{11\pi}{6} = \dfrac{\sqrt{3}}{2}$

$\tan \dfrac{11\pi}{6} = \dfrac{y}{x}, \tan \dfrac{11\pi}{6} = \dfrac{-\frac{1}{2}}{\frac{\sqrt{3}}{2}},$

$\tan \dfrac{11\pi}{6} = -\dfrac{1}{\sqrt{3}}$

$\csc \dfrac{11\pi}{6} = \dfrac{1}{y}, \csc \dfrac{11\pi}{6} = -2$

$\sec \dfrac{11\pi}{6} = \dfrac{1}{x}, \sec \dfrac{11\pi}{6} = \dfrac{2}{\sqrt{3}}$

$\cot \dfrac{11\pi}{6} = \dfrac{x}{y}, \cot \dfrac{11\pi}{6} = -\sqrt{3}$

f) The terminal arm of an angle $\dfrac{2\pi}{3}$ is in the second quadrant; the coordinates of the point of intersection are $P\left(-\dfrac{1}{2}, \dfrac{\sqrt{3}}{2}\right)$.

$\sin \dfrac{2\pi}{3} = y, \sin \dfrac{2\pi}{3} = \dfrac{\sqrt{3}}{2}$

$\cos \dfrac{2\pi}{3} = x, \cos \dfrac{2\pi}{3} = -\dfrac{1}{2}$

$\tan \dfrac{2\pi}{3} = \dfrac{y}{x}, \tan \dfrac{2\pi}{3} = \dfrac{\frac{\sqrt{3}}{2}}{-\frac{1}{2}}, \tan \dfrac{2\pi}{3} = -\sqrt{3}$

$\csc \dfrac{2\pi}{3} = \dfrac{1}{y}, \csc \dfrac{2\pi}{3} = \dfrac{2}{\sqrt{3}}$

$\sec \dfrac{2\pi}{3} = \dfrac{1}{x}, \sec \dfrac{2\pi}{3} = -2$

$\cot \dfrac{2\pi}{3} = \dfrac{x}{y}, \cot \dfrac{2\pi}{3} = -\dfrac{1}{\sqrt{3}}$

8. a) $\sin \theta = \dfrac{y}{r} = -\dfrac{1}{5}$

$y = -1, r = 5$

$x = \sqrt{r^2 - y^2}$

$x = \sqrt{5^2 - (-1)^2}$

$x = \sqrt{24}$

$\cos \theta = \dfrac{x}{r}, \cos \theta = \dfrac{\sqrt{24}}{5}$

$\tan \theta = \dfrac{y}{x}, \tan \theta = \dfrac{-1}{\sqrt{24}}$

$\csc \theta = \dfrac{r}{y}, \csc \theta = \dfrac{5}{-1}, \csc \theta = -5$

$\sec \theta = \dfrac{r}{x}, \sec \theta = \dfrac{5}{\sqrt{24}}$

$\cot \theta = \dfrac{x}{y}, \cot \theta = \dfrac{\sqrt{24}}{-1}, \cot \theta = -\sqrt{24}$

b) $\tan \theta = \dfrac{y}{x} = \dfrac{-2}{-1} = 2$

$y = -2, x = -1$

$r = \sqrt{x^2 + y^2}$

$y = \sqrt{(-1)^2 + (-2)^2}$

$r = \sqrt{5}$

$\sin \theta = \dfrac{y}{r}, \sin \theta = \dfrac{-2}{\sqrt{5}}$

$$\cos\theta = \frac{x}{r}, \cos\theta = \frac{-1}{\sqrt{5}}$$

$$\csc\theta = \frac{r}{y}, \csc\theta = -\frac{\sqrt{5}}{2}$$

$$\sec\theta = \frac{r}{x}, \sec\theta = \frac{\sqrt{5}}{-1}, \sec\theta = -\sqrt{5}$$

$$\cot\theta = \frac{x}{y}, \cot\theta = \frac{-1}{-2}, \cot\theta = \frac{1}{2}$$

c) $\csc\theta = \frac{r}{y} = \frac{2}{-1} = -2$

$r = 2, y = -1$

In the third quadrant x is negative.

$$x = -\sqrt{r^2 - y^2}$$
$$x = -\sqrt{2^2 + (-1)^2}$$
$$x = -\sqrt{3}$$

$$\sin\theta = \frac{y}{r}, \sin\theta = \frac{-1}{2}$$

$$\cos\theta = \frac{x}{r}, \cos\theta = -\frac{\sqrt{3}}{2}$$

$$\tan\theta = \frac{y}{x}, \tan\theta = \frac{-1}{-\sqrt{3}}, \tan\theta = \frac{1}{\sqrt{3}}$$

$$\sec\theta = \frac{r}{x}, \sec\theta = -\frac{2}{\sqrt{3}}$$

$$\cot\theta = \frac{x}{y}, \cot\theta = \frac{-\sqrt{3}}{-1}, \cot\theta = \sqrt{3}$$

d) $\sec\theta = \frac{r}{x} = \frac{\sqrt{3}}{1} = \sqrt{3}$

$x = 1, r = \sqrt{3}$

$$y = \sqrt{r^2 - x^2}$$
$$y = \sqrt{(\sqrt{3})^2 - 1^2}$$
$$y = \sqrt{2}$$

$$\sin\theta = \frac{y}{r}, \sin\theta = \frac{\sqrt{2}}{\sqrt{3}}$$

$$\cos\theta = \frac{x}{r}, \cos\theta = \frac{1}{\sqrt{3}}$$

$$\tan\theta = \frac{y}{x}, \tan\theta = \frac{\sqrt{2}}{1}, \tan\theta = \sqrt{2}$$

$$\csc\theta = \frac{r}{y}, \csc\theta = \frac{\sqrt{3}}{\sqrt{2}}$$

$$\cot\theta = \frac{x}{y}, \cot\theta = \frac{1}{\sqrt{2}}$$

9. a) $\tan\frac{\pi}{6}, \cot\frac{\pi}{3}, \tan\frac{7\pi}{6}, \cot\frac{4\pi}{3}$

 b) $\cos\frac{5\pi}{6}, \cos\frac{7\pi}{6}, \sin\frac{4\pi}{3}, \sin\frac{5\pi}{3}$

 c) $\sec\frac{\pi}{6}, \csc\frac{\pi}{3}, \csc\frac{2\pi}{3}, \sec\frac{11\pi}{6}$

 d) $\sec\frac{3\pi}{4}, \sec\frac{5\pi}{4}, \csc\frac{5\pi}{4}, \csc\frac{7\pi}{4}$

10. 44.3 m

11. Let the vertical side of the triangle to the left be a_1, the horizontal side of the triangle to the left be b_1, the vertical side of the triangle to the right be a_2, the horizontal side of the triangle to the right be b_2.

$\sin(0.4\pi) = \frac{a_1}{10.4}$, $a_1 = 10.4\sin(0.4\pi)$, $a_1 \cong 9.9$ m

$\cos(0.4\pi) = \frac{b_1}{10.4}$, $b_1 = 10.4\cos(0.4\pi)$, $b_1 \cong 3.2$ m

$\sin(0.15\pi) = \frac{a_2}{10.4}$, $a_2 = 10.4\sin(0.15\pi)$, $a_2 \cong 4.7$ m

$\cos(0.15\pi) = \frac{b_2}{10.4}$, $b_2 = 10.4\cos(0.15\pi)$, $b_2 \cong 9.3$ m

Horizontal displacement is 6.1 m to the left.
Vertical displacement is 5.2 m up.

12. a) i) $\frac{\sqrt{3}}{2}$ ii) -1 iii) $-\sqrt{3}$

 b) i) 0.866 and $\frac{\sqrt{3}}{2} = -0.866$ ii) -1

 iii) -1.732 and $-\sqrt{3} = -1.732$

13. Answers will vary.

14. $\sin\theta = \frac{3}{\sqrt{13}}$; $\cos\theta = -\frac{2}{\sqrt{13}}$; $\tan\theta = -\frac{3}{2}$

 $\csc\theta = \frac{\sqrt{13}}{3}$; $\sec\theta = -\frac{\sqrt{13}}{2}$; $\cot\theta = -\frac{2}{3}$

15. $146\left(\sin\left(\frac{\pi}{5}\right) - \sin\left(\frac{\pi}{6}\right)\right) = 12.8$ million km down

16. a) i) $\dfrac{\sec\frac{\pi}{4}\cos\frac{2\pi}{3}}{\tan\frac{\pi}{6}\csc\frac{3\pi}{4}} = \dfrac{\left(\frac{1}{\cos\frac{\pi}{4}}\right)\left(\cos\frac{2\pi}{3}\right)}{\left(\tan\frac{\pi}{6}\right)\left(\frac{1}{\sin\frac{3\pi}{4}}\right)}$

$$= \frac{\left(\cos\frac{2\pi}{3}\right)\left(\sin\frac{3\pi}{4}\right)}{\left(\cos\frac{\pi}{4}\right)\left(\tan\frac{\pi}{6}\right)}$$

$$= \frac{\left(-\frac{1}{2}\right)\left(\frac{1}{\sqrt{2}}\right)}{\left(\frac{1}{\sqrt{2}}\right)\left(\frac{1}{\sqrt{3}}\right)}$$

$$= \frac{\left(-\frac{1}{2\sqrt{2}}\right)}{\left(\frac{1}{\sqrt{2}\sqrt{3}}\right)}$$

$$= -\frac{\sqrt{3}}{2} \approx -0.866$$

ii) $\sin \dfrac{5\pi}{4} - \cos \dfrac{11\pi}{6} \cot \dfrac{\pi}{3}$

$= \sin \dfrac{5\pi}{4} - \left(\cos \dfrac{11\pi}{6}\right)\left(\dfrac{1}{\tan \dfrac{\pi}{3}}\right)$

$= \left(-\dfrac{1}{\sqrt{2}}\right) - \left(\dfrac{\sqrt{3}}{2}\right)\left(\dfrac{1}{\sqrt{3}}\right)$

$= -\dfrac{1}{\sqrt{2}} - \dfrac{1}{2}$

$= -\dfrac{\sqrt{2}}{2} - \dfrac{1}{2}$

$= \dfrac{-\sqrt{2} - 1}{2} \approx -1.207$

b) i) $\dfrac{\sec \dfrac{\pi}{4} \cos \dfrac{2\pi}{3}}{\tan \dfrac{\pi}{6} \csc \dfrac{3\pi}{4}} = \dfrac{(1.414)(-0.5)}{(0.577)(1.414)}$

$\cong -0.866$

ii) $\sin \dfrac{5\pi}{4} - \cos \dfrac{11\pi}{6} \cot \dfrac{\pi}{3}$

$= (-0.707) - (0.866)(0.577)$

$\cong -1.207$

17. 2.63 m²

4.3 Equivalent Trigonometric Expressions

1. $\sin \dfrac{\pi}{4} = \cos\left(\dfrac{\pi}{2} - \dfrac{\pi}{4}\right) = \cos\left(\dfrac{\pi}{4}\right) = \dfrac{\sqrt{2}}{2}$

2. $\sec \dfrac{\pi}{6} = \csc\left(\dfrac{\pi}{2} - \dfrac{\pi}{6}\right) = \csc\left(\dfrac{2\pi}{6}\right)$

$= \csc\left(\dfrac{\pi}{3}\right) = \dfrac{2}{\sqrt{3}}$

3. $\tan \dfrac{\pi}{3} = \cot\left(\dfrac{\pi}{2} - \dfrac{\pi}{3}\right) = \cot\left(\dfrac{3\pi - 2\pi}{6}\right)$

$= \cot \dfrac{\pi}{6} = \sqrt{3}$

4. $\cos \dfrac{2\pi}{9} = 0.766 = \sin\left(\dfrac{\pi}{2} + \dfrac{2\pi}{9}\right)$

$= \sin\left(\dfrac{9\pi + 4\pi}{9}\right) = \sin \dfrac{13\pi}{9} = 0.766$

5. $\dfrac{3\pi}{4}$; This answer must be added to $\dfrac{\pi}{2}$ to give $\dfrac{5\pi}{4}$, but this is also the measure of angle x.

6. Express $\dfrac{2\pi}{3}$ as a sum of $\dfrac{\pi}{2}$ and an angle.

$\dfrac{2\pi}{3} = \dfrac{\pi}{2} + \alpha$

$\alpha = \dfrac{2\pi}{3} - \dfrac{\pi}{2}$

$\alpha = \dfrac{4\pi - 3\pi}{6}$

$\alpha = \dfrac{\pi}{6}$

$\dfrac{2\pi}{3} = \dfrac{\pi}{2} + \dfrac{\pi}{6}$

Apply a trigonometric identity to determine y.

$\sin \dfrac{2\pi}{3} = \sin\left(\dfrac{\pi}{2} + \dfrac{\pi}{6}\right) = \cos \dfrac{\pi}{6}$

$\therefore y = \dfrac{\pi}{6}$

7. $\dfrac{3\pi}{8}$ **8.** $\dfrac{\pi}{10}$ **9.** $\dfrac{\pi}{5}$

10. a) Since an angle of $\dfrac{5\pi}{12}$ lies in the first quadrant, it can be expressed as a difference between $\dfrac{\pi}{2}$ and an angle α.

$\dfrac{5\pi}{12} = \dfrac{\pi}{2} - \alpha$

$\alpha = \dfrac{\pi}{2} - \dfrac{5\pi}{12}$

$\alpha = \dfrac{6\pi - 5\pi}{12}$

$\alpha = \dfrac{\pi}{12}$

Apply a co-function identity:

$\cos \dfrac{5\pi}{12} = \cos\left(\dfrac{\pi}{2} - \dfrac{\pi}{12}\right)$

$= \sin \dfrac{\pi}{12} \cong 0.2588$

b) Since an angle of $\dfrac{7\pi}{12}$ lies in the second quadrant, it can be expressed as a sum of $\dfrac{\pi}{2}$ and an angle α.

$\dfrac{7\pi}{12} = \dfrac{\pi}{2} + \alpha$

$\alpha = \dfrac{7\pi}{12} - \dfrac{\pi}{2}$

$\alpha = \dfrac{7\pi - 6\pi}{12}$

$\alpha = \dfrac{\pi}{12}$

Apply a trigonometric identity:

$\cos \dfrac{7\pi}{12} = \cos\left(\dfrac{\pi}{2} + \dfrac{\pi}{12}\right)$

$= -\sin \dfrac{\pi}{12} = -0.2588$

11. a) 1.21 **b)** 1.21 **12.** 2.92 rad

13. $b = \dfrac{\pi}{10}, b \cong 0.31$

14. $\sec x = -\csc 0.57$ rad

$\dfrac{1}{\cos x} = -\dfrac{1}{\sin 0.57}$

$\cos x = -\sin 0.57$

$\cos x = -0.5396$

$x = 2.14$ rad

15. 0.05 rad **16.** 0.73 rad

17. a) i)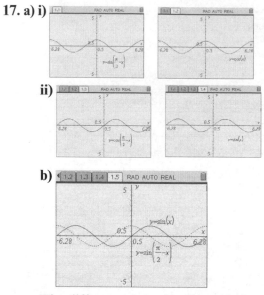

ii)

b)

The difference is in the phase shift.
Apply a phase shift of $\frac{\pi}{2}$ to the left on $y = \sin x$ and the result is
$y = \left(\sin \frac{\pi}{2} - x\right)$; $\cos x$ is also a result of applying a phase shift of $\frac{\pi}{2}$ to the left on $y = \sin x$.

Therefore, $\sin\left(\frac{\pi}{2} - x\right) = \cos x$.

18. a) -0.9749 **b)** -0.9749

19. a)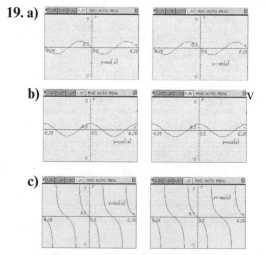

b)

c)

The same relationship would be expected for the reciprocal trigonometric functions. This means that we would expect:
$\csc(-x) = -\csc x$; $\sec(-x) = \sec x$; $\cot(-x) = -\cot x$
They represent reflection in $\theta = 0$

20. Answers will vary.

21. Use compound-angle formulas, quotient identity, and reciprocal identities:

$$\sin\left(\alpha - \frac{\pi}{2}\right) = \sin\alpha\cos\frac{\pi}{2} - \cos\alpha\sin\frac{\pi}{2}$$
$$= \sin\alpha(0) - \cos\alpha(1) = -\cos\alpha$$
$$\cos\left(\alpha - \frac{\pi}{2}\right) = \cos\alpha\cos\frac{\pi}{2} + \sin\alpha\sin\frac{\pi}{2}$$
$$= \cos\alpha(0) + \sin\alpha(1) = \sin\alpha$$
$$\tan\left(\alpha - \frac{\pi}{2}\right) = \frac{\sin\left(\alpha - \frac{\pi}{2}\right)}{\cos\left(\alpha - \frac{\pi}{2}\right)}$$
$$= \frac{-\cos\alpha}{\sin\alpha} = -\cot\alpha$$
$$\csc\left(\alpha - \frac{\pi}{2}\right) = \frac{1}{\sin\left(\alpha - \frac{\pi}{2}\right)}$$
$$= \frac{1}{-\cos\alpha} = -\sec\alpha$$
$$\sec\left(\alpha - \frac{\pi}{2}\right) = \frac{1}{\cos\left(\alpha - \frac{\pi}{2}\right)} = \frac{1}{\sin\alpha} = \csc\alpha$$
$$\cot\left(\alpha - \frac{\pi}{2}\right) = \frac{1}{\tan\left(\alpha - \frac{\pi}{2}\right)} = \frac{1}{-\cot\alpha}$$
$$= -\tan\alpha$$
$$\sin(\alpha - \pi) = \sin\alpha\cos\pi - \cos\alpha\sin\pi$$
$$= \sin\alpha(-1) - \cos\alpha(0) = -\sin\alpha$$
$$\cos(\alpha - \pi) = \cos\alpha\cos\pi + \sin\alpha\sin\pi$$
$$= \cos\alpha(-1) + \sin\alpha(0) = -\cos\alpha$$
$$\tan(\alpha - \pi) = \frac{\sin(\alpha - \pi)}{\cos(\alpha - \pi)} = \frac{-\sin\alpha}{-\cos\alpha}$$
$$= \tan\alpha$$
$$\csc(\alpha - \pi) = \frac{1}{\sin(\alpha - \pi)} = \frac{1}{-\sin\alpha}$$
$$= -\csc\alpha$$
$$\sec(\alpha - \pi) = \frac{1}{\cos(\alpha - \pi)} = \frac{1}{-\cos\alpha}$$
$$= -\sec\alpha$$
$$\cot(\alpha - \pi) = \frac{1}{\tan(\alpha - \pi)} = \frac{1}{\tan\alpha} = \cot\alpha$$
$$\sin\left(\alpha - \frac{3\pi}{2}\right) = \sin\alpha\cos\frac{3\pi}{2} - \cos\alpha\sin\frac{3\pi}{2}$$
$$= \sin\alpha(0) - \cos\alpha(-1) = \cos\alpha$$
$$\cos\left(\alpha - \frac{3\pi}{2}\right) = \cos\alpha\cos\frac{3\pi}{2} + \sin\alpha\sin\frac{3\pi}{2}$$
$$= \cos\alpha(0) + \sin\alpha(-1) = -\sin\alpha$$
$$\tan\left(\alpha - \frac{3\pi}{2}\right) = \frac{\sin\left(\alpha - \frac{3\pi}{2}\right)}{\cos\left(\alpha - \frac{3\pi}{2}\right)} = \frac{\cos\alpha}{-\sin\alpha}$$
$$= -\cot\alpha$$

$$\csc\left(\alpha - \frac{3\pi}{2}\right) = \frac{1}{\sin\left(\alpha - \frac{3\pi}{2}\right)} = \frac{1}{\cos\alpha}$$
$$= \sec\alpha$$

$$\sec\left(\alpha - \frac{3\pi}{2}\right) = \frac{1}{\cos\left(\alpha - \frac{3\pi}{2}\right)} = \frac{1}{-\sin\alpha}$$
$$= -\csc\alpha$$

$$\cot\left(\alpha - \frac{3\pi}{2}\right) = \frac{1}{\tan\left(\alpha - \frac{3\pi}{2}\right)} = \frac{1}{-\cot\alpha}$$
$$= -\tan\alpha$$

a) $\sin\alpha = \cos\left(\alpha - \frac{\pi}{2}\right) = -\sin(\alpha - \pi)$
$$= -\cos\left(\alpha - \frac{3\pi}{2}\right)$$

b) $\cos\alpha = -\sin\left(\alpha - \frac{\pi}{2}\right) = -\cos(\alpha - \pi)$
$$= \sin\left(\alpha - \frac{3\pi}{2}\right)$$

c) $\tan\alpha = -\cot\left(\alpha - \frac{\pi}{2}\right) = \tan(\alpha - \pi)$
$$= -\cot\left(\alpha - \frac{3\pi}{2}\right)$$

d) $\csc\alpha = \sec\left(\alpha - \frac{\pi}{2}\right) = -\csc(\alpha - \pi)$
$$= -\sec\left(\alpha - \frac{3\pi}{2}\right)$$

e) $\sec\alpha = -\csc\left(\alpha - \frac{\pi}{2}\right) = -\sec(\alpha - \pi)$
$$= \csc\left(\alpha - \frac{3\pi}{2}\right)$$

f) $\cot\alpha = -\tan\left(\alpha - \frac{\pi}{2}\right) = \cot(\alpha - \pi)$
$$= -\tan\left(\alpha - \frac{3\pi}{2}\right)$$

22. a) $\sin\alpha = -\cos\left(\alpha + \frac{\pi}{2}\right) = -\sin(\alpha + \pi)$
$$= \cos\left(\alpha + \frac{3\pi}{2}\right)$$

$\cos\alpha = \sin\left(\alpha + \frac{\pi}{2}\right) = -\cos(\alpha + \pi)$
$$= -\sin\left(\alpha + \frac{3\pi}{2}\right)$$

$\tan\alpha = -\cot\left(\alpha + \frac{\pi}{2}\right) = \tan(\alpha + \pi)$
$$= -\cot\left(\alpha + \frac{3\pi}{2}\right)$$

$\csc\alpha = -\sec\left(\alpha + \frac{\pi}{2}\right) = -\csc(\alpha + \pi)$
$$= \sec\left(\alpha + \frac{3\pi}{2}\right)$$

$\sec\alpha = \csc\left(\alpha + \frac{\pi}{2}\right) = -\sec(\alpha + \pi)$
$$= -\csc\left(\alpha + \frac{3\pi}{2}\right)$$

$\cot\alpha = -\tan\left(\alpha + \frac{\pi}{2}\right) = \cot(\alpha + \pi)$
$$= -\tan\left(\alpha + \frac{3\pi}{2}\right)$$

b) They also represent phase shifts of the original function.

23. a) 0.8391 **b)** -0.8391

24. a) $-\frac{\pi}{2}$ **b)** Answers will vary.

25. a) $\sin x$ **b)** $-\sin x - \cos^2 x$

26. L.S. $= \dfrac{\sin\left(x + \frac{\pi}{2}\right)}{\sin x}$

$$= \frac{\sin x \cos\frac{\pi}{2} + \cos x \sin\frac{\pi}{2}}{\sin x}$$

$$= \frac{\sin x(0) + \cos x(1)}{\sin x} = \frac{\cos x}{\sin x} = \cot x$$

R.S. $= \tan x$

L.S. $\neq$ R.S.

4.4 Compound-Angle Formulas

1. a) $\sin\dfrac{\pi}{4} = \dfrac{1}{\sqrt{2}}$ **b)** $\sin\dfrac{5\pi}{3} = -\dfrac{\sqrt{3}}{2}$

c) $\cos\dfrac{11\pi}{12} = \dfrac{-\sqrt{6} - \sqrt{2}}{4}$ **d)** $\cos\left(-\dfrac{5\pi}{3}\right) = \dfrac{1}{2}$

2. $\dfrac{\sqrt{2} + \sqrt{6}}{4}$

3. a) $\dfrac{1 + \sqrt{3}}{2\sqrt{2}}$ **b)** $\dfrac{1 + \sqrt{3}}{2\sqrt{2}}$ **c)** $\dfrac{-1 - \sqrt{3}}{2\sqrt{2}}$ **d)** $\dfrac{1 - \sqrt{3}}{2\sqrt{2}}$

4. Answers may vary. For example:
$$\sin\frac{13\pi}{36} = \sin\left(\frac{\pi}{4} + \frac{\pi}{9}\right)$$
$$= \sin\frac{\pi}{4}\cos\frac{\pi}{9} + \cos\frac{\pi}{4}\sin\frac{\pi}{9}$$
$$= \left(\frac{1}{\sqrt{2}}\right)\cos\frac{\pi}{9} + \left(\frac{1}{\sqrt{2}}\right)\sin\frac{\pi}{9}$$
$$= \frac{1}{\sqrt{2}}\left(\cos\frac{\pi}{9} + \sin\frac{\pi}{9}\right)$$

5. Answers may vary. For example:
$$x2\;\frac{-\sqrt{3} + \tan\frac{\pi}{8}}{1 + \sqrt{3}\tan\frac{\pi}{8}}$$

6. a) $\dfrac{\sqrt{2} - \sqrt{6}}{4}$ **b)** $\dfrac{\sqrt{6} - \sqrt{2}}{4}$ **c)** $\dfrac{\sqrt{6} - \sqrt{2}}{4}$ **d)** $\dfrac{\sqrt{2} + \sqrt{6}}{4}$

7. a) $\sin \dfrac{23\pi}{12} = \sin\left(-\dfrac{\pi}{12}\right) = \sin\left(\dfrac{\pi}{4} - \dfrac{\pi}{3}\right)$

$= \sin \dfrac{\pi}{4} \cos \dfrac{\pi}{3} - \cos \dfrac{\pi}{4} \sin \dfrac{\pi}{3}$

$= \left(\dfrac{1}{\sqrt{2}}\right)\left(\dfrac{1}{2}\right) - \left(\dfrac{1}{\sqrt{2}}\right)\left(\dfrac{\sqrt{3}}{2}\right) = \dfrac{1 - \sqrt{3}}{2\sqrt{2}}$

b) $\cos \dfrac{13\pi}{12} = \cos\left(\dfrac{3\pi}{4} + \dfrac{\pi}{3}\right)$

$= \cos \dfrac{3\pi}{4} \cos \dfrac{\pi}{3} - \sin \dfrac{3\pi}{4} \sin \dfrac{\pi}{3}$

$= \left(-\dfrac{1}{\sqrt{2}}\right)\left(\dfrac{1}{2}\right) - \left(\dfrac{1}{\sqrt{2}}\right)\left(\dfrac{\sqrt{3}}{2}\right) = \dfrac{-1 - \sqrt{3}}{2\sqrt{2}}$

c) $\tan \dfrac{23\pi}{12} = \tan\left(-\dfrac{\pi}{12}\right) = \tan\left(\dfrac{\pi}{4} - \dfrac{\pi}{3}\right)$

$= \dfrac{\tan \dfrac{\pi}{4} - \tan \dfrac{\pi}{3}}{1 + \tan \dfrac{\pi}{4} \tan \dfrac{\pi}{3}}$

$= \dfrac{1 - \sqrt{3}}{1 + (1)(\sqrt{3})} = \dfrac{1 - \sqrt{3}}{1 + \sqrt{3}}$

d) $\csc \dfrac{5\pi}{12} = \csc\left(\dfrac{3\pi}{4} - \dfrac{\pi}{3}\right) = \dfrac{1}{\sin\left(\dfrac{3\pi}{4} - \dfrac{\pi}{3}\right)}$

$= \dfrac{1}{\sin \dfrac{3\pi}{4} \cos \dfrac{\pi}{3} - \cos \dfrac{3\pi}{4} \sin \dfrac{\pi}{3}}$

$= \dfrac{1}{\left(\dfrac{1}{\sqrt{2}}\right)\left(\dfrac{1}{2}\right) - \left(-\dfrac{1}{\sqrt{2}}\right)\left(\dfrac{\sqrt{3}}{2}\right)} = \dfrac{1}{\dfrac{1 + \sqrt{3}}{2\sqrt{2}}}$

$= \dfrac{2\sqrt{2}}{1 + \sqrt{3}}$

8. a) $\cos x = \dfrac{\sqrt{3}}{2};\ \cos y = \dfrac{\sqrt{15}}{4}$

b) i) $\dfrac{\sqrt{15} + \sqrt{3}}{8}$ **ii)** $\dfrac{\sqrt{15} - \sqrt{3}}{8}$

iii) $\dfrac{3\sqrt{5} - 1}{8}$ **iv)** $\dfrac{3\sqrt{5} + 1}{8}$

9. a) $\cos x = -\dfrac{\sqrt{77}}{9};\ \cos y = \dfrac{3}{5}$

b) i) $\dfrac{-8 - 3\sqrt{77}}{45}$ **ii)** $\dfrac{-8 + 3\sqrt{77}}{45}$

iii) $\dfrac{4\sqrt{77} - 6}{45}$ **iv)** $\dfrac{4\sqrt{77} + 6}{45}$

10. a) $\cos x = \dfrac{3}{5}$ and x is in the first quadrant

$\sin x = \dfrac{\sqrt{5^2 - 3^2}}{5} = \dfrac{\sqrt{16}}{5} = \dfrac{4}{5}$

$\sin y = \dfrac{24}{25}$ and y is in the first quadrant

$\cos y = \dfrac{\sqrt{25^2 - 24^2}}{25} = \dfrac{\sqrt{49}}{25} = \dfrac{7}{25}$

$\sin(x - y) = \sin x \cos y - \cos x \sin y$

$= \left(\dfrac{4}{5}\right)\left(\dfrac{7}{25}\right) - \left(\dfrac{3}{5}\right)\left(\dfrac{24}{25}\right) = \dfrac{28}{125} - \dfrac{72}{125} = -\dfrac{44}{125}$

b) $\sin x = \dfrac{5}{13}$ and x is in the first quadrant

$\cos x = \dfrac{\sqrt{13^2 - 5^2}}{13} = \dfrac{\sqrt{144}}{13} = \dfrac{12}{13}$

$\sin y = \dfrac{12}{13}$ and y is in the first quadrant

$\cos y = \dfrac{\sqrt{13^2 - 12^2}}{13} = \dfrac{\sqrt{25}}{13} = \dfrac{5}{13}$

$\sin(x + y) = \sin x \cos y + \cos x \sin y$

$= \left(\dfrac{5}{13}\right)\left(\dfrac{5}{13}\right) + \left(\dfrac{12}{13}\right)\left(\dfrac{12}{13}\right) = \dfrac{25}{169} + \dfrac{144}{169}$

$= \dfrac{169}{169} = 1$

c) $\cos x = \dfrac{2}{3}$ and x is in the first quadrant

$\sin x = \dfrac{\sqrt{3^2 - 2^2}}{3} = \dfrac{\sqrt{5}}{3}$

$\sin y = \dfrac{10}{13}$ and y is in the first quadrant

$\cos y = \dfrac{\sqrt{13^2 - 10^2}}{13} = \dfrac{\sqrt{69}}{13}$

$\cos(x + y) = \cos x \cos y - \sin x \sin y$

$= \left(\dfrac{2}{3}\right)\left(\dfrac{\sqrt{69}}{13}\right) - \left(\dfrac{\sqrt{5}}{3}\right)\left(\dfrac{10}{13}\right) = \dfrac{2\sqrt{69}}{39} - \dfrac{10\sqrt{5}}{39}$

$= \dfrac{2\sqrt{69} - 10\sqrt{5}}{39}$

d) $\cos x = \dfrac{3}{5}$ and x is in the first quadrant

$\sin x = \dfrac{\sqrt{5^2 - 3^2}}{5} = \dfrac{\sqrt{16}}{5} = \dfrac{4}{5}$

$\sin y = \dfrac{4}{5}$ and y is in the first quadrant

$\cos y = \dfrac{\sqrt{5^2 - 4^2}}{5} = \dfrac{\sqrt{9}}{5} = \dfrac{3}{5}$

$\cos(x - y) = \cos x \cos y + \sin x \sin y$

$= \left(\dfrac{3}{5}\right)\left(\dfrac{4}{5}\right) + \left(\dfrac{4}{5}\right)\left(\dfrac{3}{5}\right) = \dfrac{12}{25} + \dfrac{12}{25} = \dfrac{24}{25}$

e) $\cot x = \dfrac{6}{5}$ and x is in the first quadrant

$\tan x = \dfrac{1}{\cot x} = \dfrac{5}{6}$

$\sec y = \dfrac{4}{5}$ and y is in the first quadrant

$\tan y = \dfrac{\sqrt{3^2 - 2^2}}{2} = \dfrac{\sqrt{5}}{2}$

$\tan(x + y) = \dfrac{\tan x + \tan y}{1 + \tan x \tan y}$

$$= \frac{\left(\frac{5}{6}\right) + \left(\frac{\sqrt{5}}{2}\right)}{1 + \left(\frac{5}{6}\right)\left(\frac{\sqrt{5}}{2}\right)} = \frac{\frac{5 + 3\sqrt{5}}{6}}{1 + \frac{5\sqrt{5}}{12}} = \frac{\frac{5 + 3\sqrt{5}}{6}}{\frac{12 - 5\sqrt{5}}{12}}$$

$$= \frac{12(5 + 3\sqrt{5})}{6(12 - 5\sqrt{5})} = \frac{2(5 + 3\sqrt{5})}{12 - 5\sqrt{5}}$$

f) $\sec x = \frac{4}{3}$ and x is in the first quadrant

$$\cos x = \frac{1}{\sec x} = \frac{3}{4}$$

$$\sin x = \frac{\sqrt{4^2 - 3^2}}{4} = \frac{\sqrt{7}}{4}$$

$\tan y = \frac{13}{5}$ and y is in the first quadrant

$$\sin y = \frac{13}{\sqrt{13^2 + 5^2}} = \frac{13}{\sqrt{194}}$$

$$\cos y = \frac{5}{\sqrt{13^2 + 5^2}} = \frac{5}{\sqrt{194}}$$

$$\csc(x - y) = \frac{1}{\sin(x - y)}$$

$$= \frac{1}{\sin x \cos y - \cos x \sin y}$$

$$= \frac{1}{\left(\frac{\sqrt{7}}{4}\right)\left(\frac{5}{\sqrt{194}}\right) - \left(\frac{3}{4}\right)\left(\frac{13}{\sqrt{194}}\right)}$$

$$= \frac{4\sqrt{194}}{5\sqrt{7} - 39}$$

11. $\dfrac{\sqrt{3} \cos \alpha - \sin \alpha}{2}$

12. $\csc\left(\dfrac{3\pi}{2} + \theta\right) = \dfrac{1}{\sin \dfrac{3\pi}{2} \cos \theta + \cos \dfrac{3\pi}{2} \sin \theta}$

$$= \frac{1}{(-1) \cos \theta + (0) \sin \theta}$$

$$= \frac{1}{-\cos \theta + 0} = -\sec \theta$$

13. $\cos \dfrac{13\pi}{4} = -\cos \dfrac{\pi}{4}$

14. a)

b) second quadrant **c)** $-\sqrt{\dfrac{3}{10}}$ **d)** 2.15

e) -0.548 and $-\sqrt{\dfrac{3}{10}} = -0.5477225575$

15. a) $\sin b = \dfrac{4}{5}$, $\tan b = -\dfrac{4}{3}$ **b)** $-\dfrac{7}{25}$ **c)** $-\dfrac{24}{25}$

d) $\dfrac{24}{7}$ **e)** 2.21 rad **f)** The angle $2b$ lies in the third quadrant, as indicated by the signs of the three primary ratios.

16. a) $\dfrac{\sqrt{2 - \sqrt{3}}}{2}$ **b)** Answers will vary.

17. $\sin 2x = -\dfrac{24}{25}$; $\cos 2x = -\dfrac{7}{25}$

18. a) $\sin 2x = \dfrac{24}{25}$; $\cos 2x = \dfrac{7}{25}$ **b)** $\sin 2x = -1$;

$\cos 2x = 0$ **c)** $\sin 2x = \dfrac{\sqrt{15}}{8}$; $\cos 2x = \dfrac{7}{8}$

d) $\sin 2x = -\dfrac{12}{13}$; $\cos 2x = -\dfrac{5}{13}$

19. $\sin 3x = 3 \sin x - 4 \sin^3 x$

20. $\cos 3x = 4 \cos^3 x - 3 \cos x$

21. a) $\sqrt{\dfrac{2 + \sqrt{3}}{2}}$ **b)** $\sqrt{\dfrac{2 + \sqrt{2}}{2}}$

22. $\cos x \cos y = \dfrac{1}{2}[\cos(x + y) + \cos(x - y)]$

$$\text{RS} = \frac{1}{2}[\cos x \cos x + \sin x \sin y$$
$$+ \cos x \cos y - \sin x \sin y]$$

$$= \frac{1}{2}[2 \cos x \cos y]$$

$$= \cos x \cos y$$

$$= \text{LS}$$

23. $R = \dfrac{2v^2 \cos \theta \sin(\theta - \beta)}{g \cos^2 \beta}$

$$\beta = \frac{\pi}{6}$$

$$R = \frac{2v^2 \cos \theta \sin\left(\theta - \dfrac{\pi}{6}\right)}{g \cos^2 \dfrac{\pi}{6}}$$

$$= \frac{2v^2 \cos \theta \left(\sin \theta \cos \dfrac{\pi}{6} - \cos \theta \sin \dfrac{\pi}{6}\right)}{g \cos^2 \dfrac{\pi}{6}}$$

$$= \frac{2v^2 \cos \theta \left(\sin \theta \left(\dfrac{\sqrt{3}}{2}\right) - \cos \theta \left(\dfrac{1}{2}\right)\right)}{g\left(\dfrac{\sqrt{3}}{2}\right)^2}$$

$$= \frac{2v^2 \cos \theta \left(\dfrac{1}{2}\right)(\sqrt{3} \sin \theta - \cos \theta)}{g\left(\dfrac{3}{4}\right)}$$

$$= \frac{4v^2 \cos \theta (\sqrt{3} \sin \theta - \cos \theta)}{3g}$$

The range of the rocket is

$$R = \frac{4v^2 \cos \theta (\sqrt{3} \sin \theta - \cos \theta)}{3g}$$

4.5 Prove Trigonometric Identities

1. a) 1 **b)** $\csc x$ **c)** $\csc x$ **d)** 2
2. a) yes **b)** yes **c)** no **d)** no **e)** yes **f)** yes

3. a)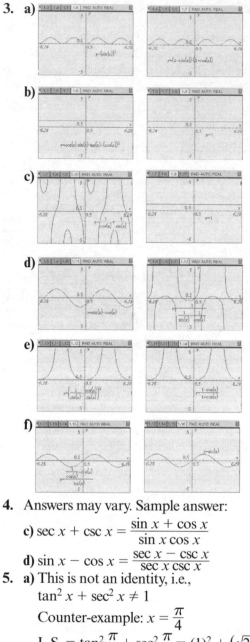

b)

c)

d)

e)

f)

4. Answers may vary. Sample answer:

c) $\sec x + \csc x = \dfrac{\sin x + \cos x}{\sin x \cos x}$

d) $\sin x - \cos x = \dfrac{\sec x - \csc x}{\sec x \csc x}$

5. a) This is not an identity, i.e.,

$\tan^2 x + \sec^2 x \neq 1$

Counter-example: $x = \dfrac{\pi}{4}$

L.S. $= \tan^2 \dfrac{\pi}{4} + \sec^2 \dfrac{\pi}{4} = (1)^2 + (\sqrt{2})^2$

$= 1 + 2 = 3$

R.S. $= 1$

L.S. $\neq$ R.S.

Therefore, $\tan^2 x + \sec^2 x \neq 1$.

b) This is an identity, i.e.,

$\cos x \tan^2 x = \sin x \tan x$

L.S. $= \cos x \tan^2 x$ Use quotient identity.

$= \cos x \dfrac{\sin^2 x}{\cos^2 x}$

$= \dfrac{\sin^2 x}{\cos x}$

$= \sin x \dfrac{\sin x}{\cos x}$ Use quotient identity.

$= \sin x \tan x$

$=$ R.S.

L.S. $=$ R.S.

Therefore, $\cos x \tan^2 x = \sin x \tan x$ is an identity.

c) This is an identity, i.e.,

$\tan 2x - \sin 2x = 2 \tan 2x \sin^2 x$

L.S. $= \tan 2x - \sin 2x$ Use quotient identity.

$= \dfrac{\sin 2x}{\cos 2x} - \sin 2x$

$= \dfrac{\sin 2x - \sin 2x \cos 2x}{\cos 2x}$

$= \dfrac{\sin 2x (1 - \cos 2x)}{\cos 2x}$

$= \dfrac{\sin 2x}{\cos 2x}(1 - \cos 2x)$ Use quotient identity and double-angle formula.

$= \tan 2x \left(1 - (1 - 2\sin^2 x)\right)$

$= \tan 2x (1 - 1 + 2\sin^2 x)$

$= \tan 2x (2\sin^2 x)$

$= 2 \tan 2x \sin^2 x$

$=$ R.S.

L.S. $=$ R.S.

Therefore, $\tan 2x - \sin 2x = 2 \tan 2x \sin^2 x$ is an identity.

d) This is an identity, i.e.,

$\sin 2x = \tan x(1 + \cos 2x)$

R.S. $= \tan x(1 + \cos 2x)$ Use double-angle formula.

$= \tan x (2\cos^2 x)$ Use quotient identity.

$= \dfrac{\sin x}{\cos x}(2\cos^2 x)$

$= 2 \sin x \cos x$ Use double-angle formula.

$= \sin 2x$

$=$ L.S.

L.S. $=$ R.S.

Therefore, $\sin 2x = \tan x(1 + \cos 2x)$ is an identity.

e) This is not an identity, i.e.,

$\sec 2x \neq \dfrac{\sec x \csc x}{2}$

Counter-example: $x = \dfrac{\pi}{6}$

L.S. $= \sec\left(2\frac{\pi}{6}\right) = \sec\frac{\pi}{3} = 2$

R.S. $= \dfrac{\sec\left(\frac{\pi}{6}\right)\csc\left(\frac{\pi}{6}\right)}{2} = \dfrac{\left(\frac{2}{\sqrt{3}}\right)(2)}{2} = \dfrac{2}{\sqrt{3}}$

L.S. $\neq$ R.S.

Therefore, $\sec 2x \neq \dfrac{\sec x \csc x}{2}$.

f) This is an identity, i.e.,

$\sin^2 x + \cos^2 x + \tan^2 x = \sec^2 x$

L.S. $= \sin^2 x + \cos^2 x + \tan^2 x$

$= 1 + \tan^2 x$ Use quotient identity.

$= 1 + \dfrac{\sin^2 x}{\cos^2 x}$

$= \dfrac{\cos^2 x + \sin^2 x}{\cos^2 x}$ Use Pythagorean identity.

$= \dfrac{1}{\cos^2 x}$ Use reciprocal identity.

$= \sec^2 x$

$=$ R.S.

L.S. $=$ R.S.

Therefore, $\sin^2 x + \cos^2 x + \tan^2 x = \sec^2 x$ is an identity.

g) $\dfrac{\cos^2 x - \sin^2 x}{\cos^2 x + \sin x \cos x} = 1 - \tan x$

L.S. $= \dfrac{\cos^2 x - \sin^2 x}{\cos^2 x + \sin x \cos x}$

$= \dfrac{(\cos x - \sin x)(\cos x + \sin x)}{\cos x(\cos x + \sin x)}$

$= \dfrac{\cos x - \sin x}{\cos x}$

$= 1 - \dfrac{\sin x}{\cos x}$ Use quotient identity.

$= 1 - \tan x$

$=$ R.S.

L.S. $=$ R.S.

Therefore, $\dfrac{\cos^2 x - \sin^2 x}{\cos^2 x + \sin x \cos x} =$

$1 - \tan x$ is an identity.

6. Answers may vary. For example:

a) counter-example: $x = \dfrac{\pi}{6}$

b) counter-example: $x = \dfrac{\pi}{3}$

c) counter-example: $x = \dfrac{2\pi}{3}$

d) counter-example: $x = \dfrac{\pi}{4}$

7. $\sin\left(\frac{\pi}{2} + \theta\right) = \sin\left(\frac{\pi}{2}\right)\cos\theta + \cos\left(\frac{\pi}{2}\right)\sin\theta$

$= (1)\cos\theta + (0)\sin\theta = \cos\theta$

8. a) $-\sin x$ **b)** $-\cos x$ **c)** $-\cos y$ **d)** $\cos y$

9. $\tan\dfrac{3\pi}{2}$ is undefined

Use quotient identity and compound-angle formula instead.

10. $\sin\left(x - \dfrac{4\pi}{3}\right) = \dfrac{\sqrt{3}\cos x - \sin x}{2}$

L.S. $= \sin\left(x - \dfrac{4\pi}{3}\right)$ Use double angle formula.

$= 2\sin\left[\frac{1}{2}\left(x - \frac{4\pi}{3}\right)\right]\cos\left[\frac{1}{2}\left(x - \frac{4\pi}{3}\right)\right]$

$= 2\sin\left(\dfrac{x}{2} - \dfrac{2\pi}{3}\right)\cos\left(\dfrac{x}{2} - \dfrac{2\pi}{3}\right)$

Use compound-angle formula.

$= 2\left[\sin\dfrac{x}{2}\cos\dfrac{2\pi}{3} - \cos\dfrac{x}{2}\sin\dfrac{2\pi}{3}\right]$

$\left[\cos\dfrac{x}{2}\cos\dfrac{2\pi}{3} + \sin\dfrac{x}{2}\sin\dfrac{2\pi}{3}\right]$

$= 2\left[\sin\dfrac{x}{2}\left(-\dfrac{1}{2}\right) - \cos\dfrac{x}{2}\left(\dfrac{\sqrt{3}}{2}\right)\right]$

$\left[\cos\dfrac{x}{2}\left(-\dfrac{1}{2}\right) + \sin\dfrac{x}{2}\left(\dfrac{\sqrt{3}}{2}\right)\right]$

$= 2\left(\dfrac{1}{2}\right)\left(\dfrac{1}{2}\right)\left(-\sin\dfrac{x}{2} - \sqrt{3}\cos\dfrac{x}{2}\right)$

$\left(-\cos\dfrac{x}{2} + \sqrt{3}\sin\dfrac{x}{2}\right)$

$= \left(\dfrac{1}{2}\right)\left(\sin\dfrac{x}{2}\cos\dfrac{x}{2} - \sqrt{3}\sin^2\dfrac{x}{2}\right.$

$\left. + \sqrt{3}\cos^2\dfrac{x}{2} - 3\sin\dfrac{x}{2}\cos\dfrac{x}{2}\right)$

$= \left(\dfrac{1}{2}\right)\left[-2\sin\dfrac{x}{2}\cos\dfrac{x}{2} + \right.$

$\left. \sqrt{3}\left(\cos^2\dfrac{x}{2} - \sin^2\dfrac{x}{2}\right)\right]$ Use double-angle formula.

$= \left(\dfrac{1}{2}\right)\left[-\sin x + \sqrt{3}\left(\cos^2\dfrac{x}{2} - \sin^2\dfrac{x}{2}\right)\right]$

Use double-angle formula.

$= \left(\dfrac{1}{2}\right)(\sqrt{3}\cos x - \sin x)$

$= \dfrac{\sqrt{3}\cos x - \sin x}{2}$

$=$ R.S.

L.S. $=$ R.S.

Therefore, $\sin\left(x - \dfrac{4\pi}{3}\right) = \dfrac{\sqrt{3}\cos x - \sin x}{2}$ is an identity.

11. $\cos\left(2x + \dfrac{\pi}{2}\right) = -\sin 2x$

$\quad$ L.S. $= \cos\left(2x + \dfrac{\pi}{2}\right)$

$\qquad = \cos\left[2\left(x + \dfrac{\pi}{4}\right)\right]$ $\quad$ Use double-angle formula

$\qquad = 1 - 2\sin^2\left(x + \dfrac{\pi}{4}\right)$ $\quad$ Use compound-angle formula

$\qquad = 1 - 2\left(\sin x \cos\dfrac{\pi}{4} + \cos x \sin\dfrac{\pi}{4}\right)^2$

$\qquad = 1 - 2\left[\sin x\left(\dfrac{1}{\sqrt{2}}\right) + \cos x\left(\dfrac{1}{\sqrt{2}}\right)\right]^2$

$\qquad = 1 - 2\left[\left(\dfrac{1}{\sqrt{2}}\right)(\sin x + \cos x)\right]^2$

$\qquad = 1 - 2\left(\dfrac{1}{2}\right)[(\sin x + \cos x)]^2$

$\qquad = 1 - (\sin x + \cos x)^2$

$\qquad = 1 - (\sin^2 x + 2\sin x \cos x + \cos^2 x)$
$\qquad\qquad$ Use Pythagorean identity

$\qquad = 1 - (1 + 2\sin x \cos x)$

$\qquad = -2\sin x \cos x$ $\quad$ Use double angle formula

$\qquad = -\sin 2x$

$\qquad =$ R.S.

12. Answers may vary.

13. a) $\sin 4x = \sin(2(2x)) = 2\sin 2x \cos 2x$

$\quad$ **b)** $\sin 6x = \sin(2(3x)) = 2\sin 3x \cos 3x$

$\quad\ \sin 8x = \sin(2(4x)) = 2\sin 4x \cos 4x$

$\quad$ These identities will hold for all $\sin kx$, where k is a positive integer because the angle kx can be expressed as $2\left(\dfrac{kx}{2}\right)$; therefore,

$\quad \sin kx = \sin\left(2\left(\dfrac{kx}{2}\right)\right) = 2\sin\dfrac{kx}{2}\cos\dfrac{kx}{2}.$

14. a) $\dfrac{\pi}{2}, \dfrac{3\pi}{2}, \dfrac{7\pi}{6}, \dfrac{11\pi}{6}$ **b)** $\dfrac{3\pi}{8}, \dfrac{7\pi}{8}, \dfrac{11\pi}{8}, \dfrac{15\pi}{8}$

$\quad$ **c)** $0, \pi, 2\pi, \dfrac{\pi}{2}, \dfrac{3\pi}{2}$ **d)** $\dfrac{3\pi}{4}, \dfrac{7\pi}{4}$

$\quad$ **e)** $0 \le x \le 2\pi$ **f)** $\dfrac{\pi}{3}, \dfrac{5\pi}{3}$

15. a–b) Answers will vary.

16. Answers will vary.

17. a–b) Answers will vary.

18. Answers will vary.

19. a) No, the graphs are not the same for all values. **b)** Answers may vary. For example: Let $x = 0$; L.S. $\ne$ R.S.

20. $B = \dfrac{F \csc \theta}{I\ell}$

$\quad$ Use reciprocal identity $\csc \theta = \dfrac{1}{\sin \theta}$.

$\quad B = \dfrac{F\left(\dfrac{1}{\sin \theta}\right)}{I\ell}$ $\qquad B = \dfrac{F}{I\ell \sin \theta}$

21. a) $I = I_0 \cos^2 \theta$ **b)** half the original intensity

22. $\sin(x + y)\sin(x - y) = \sin^2 x - \sin^2 y$

$\quad (\sin x \cos y + \cos x \sin y)$

$\qquad (\sin x \cos y - \cos x \sin y) =$ LS

$\quad \sin^2 x \cos^2 y - \cos^2 x \sin^2 y =$ LS

$\quad \sin^2 x (1 - \sin^2 y) -$

$\qquad\qquad (1 - \sin^2 x)\sin^2 y =$ LS

$\quad \sin^2 x - \sin^2 x \sin^2 y$

$\qquad - \sin^2 y + \sin^2 x \sin^2 y =$ LS

$\qquad\qquad \sin^2 x - \sin^2 y =$ LS

$\qquad\qquad\qquad\qquad\quad =$ RS

23. a) R.S. $= \dfrac{1}{2}[\cos(x - y) - \cos(x + y)]$

$\qquad = \dfrac{1}{2}[(\cos x \cos y + \sin x \sin y)$

$\qquad\qquad\qquad - (\cos x \cos y - \sin x \sin y)]$

$\qquad = \dfrac{1}{2}[2\sin x \sin y]$

$\qquad = \sin x \sin y$

$\qquad =$ L.S.

$\quad$ **b) i)** $\dfrac{1}{2}[\cos(x + y) + \cos(x - y)]$

$\qquad\quad = \cos x \cos y$

$\quad$ **ii)** $\dfrac{1}{2}[\sin(x + y) - \sin(x - y)]$

$\qquad\quad = \cos x \sin y$

$\quad$ **iii)** $\dfrac{1}{2}[\sin(x + y) + \sin(x - y)]$

$\qquad\quad = \sin x \cos y$

24. a) $\sin\dfrac{x + y}{2} \sin\dfrac{x - y}{2} = \dfrac{1}{2}[\cos y - \cos x]$

$\quad$ **b)** $\sin\dfrac{x + y}{2} \cos\dfrac{x - y}{2} = \dfrac{1}{2}[\sin x + \sin y]$

$\quad$ **c)** $\cos\dfrac{x + y}{2} \sin\dfrac{x - y}{2} = \dfrac{1}{2}[\sin x - \sin y]$

$\quad$ **d)** $\cos\dfrac{x + y}{2} \cos\dfrac{x - y}{2} = \dfrac{1}{2}[\cos x + \cos y]$

25. a–c) Answers may vary.

Chapter 4 Challenge Questions

C1. 94.6 m

C2. Any values for the radius and the radian measure that satisfy the relationship $52 = r^2\theta$ are possible solutions.

C3. 1.7425 m/s

C4. As you move from the equator (where the circumference is a maximum) to the poles, the circumference decreases by a factor of cos L. At the poles, the circumference is 0 (because of the fact that at the poles the angle is 90° and cos 90° is zero).

C5. $3.43°$. As the angle increases, the speed must also increase, as these two variables are in direct proportionality to each other in this formula.

C6. $\dfrac{\pi}{4}$ radians or $45°$

C7. a) $\dfrac{\cos(x + h) - \cos x}{h}$

b) $\dfrac{\cos(x + 0.1) - \cos x}{0.1}$

$= \dfrac{\cos x \cos(0.1) - \sin x \sin(0.1) - \cos x}{0.1}$

$= \cos x \left(\dfrac{\cos(0.1) - 1}{0.1}\right) - \sin x \left(\dfrac{\sin(0.1)}{0.1}\right)$

$= -0.050 \cos x - 0.998 \sin x$

c)

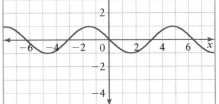

The expression after the $\cos x$ is approximately equal to zero [and gets closer to zero if h is smaller than 0.1 (0.001, for example)], and the expression after the $\sin x$ is approximately equal to 1 [and gets closer to 1 if h is smaller than 0.1 (0.001, for example)]. Therefore, the expression is approximately equal to $-\sin x$.

C8. a)

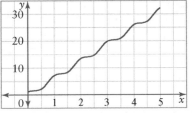

b) moving left: (0.5, 1), (1.5, 2), (2.5, 3), (3.5, 4), (4.5, 5)
moving right: (0, 0.5), (1, 1.5), (2, 2.5), (3, 3.5), (4, 4.5)

c) Answers may vary. **d)** 2π

e) When $t = 0, 1, 2, 3, 4,$ and 5, the velocity has the same value of approximately 6.3.

C9. $60°$

C10. max $= 129.9 \, V$ and min $= -129.9 \, V$

Chapter 5

5.1 Graphs of Sine, Cosine, and Tangent Functions

1. a) max -4 at $x = -\dfrac{3\pi}{2}, \dfrac{\pi}{2}$

min -6 at $x = -\dfrac{\pi}{2}, \dfrac{3\pi}{2}$

b) max 8 at $x = -2\pi, 0, \pi$
min 6 at $x = -\pi, \pi$

c) max 2 at $x = -\dfrac{3\pi}{2}, \dfrac{\pi}{2}$

min 0 at $x = -\dfrac{\pi}{2}, \dfrac{3\pi}{2}$

d) max -2 at $x = -2\pi, 0, \pi$
min -4 at $x = -\pi, \pi$

2. a)

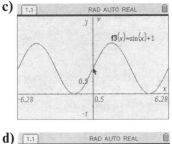

b)

c)

d)

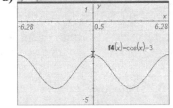

3. a) $y = \dfrac{1}{2}\sin x$ **b)** $y = 3 \cos x$

c) $y = -7 \sin x$ **d)** $y = -\dfrac{1}{4}\cos x$

4. a) $y = \sin\left(x - \dfrac{2\pi}{3}\right)$ **b)** $y = \cos\left(x - \dfrac{4\pi}{5}\right)$

c) $y = \sin\left(x + \dfrac{5\pi}{7}\right)$ **d)** $y = \cos\left(x + \dfrac{11\pi}{7}\right)$

5. a) $y = \sin\dfrac{1}{2}x$ **b)** $y = \cos 4x$

c) $y = \sin\dfrac{4}{3}x$ **d)** $y = \cos\dfrac{8}{5}x$

6. a) $y = 5\sin\dfrac{1}{2}x$

b)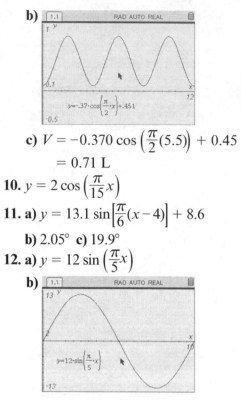

7. a) 3 **b)** 2 down **c)** $y = 3\cos x - 2$

d)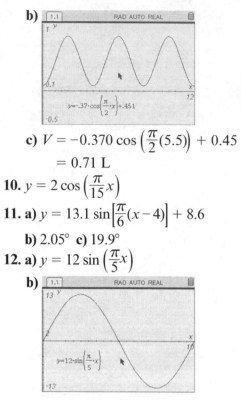

8. a) π **b)** $\dfrac{2\pi}{3}$ left **c)** $y = \sin\left[2\left(x + \dfrac{2\pi}{3}\right)\right]$

d)

9. a) To determine the amplitude:
$$\dfrac{\text{max} - \text{min}}{2} = \dfrac{0.82 - 0.08}{2} = 0.370$$
The period is 4 seconds, so
$$\dfrac{2\pi}{k} = 4$$
$$4k = 2\pi; \ k = \dfrac{\pi}{2}$$
Since the minimum amount of air is in the lungs at $t = 0$, the cosine function needs to be reflected in the t-axis. The point $(0, 0.08)$ must be on the function, so
$$V = -0.370\cos\left(\dfrac{\pi}{2}t\right) + d \text{ becomes}$$
$$0.08 = -0.370\cos\left(\dfrac{\pi}{2}(0)\right) + d$$
$$0.08 = -0.370 + d$$
$$d = 0.45$$
Therefore, $V = -0.370\cos\left(\dfrac{\pi}{2}t\right) + 0.45$ L

b)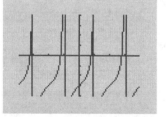

c) $V = -0.370\cos\left(\dfrac{\pi}{2}(5.5)\right) + 0.45$
$\qquad = 0.71$ L

10. $y = 2\cos\left(\dfrac{\pi}{15}x\right)$

11. a) $y = 13.1\sin\left[\dfrac{\pi}{6}(x - 4)\right] + 8.6$

b) 2.05° **c)** 19.9°

12. a) $y = 12\sin\left(\dfrac{\pi}{5}x\right)$

b)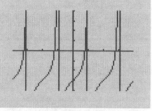

c) 11.4 cm below equilibrium position

d) 6.3 s, 8.7 s

13. a) 25 **b)** 30 up **c)** 90 **d)** $\dfrac{\pi}{45}$

14. a) vertical translation 3 down

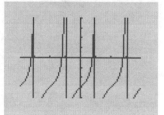

b) vertical stretch by factor of 2

c) phase shift $\dfrac{\pi}{6}$ right

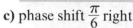

d) change of period to $\frac{\pi}{4}$

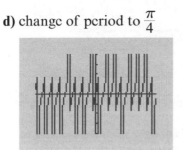

15. a) The solutions must be from the interval $-4 \le x \le 4$, since beyond this, $y = \frac{1}{4}x$ exceeds the amplitude of $\cos x$ (which is 1). For $0 < x < 4$, $y = \frac{1}{4}x$ is positive. According to the CAST rule, for $0 < x < 4$, $\cos x$ is only positive once ($\cos x$ is positive in the first quadrant, but negative in the second and third [which is where $x = 4$ stops]). For $-4 < x < 0$, $y = \frac{1}{4}x$ is negative. According to the CAST rule, for $-4 < x < 0$, $\cos x$ is negative twice ($\cos x$ is positive in the fourth quadrant, but negative in the third and second [which is where $x = -4$ stops]). Therefore, there will be three points of intersection in total.

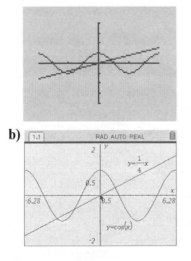

b)

5.2 Graphs of Reciprocal Trigonometric Functions

1. 3.28, 6.14 **2.** 1.37, 4.91 **3.** 3.06, 6.20

4. a) $y = \sec\left(x - \frac{\pi}{2}\right)$

b) Yes. The secant function is periodic, with period 2π; therefore adding a multiple of 2π to the phase shift will not change the

graph. The following transformations are all equivalent to $y = \csc x$:

$$y = \sec\left(x - \left(\frac{\pi}{2} + 2\pi n\right)\right), n \text{ is an integer}$$

$$y = \sec\left(x + \left(\frac{3\pi}{2} + 2\pi n\right)\right), n \text{ is an integer}$$

5. a)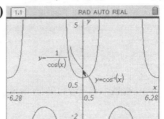

b) approximately 0.446 rad

6. 2215.4 m

7. a) According to the diagram,

$$\cos x = \frac{1200}{d}$$

So $d = \frac{1200}{\cos x}$

Since the function d is in terms of x and $\frac{1}{\cos x} = \sec x$, this function can be written as $d(x) = 1200 \sec x$

b) $d\left(\frac{7\pi}{12}\right) = 1200 \sec\left(\frac{7\pi}{12}\right)$

$$= \frac{1200}{\cos\left(\frac{7\pi}{12}\right)} \text{ or } 1200\left(\frac{1}{\cos\left(\frac{7\pi}{12}\right)}\right)$$

$$\cos\left(\frac{7\pi}{12}\right) = \cos\left(\frac{\pi}{4} + \frac{\pi}{3}\right)$$

$$= \cos\left(\frac{\pi}{4}\right)\cos\left(\frac{\pi}{3}\right) - \sin\left(\frac{\pi}{4}\right)\sin\left(\frac{\pi}{3}\right)$$

$$= \left(\frac{1}{\sqrt{2}}\right)\left(\frac{1}{2}\right) - \left(\frac{1}{\sqrt{2}}\right)\left(\frac{\sqrt{3}}{2}\right)$$

$$= \frac{1 - \sqrt{3}}{2\sqrt{2}}$$

So $\dfrac{1}{\cos\left(\frac{7\pi}{12}\right)} = \dfrac{2\sqrt{2}}{1 - \sqrt{3}}$

$d\left(\frac{7\pi}{12}\right)$ becomes

$$d\left(\frac{7\pi}{12}\right) = 1200\left(\frac{2\sqrt{2}}{1 - \sqrt{3}}\right)$$

$$= \frac{2400\sqrt{2}}{1 - \sqrt{3}}$$

c)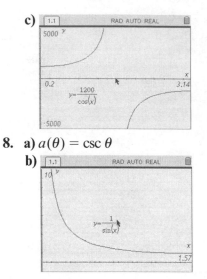

8. a) $a(\theta) = \csc \theta$

b)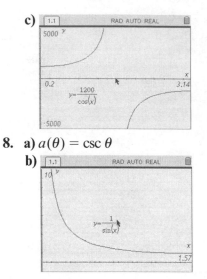

9. $\tan \theta = \dfrac{d}{5}$ or $d = 5 \tan \theta$

One complete revolution every 3 seconds means that the period is 3.

$$\frac{2\pi}{k} = 3$$

So $3k = 2\pi$

$$k = \frac{2\pi}{3}$$

Therefore, the function $d = 5 \tan \theta$ can be written as a function of time, using the period of rotation

$$d(t) = 5 \tan\left(\frac{2\pi}{3}t\right)$$

10. a) The cotangent function is the reciprocal of the tangent function and $\tan^{-1}$ is the opposite operation of tangent.

b) $\cot \dfrac{1}{\sqrt{3}} = 1.5352$, $\tan^{-1}\left(\dfrac{1}{\sqrt{3}}\right) = \dfrac{\pi}{6}$

11. No. Answers may vary. Sample answer:

$$\sec^2 x = \csc^2\left(x - \frac{\pi}{2}\right)$$

12. a) $d = 150 \sec x$ **b)** $100\sqrt{3}$ m **c)** 173.2 m

d)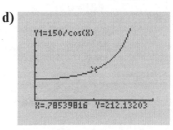

13. a)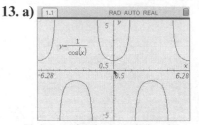

b) i) vertical stretch by factor of 2

ii) change of period to $\dfrac{2\pi}{3}$

iii) vertical translation 4 down

iv) phase shift 2 left

14. a)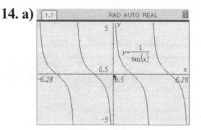

b) i) vertical stretch by factor of 4

ii) change of period to $\dfrac{\pi}{3}$ **iii)** vertical translation 5 up **iv)** phase shift 2 right

15. a)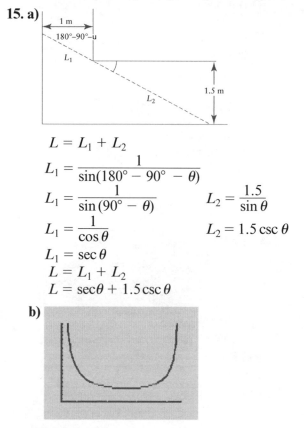

$$L = L_1 + L_2$$

$$L_1 = \frac{1}{\sin(180° - 90° - \theta)}$$

$$L_1 = \frac{1}{\sin(90° - \theta)} \qquad L_2 = \frac{1.5}{\sin \theta}$$

$$L_1 = \frac{1}{\cos \theta} \qquad L_2 = 1.5 \csc \theta$$

$$L_1 = \sec \theta$$

$$L = L_1 + L_2$$

$$L = \sec \theta + 1.5 \csc \theta$$

b)

c) 48.86° **d)** 3.5 m

5.3 Sinusoidal Functions of the Form
$f(x) = a \sin[k(x - d)] + c$ and
$f(x) = \cos[k(x - d)] + c$

1. **a)** $4; \dfrac{2\pi}{9}$

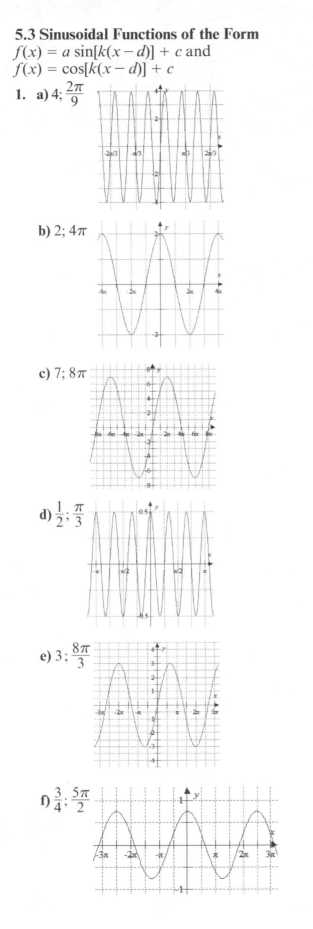

b) $2; 4\pi$

c) $7; 8\pi$

d) $\dfrac{1}{2}; \dfrac{\pi}{3}$

e) $3; \dfrac{8\pi}{3}$

f) $\dfrac{3}{4}; \dfrac{5\pi}{2}$

2. **a)** $y = 5 \sin(3x)$ **b)** $y = 2 \cos\left(\dfrac{1}{2}x\right)$

3. **a)** $\dfrac{1}{2}$ **b)** $\dfrac{2\pi}{3}$ **c)** $\dfrac{\pi}{6}$ left **d)** 5 down

e)

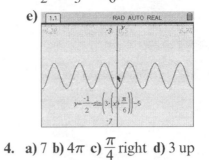

4. **a)** 7 **b)** 4π **c)** $\dfrac{\pi}{4}$ right **d)** 3 up

e)

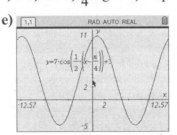

5. **a)** amplitude 6; period π; phase shift
$\dfrac{\pi}{12}$ right; vertical tra nslation 0

b) $y = 6 \sin\left[2\left(x - \dfrac{\pi}{12}\right)\right]$

c)

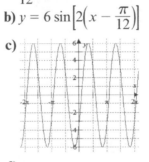

d) same

6. **a)** amplitude $\dfrac{1}{2}$; period 2π; phase shift $\dfrac{\pi}{8}$ left;
vertical translation 4 down

b) $y = -\dfrac{1}{2} \cos\left(x + \dfrac{\pi}{8}\right) - 4$

c)

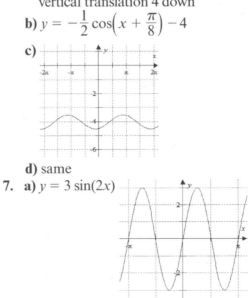

d) same

7. **a)** $y = 3 \sin(2x)$

b) $y = 3 \sin\left[\frac{1}{2}\left(x + \frac{\pi}{12}\right)\right]$

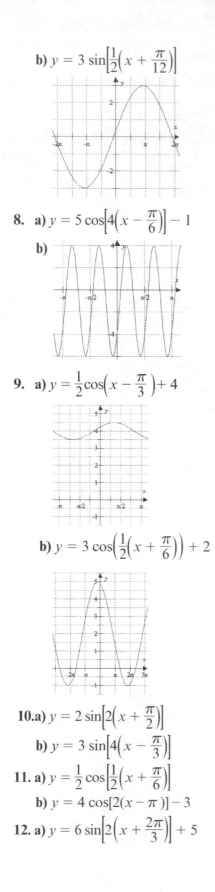

8. a) $y = 5 \cos\left[4\left(x - \frac{\pi}{6}\right)\right] - 1$

b)

9. a) $y = \frac{1}{2}\cos\left(x - \frac{\pi}{3}\right) + 4$

b) $y = 3 \cos\left(\frac{1}{2}\left(x + \frac{\pi}{6}\right)\right) + 2$

10. a) $y = 2 \sin\left[2\left(x + \frac{\pi}{2}\right)\right]$

b) $y = 3 \sin\left[4\left(x - \frac{\pi}{3}\right)\right]$

11. a) $y = \frac{1}{2} \cos\left[\frac{1}{2}\left(x + \frac{\pi}{6}\right)\right]$

b) $y = 4 \cos[2(x - \pi)] - 3$

12. a) $y = 6 \sin\left[2\left(x + \frac{2\pi}{3}\right)\right] + 5$

b)

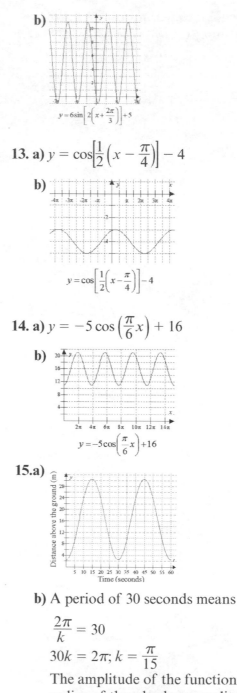

$y = 6\sin\left[2\left(x + \frac{2\pi}{3}\right)\right] + 5$

13. a) $y = \cos\left[\frac{1}{2}\left(x - \frac{\pi}{4}\right)\right] - 4$

b)

$y = \cos\left[\frac{1}{2}\left(x - \frac{\pi}{4}\right)\right] - 4$

14. a) $y = -5 \cos\left(\frac{\pi}{6}x\right) + 16$

b)

$y = -5\cos\left(\frac{\pi}{6}x\right) + 16$

15. a)

Distance above the ground (m)

Time (seconds)

b) A period of 30 seconds means

$$\frac{2\pi}{k} = 30$$

$$30k = 2\pi; k = \frac{\pi}{15}$$

The amplitude of the function is the radius of the wheel, so amplitude = 14. The centre of the wheel is $14 + 2.5 = 16.5$ m off the ground, so $d = 16.5$. As well, if the wheel position starts at the lowest position at $t = 0$, then the cosine function must be reflected in the x-axis to have a minimum value at $t = 0$. All of this together means that

$$y = -14 \cos\left(\frac{\pi}{15}t\right) + 16.5$$

c) If the wheel speeds up, the period of the function gets shorter, so k increases.

16. a)

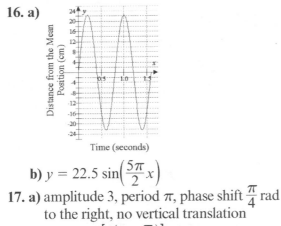

b) $y = 22.5 \sin\left(\dfrac{5\pi}{2} x\right)$

17. a) amplitude 3, period π, phase shift $\dfrac{\pi}{4}$ rad to the right, no vertical translation

b) $y = 3 \sin\left[2\left(x - \dfrac{\pi}{4}\right)\right]$

c)

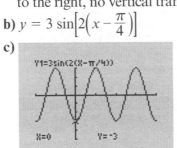

d) Answers may vary. Sample answer:

$y = 3 \cos\left[2\left(x - \dfrac{\pi}{2}\right)\right]$

18. a) $\dfrac{2\pi}{23}, \dfrac{\pi}{14}, \dfrac{2\pi}{33}$

b)

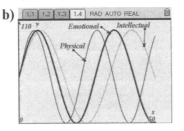

c) yes, at approximately 10 171.5 days

d) at $t = 7305$ days; intellectual: 87.79%; emotional: 18.83%; physical: 18.45% Potential for the next 30 days:

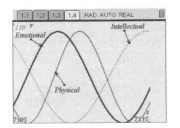

19. a) approximately 4:08 p.m. (16.133 3 hours)

b) $h(t) = 4.4 \sin[0.16\pi(x - 0.508\,3)] + 3.8$

c)

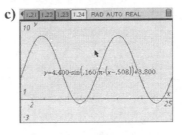

d) 8.2 m

20. a) The amplitude can be found as follows: $\dfrac{\text{max} - \text{min}}{2} = \dfrac{350 - 50}{2} = 150$

The function has a period of 12 months so

$\dfrac{2\pi}{k} = 12$

$12k = 2\pi; k = \dfrac{\pi}{6}$

If February is the starting month of the data at $t = 1$, then the phase shift is 1 unit to the right. The point $(1, 50)$ is on the function, which means that:

$s(t) = $ a minimum point

$150 \cos\left[\dfrac{\pi}{6}(t - 1)\right] + d$

Becomes $s(1) = 150 \cos\left[\dfrac{\pi}{6}(1 - 1)\right] + d$

$50 = -150 + d$

$d = 200$

All of this information produces the function

$s(t) = -150 \cos\left[\dfrac{\pi}{6}(t - 1)\right] + 200.$

b)

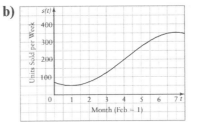

21. a) $y = 8 \sin\left(\dfrac{\pi}{20}(x - 10)\right) + 12$

b)

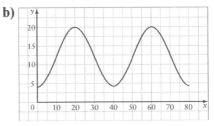

5.4 Solving Trigonometric Equations

1. **a)** 0.52, 2.62 **b)** 2.69, 3.59 **c)** 0.79, 3.93
   d) 1.77, 4.51 **e)** 2.09, 5.24 **f)** 3.48, 5.94

2. **a)** $\dfrac{5\pi}{4}, \dfrac{7\pi}{4}$ **b)** $\dfrac{5\pi}{6}, \dfrac{7\pi}{6}$ **c)** $\dfrac{\pi}{3}, \dfrac{4\pi}{3}$ **d)** 2.94, 6.09

3. **a)** 0.78, 2.37, 3.92, 5.51 **b)** 0.84, 2.30, 3.98,
   5.44 **c)** 1.48, 1.66, 4.62, 4.80 **d)** 1.10, 2.04,
   4.24, 5.18 **e)** 0.49, 2.66, 3.63, 5.80

4. **a)** $\dfrac{\pi}{3}, \dfrac{2\pi}{3}, \dfrac{4\pi}{3}, \dfrac{5\pi}{3}$ **b)** $\dfrac{\pi}{3}, \dfrac{2\pi}{3}, \dfrac{4\pi}{3}, \dfrac{5\pi}{3}$
   c) $\dfrac{\pi}{3}, \dfrac{2\pi}{3}, \dfrac{4\pi}{3}, \dfrac{5\pi}{3}$ **d)** $\dfrac{\pi}{6}, \dfrac{5\pi}{6}, \dfrac{7\pi}{6}, \dfrac{11\pi}{6}$

5. **a)** 1.98. 3.84 **b)** 0, 2.47 **c)** 1.26 **d)** 1.02

6. **a)** $0, \dfrac{\pi}{4}, \pi, \dfrac{5\pi}{4}, 2\pi$ **b)** $\dfrac{\pi}{2}, \dfrac{2\pi}{3}, \dfrac{4\pi}{3}, \dfrac{3\pi}{2}$
   c) $\dfrac{\pi}{2}, \dfrac{7\pi}{6}, \dfrac{11\pi}{6}$ **d)** $\dfrac{2\pi}{3}, \dfrac{4\pi}{3}, 1.23, 5.05$
   e) 1.82, 4.46 **f)** no solution **g)** $\dfrac{\pi}{3}, \dfrac{5\pi}{3}$,
   1.82, 4.46 **h)** $\dfrac{\pi}{3}, \dfrac{5\pi}{3}$ **i)** $\dfrac{\pi}{2}, 3.31, 6.12$

7. **a)** $2\cos^2\theta + \cos\theta - 1 = 0$
   $(\cos\theta + 1)(2\cos\theta - 1 = 0)$
   $\cos\theta + 1 = 0$ or $2\cos\theta - 1 = 0$
   $\cos\theta = -1 \qquad \cos\theta = \dfrac{1}{2}$
   $\theta = 180° \qquad \theta = 60°$
   We eliminate the solution 180° due to
   the restriction on the variable given in
   the question, so the solution is 60°.
   b) $A = 16\sin 60°\,(\cos 60° + 1)$
   $= 16\left(\dfrac{\sqrt{3}}{2}\right)\left(\dfrac{1}{2} + 1\right)$
   $= 16\left(\dfrac{\sqrt{3}}{2}\right)\left(\dfrac{3}{2}\right)$
   $= \dfrac{48\sqrt{3}}{4}$
   $= 12\sqrt{3} = 20.8$
   Therefore the maximum area is 20.8 cm²
   c)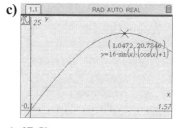

8. **a)** 67.5°
   b) 18.75 m

c)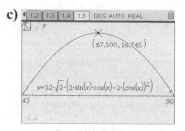

max $R = 18.745$ m at $\theta = 67.5°$

9. **a)** 30°, 60° **b)** 123.6 m

10. $-\dfrac{5\pi}{3}, -\dfrac{4\pi}{3}, -\dfrac{2\pi}{3}, -\dfrac{\pi}{3}, \dfrac{\pi}{3}, \dfrac{2\pi}{3}, \dfrac{4\pi}{3}, \dfrac{5\pi}{3}$

11.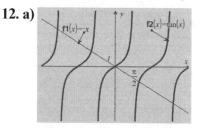

$$\dfrac{1 + \sec x}{\sec x} = \dfrac{\sin^2 x}{1 - \cos x}$$

$$\dfrac{1 + \dfrac{1}{\cos x}}{\dfrac{1}{\cos x}} = \dfrac{1 - \cos^2 x}{1 - \cos x}$$

$$\dfrac{\dfrac{\cos x}{\cos x} + \dfrac{1}{\cos x}}{\dfrac{1}{\cos x}} = \dfrac{(1 - \cos x)(1 + \cos x)}{(1 - \cos x)}$$

$$\dfrac{\dfrac{\cos x + 1}{\cos x}}{\dfrac{1}{\cos x}} = 1 + \cos x$$

$$\dfrac{\cos x + 1}{\cos x} \times \dfrac{\cos x}{1} = 1 + \cos x$$

$$\cos x + 1 = 1 + \cos x$$

$$0 = 0$$

Since this is always true, all values are
solutions to the original expression, as a
result the solution is $x \in [-2\pi, 2\pi]$.

12. **a)**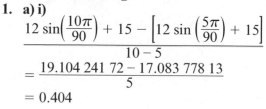

b) 2.02, 4.91

5.5 Making Connections and Instantaneous Rates of Change

1. **a) i)**
   $$\dfrac{12\sin\left(\dfrac{10\pi}{90}\right) + 15 - \left[12\sin\left(\dfrac{5\pi}{90}\right) + 15\right]}{10 - 5}$$
   $$= \dfrac{19.104\,241\,72 - 17.083\,778\,13}{5}$$
   $$= 0.404$$

ii) $\dfrac{12\sin\left(\dfrac{10\pi}{90}\right)+15-\left[12\sin\left(\dfrac{9\pi}{90}\right)+15\right]}{10-9}$

$=\dfrac{19.104\,241\,72-18.708\,203\,93}{1}$

$=0.396$

iii) $\dfrac{12\sin\left(\dfrac{10\pi}{90}\right)+15-\left[12\sin\left(\dfrac{9.9\pi}{90}\right)+15\right]}{10-9.9}$

$=\dfrac{19.104\,241\,72-19.064\,855\,04}{0.1}$

$=0.394$

iv) $\dfrac{12\sin\left(\dfrac{10\pi}{90}\right)+15-\left[12\sin\left(\dfrac{9.99\pi}{90}\right)+15\right]}{10-9.99}$

$=\dfrac{19.104\,241\,72-19.100\,305\,29}{0.01}$

$=0.394$

b) As the two points from part a) get closer and closer together at the value of $x=10$, the behaviour of the secant slopes becomes the value of the tangent slope at $x=10$. As a result, the tangent slope is approximately 0.394 m/s.

c) The instantaneous rate of change represents the speed of the particle at $t=10\ s$.

d) The slope of points on a sinusoidal function that are in phase to each other should have the same slope. Therefore, with this function having a period of 180 seconds $\dfrac{2\pi}{k}=\dfrac{2\pi}{\dfrac{\pi}{90}}$ or 180, we would expect the speed to be the same at $t=194$ s, $t=374$ s, and so on.

2. a) $d(t)=6\cos\left(\dfrac{\pi}{6}t\right)+14$

b)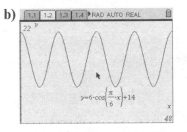

c) i) -0.804 **ii)** -0.409 **iii)** -0.273 **iv)** -0.137 **v)** -0.069 **vi)** -0.014

d) approximately -0.016 **e)** speed by which water depth changes at time $t=9{:}00$ a.m.

3. a) $120;\ 40\pi$ **b)** $E=120\sin(40\pi t)$

4. a) $y=12.2\sin\left[\dfrac{\pi}{6}(x-4)\right]+10.9$

b)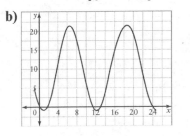

c) $y=11.76\sin(0.55x-2.35)+10.66$

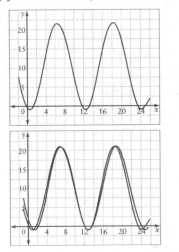

The two graphs are very close to each other.

d) Answers may vary. For example: $(x,\,y)=(4.27,\,10.9)$ **e)** 6.49 °C/month **f)** the rate by which average monthly temperature changes at month x

5. a)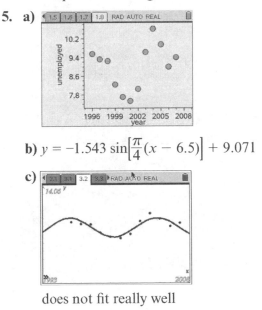

b) $y=-1.543\sin\left[\dfrac{\pi}{4}(x-6.5)\right]+9.071$

c)

does not fit really well

d)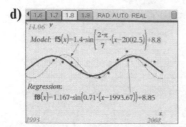

Answers may vary. For example: The regression equation and the model are pretty close.

e) 1998 **f)** -0.8 **g)** the rate by which the number of unemployed people changes at year x

6. a) Answers may vary. For example: At $t = 5$, the weight is at its minimum position, and would have a slope of zero. The speed would be a max at a time of $t = 1.5$ seconds, half way from a min (at $t = 1$) and a max ($t = 2$). **b)** 9.5 cm/s
c) speed of the weight (going up) at time $t = 1.5$ s

7. a) i) 0.8363 m/s **ii)** 0.7766 m/s
iii) 0.7639 m/s **iv)** 0.7626 m/s
b) 0.763 m/s
c) No, the graph of the sine function changes its slope continually and would not likely yield the same value at a different value of t.

8. a)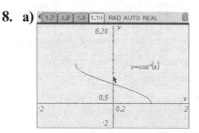

No, fails the vertical line test. Restrict range to $[0, \pi]$.

b) $x = 0$ **c)** -1

9. a)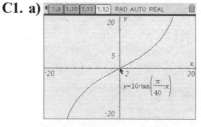

$0, \pi, 2\pi; x \to \dfrac{\pi}{2}; x \to \dfrac{3\pi}{2}$

b)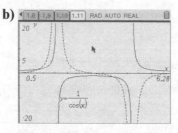

c) Answers may vary.

10. a)

Value of θ	Instantaneous Rate of Change
$-\pi$	-1
$\dfrac{-\pi}{2}$	0
0	1
$\dfrac{\pi}{2}$	0
π	-1

b)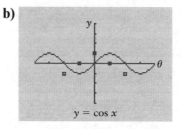

$y = \cos x$

c) The instantaneous rate of change of the sine function is the cosine function.

Challenge Questions

C1. a)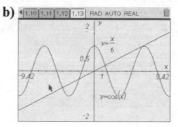

b) 2.4 m **c)** 24.1 m

C2. a) 1.72 **b)** 2.27 **c)** 12.27
d) $d(t) = 1.72 \cos[0.163\pi (t - 0.05)] + 2.27$
e) 3.98 m

C3. a) 3

b)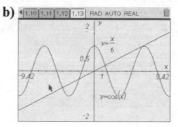

C4. $\frac{\pi}{4}$

C5. a) From the diagram, in the summer:

$\tan \theta = \frac{2}{d}$ so $d = \frac{2}{\tan \theta}$, and since the

angle is a function of the latitude, given

by $23.5 + l$, we have $d(l) = \frac{2}{\tan(23.5 + l)}$

b)

c) Answers may vary.

C6. a)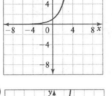

b) 2.034 *s*, 5.176 *s*; 3.605 *s*

C7. 0.001335 s **C8.** April, October

C9. $-\frac{5\pi}{3}, -\frac{\pi}{3}, \frac{\pi}{3}, \frac{5\pi}{3}$

C10. $-\frac{3\pi}{2}, -\frac{\pi}{2}, \frac{\pi}{2}, \frac{3\pi}{2}$

C11. 26 **C12.** $\frac{\sqrt{2}}{2}$

C13. a) 2.6° **b)** 190 km/h

C14. a) $y = 3.2 \sin\left[\frac{\pi}{6}(x - 9)\right] + 7.7$

b)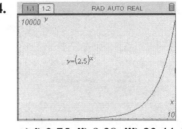

Excellent fit.

c) $y = 3.293 \sin(0.527x + 1.534) + 7.647$

Very close.

d) months 0, 6, 12; month 9

Chapter 6

6.1 The Exponential Function and Its Inverse

1. **a) i)** domain $\{x \in \mathbb{R}\}$ and range $\{y > 0, y \in \mathbb{R}\}$,
    ii) no *x*-intercept
    iii) *y*-intercept at (0, 1)
    iv) the function is always positive
    v) the function is always increasing
    vi) $y = 0$

    b)

    c)

    d) i) domain $\{x > 0, x \in \mathbb{R}\}$ and range $\{y \in \mathbb{R}\}$
    ii) *x*-intercept at (0, 1)
    iii) no *y*-intercept
    iv) the function is positive for $x > 1$ and is negative for $0 < x < 1$
    v) the function is always increasing
    vi) $x = 0$

2. **a)** Data set (ii) is exponential. Successive terms have constant ratios. **b)** $y = 5^x$

3. Tables b) and d) represent exponential functions. Functions are $y = 1.5(3)^x$ and $y = 4(0.8)^x$, respectively.

4.

    a) i) 3.75 **ii)** 9.38 **iii)** 23.44 **iv)** 58.59
    b) i) 5.73 **ii)** 14.32 **iii)** 35.79 **iv)** 89.48
    c) positive and increasing

5.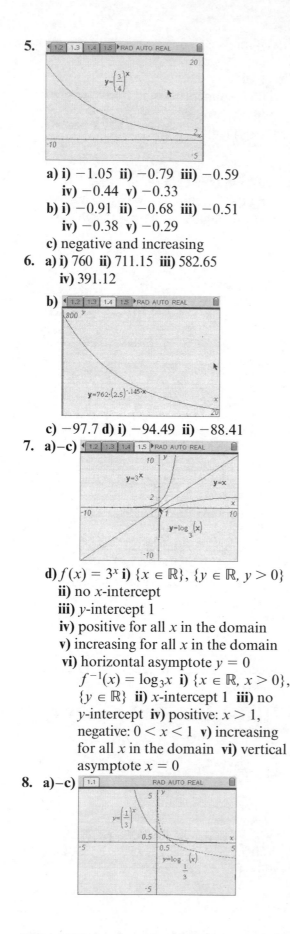

a) i) -1.05 ii) -0.79 iii) -0.59
   iv) -0.44 v) -0.33
b) i) -0.91 ii) -0.68 iii) -0.51
   iv) -0.38 v) -0.29
c) negative and increasing

6. a) i) 760 ii) 711.15 iii) 582.65
   iv) 391.12

b)

c) -97.7 d) i) -94.49 ii) -88.41

7. a)–c)

d) $f(x) = 3^x$ i) $\{x \in \mathbb{R}\}$, $\{y \in \mathbb{R}, y > 0\}$
   ii) no x-intercept
   iii) y-intercept 1
   iv) positive for all x in the domain
   v) increasing for all x in the domain
   vi) horizontal asymptote $y = 0$
   $f^{-1}(x) = \log_3 x$ i) $\{x \in \mathbb{R}, x > 0\}$,
   $\{y \in \mathbb{R}\}$ ii) x-intercept 1 iii) no
   y-intercept iv) positive: $x > 1$,
   negative: $0 < x < 1$ v) increasing
   for all x in the domain vi) vertical
   asymptote $x = 0$

8. a)–c)

i) $\{x \in \mathbb{R}\}$, $\{y \in \mathbb{R}, y > 0\}$
ii) no x-intercepts iii) y-intercept 1
iv) positive for all x in the domain
v) decreasing for all x in the domain
vi) horizontal asymptote at $y = 0$

d) $g^{-1}(x) = \log_{1/3} x$

i) $\{x \in \mathbb{R}, x > 0\}$, $\{y \in \mathbb{R}\}$
ii) x-intercept 1 iii) no y-intercept
iv) positive: $0 < x < 1$, negative: $x > 1$
v) decreasing for all x in the domain
vi) vertical asymptote at $x = 0$

9. a)–c)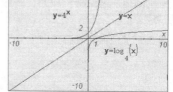

d) $y = 4^x$

10. a) 21.46 b) 0.18
11. a) 46.75 watts b) 22.09 watts c) -0.101,
   -0.051 d) -0.105, -0.049
12. a) 0.01 b) 0.86 c) 5.03

d)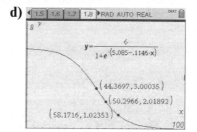

approximately 58.2 F, 50.3 F, 44.4 F
e) -0.021, -0.139

13. a)

b)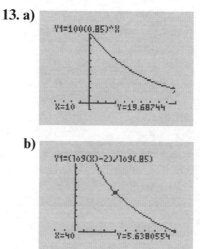

c) 4.3 m **d)** -11.3%/m **e)** -7.21%/m; greater, magnitude of slope is increasing as d increases

14.

	$f(x) = \left(\dfrac{1}{2}\right)^x$	Inverse of f
Domain	$\{x \in \mathbb{R}\}$	$\{x \in \mathbb{R}, x > 0\}$
Range	$\{y \in \mathbb{R}, y > 0\}$	$\{y \in \mathbb{R}\}$
X-intercept	none	1
Y-intercept	1	none
Intervals for which $f(x)$ is positive	$(-\infty, +\infty)$	$(0,1)$
Intervals for which $f(x)$ is increasing	none	none
Equation of asymptote	$y = 0$	$x = 0$

6.2 Logarithms

1. a) $\log_3 243 = 5$ **b)** $\log_6 \dfrac{1}{216} = -3$

2. a) 2 **b)** -6 **c)** 2 **d)** -2.6

3. a) $4^3 = 64$ **b)** $10^y = 30$

4. $x = \log_5 125$ **5.** -3

6. $5^4 = 625$

7. a) $\log_3 9 = 2$ **b)** $\log_4 16 = 2$
   c) $\log_6\left(\dfrac{1}{36}\right) = -2$ **d)** $\log_{\frac{1}{3}}\left(\dfrac{1}{27}\right) = 3$
   e) $\log_7 y = x$ **f)** $\log_{10} 10000 = 4$
   g) $\log_5\left(\dfrac{1}{125}\right) = -3$ **h)** $\log_b a = x$

8. a) 3 **b)** 5 **c)** -2 **d)** -4 **e)** -4 **f)** 4 **g)** 5
   h) 7 **i)** 8 **j)** 9

9. a) 5 **b)** -3 **c)** -3 **d)** -9 **e)** 2 **f)** -7

10. a) $2^3 = 8$ **b)** $3^{-2} = \dfrac{1}{9}$ **c)** $a^6 = 3$ **d)** $3^x = 2$
   e) $2^x = 6$ **f)** $2^{1.3} = x$ **g)** $\sqrt{2}^x = \pi$ **h)** $5^{7y} = 3x$

11. a)

b)
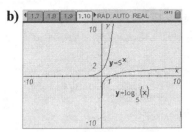

12. a) 2.1 **b)** -0.9 **c)** 1.1 **d)** 3.3 **e)** -1.9 **f)** 3.9
13. a) 6.3 **b)** 12.6 **14. a)** 11.56 **b)** 13.78
15. a) 218.7 km **b)** 76 158 859.21 s
   (or approximately 21 155 hours)
16. a) 2.36×10^{25} **b)** 10.5 h **c)** 14.9 h
17. a) 4.3 **b)** 10^{-11} mol/L
18. a) Sirius is 23 times more luminous than the Sun. Vega is 53.8 times more luminous than the Sun. The North Star is 5875 times more luminous than the Sun. Deneb is 63 715 times more luminous than the Sun. **b)** Answers may vary.
19. a) 2374 years **b)** 19 000 years **c)** $R = 10^{\frac{A}{19000}}$
   d) 99%

6.3 Transformations of Logarithmic Functions

1. a)
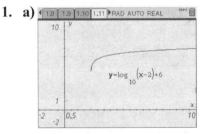

b) i) $\{x \in \mathbb{R}, x > 2\}$, $\{y \in \mathbb{R}\}$ **ii)** x-intercept 2.000001 **iii)** no y-intercept **iv)** vertical asymptote $x = 2$

2. a)
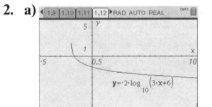

b) i) $\{x \in \mathbb{R}, x > -2\}$, $\{y \in \mathbb{R}\}$
   ii) x-intercept $-\dfrac{5}{3}$ **iii)** y-intercept -1.56
   iv) vertical asymptote $x = -2$
3. a) and iv); b) and iii); c) and ii); d) and i)
4. a) translation 3 units to the left
   b) translation 2 units to the right and 4 up

c) translation 3 units to the right and 2 up
d) translation 2 units to the left and 3 up

5. a)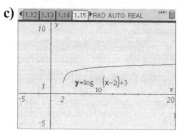

domain $\{x \in \mathbb{R}, x > 0\}$, range $\{y \in \mathbb{R}\}$; no y-intercept; x-intercept 1000; vertical asymptote $x = 0$

b)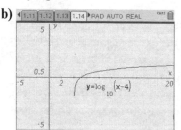

domain $\{x \in \mathbb{R}, x > 4\}$, range $\{y \in \mathbb{R}\}$; no y-intercept; x-intercept 5; vertical asymptote $x = 4$

c)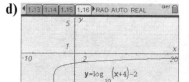

domain $\{x \in \mathbb{R}, x > 2\}$, range $\{y \in \mathbb{R}\}$; no y-intercept; x-intercept 2.001; vertical asymptote $x = 2$

d)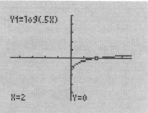

domain $\{x \in \mathbb{R}, x > -4\}$, range $\{y \in \mathbb{R}\}$; y-intercept -1.4; x-intercept 96; vertical asymptote $x = -4$

6. a) $y = 2 \log x$ **b)** $y = \dfrac{1}{4} \log x$ **c)** $y = 5 \log x$
d) $y = \dfrac{1}{2} \log x$

7. a) $\{x \in \mathbb{R}, x > 0\}, \{y \in \mathbb{R}\}$

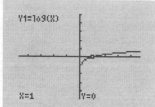

b) $\{x \in \mathbb{R}, x > 0\}, \{y \in \mathbb{R}\}$

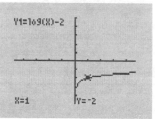

c) $\{x \in \mathbb{R}, x > 0\}, \{y \in \mathbb{R}\}$

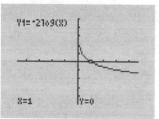

d) $\{x \in \mathbb{R}, x < 0\}, \{y \in \mathbb{R}\}$

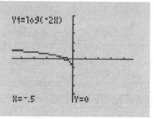

e) $\{x \in \mathbb{R}, x > 0\}, \{y \in \mathbb{R}\}$

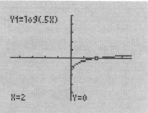

f) $\{x \in \mathbb{R}, x > 2\}, \{y \in \mathbb{R}\}$

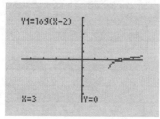

8. a)

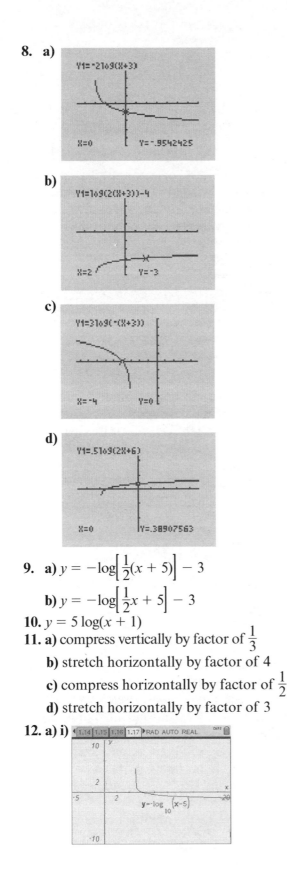

9. a) $y = -\log\left[\frac{1}{2}(x + 5)\right] - 3$

   b) $y = -\log\left[\frac{1}{2}x + 5\right] - 3$

10. $y = 5\log(x + 1)$

11. a) compress vertically by factor of $\frac{1}{3}$

   b) stretch horizontally by factor of 4

   c) compress horizontally by factor of $\frac{1}{2}$

   d) stretch horizontally by factor of 3

12. a) i)

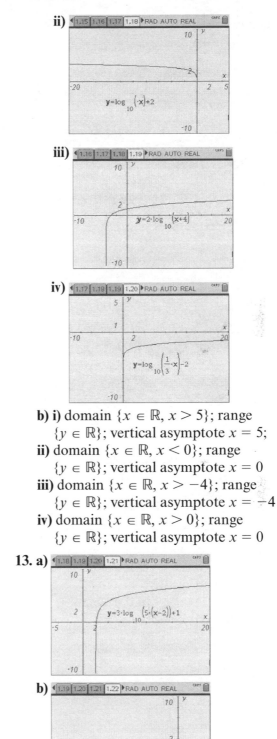

b) i) domain $\{x \in \mathbb{R}, x > 5\}$; range $\{y \in \mathbb{R}\}$; vertical asymptote $x = 5$;

   ii) domain $\{x \in \mathbb{R}, x < 0\}$; range $\{y \in \mathbb{R}\}$; vertical asymptote $x = 0$

   iii) domain $\{x \in \mathbb{R}, x > -4\}$; range $\{y \in \mathbb{R}\}$; vertical asymptote $x = -4$

   iv) domain $\{x \in \mathbb{R}, x > 0\}$; range $\{y \in \mathbb{R}\}$; vertical asymptote $x = 0$

13. a)

b)

c)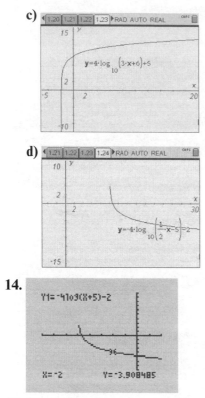

d)

14.

15. 127.155 h

16. a–c)

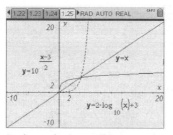

d) i) domain$\{x \in \mathbb{R}\}$ **ii)** range
$\{y \in \mathbb{R}, y > 0\}$ **iii)** horizontal
asymptote $y = 0$

17. a)

b)

18. a) domain $\left\{x \in ..., \left(-\dfrac{5\pi}{2}, \dfrac{3\pi}{2}\right), \left(-\dfrac{\pi}{2}, \dfrac{\pi}{2}\right), \right.$
$\left. \left(-\dfrac{3\pi}{2}, \dfrac{5\pi}{2}\right), ...\right\}$ The function S(x) is
defined only when cos x is positive. The
cos x function is positive in the intervals:
$...,\left(-\dfrac{5\pi}{2}, \dfrac{3\pi}{2}\right), \left(-\dfrac{\pi}{2}, \dfrac{\pi}{2}\right), \left(-\dfrac{3\pi}{2}, \dfrac{5\pi}{2}\right), ...$
range $\{y \in \mathbb{R}, y < -3\}$, due to the fact
that cos x will always be positive and
less than one, and the log of this will be
negative, causing the value of the function
to always be less than -3.

b)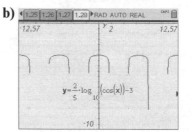

c) Answers may vary. Sample answer:
No, because pattern is too cyclic, most
likely created by a naturally occurring,
repeating event such as the rotation of
a pulsar.

19. a) i) 12 years **ii)** 19 years
b) approximately $1585

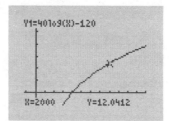

c) $A \geq 1000$ because $n \geq 0$
20. a) compress horizontally by a factor of $\dfrac{1}{2}$,
translate left 3 units, reflect in the x-axis
b) reflect in the y-axis, stretch vertically by
a factor of 3, translate up 4 units
21. The function $y = -\log(-x)$ can be obtained
by reflecting $y = \log x$ in the y-axis and
reflecting in the x-axis, so that a point (a, b)
is transformed to $(-a, -b)$. Reflection of the
function $y = \log x$ in the line $y = x$ has the
exact effect, so the two functions are inverses.
22. a) Each pair of graphs is identical.

b) translated up 4 units

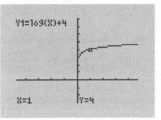

6.4 Power Laws of Logarithms

1. 9
2. 1.76
3. 1.75
4.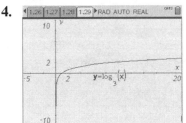

5. **a) i)** $1500 **ii)** $1881.60 **iii)** $2360.28
   b) i) 6.1 years **ii)** 12.2 years
6. **a)** 15 **b)** 3.37 **c)** -6 **d)** -1
7. **a)** $\frac{2}{3}$ **b)** 4 **c)** 18 **d)** -9
8. **a)** 1.29 **b)** 0.43 **c)** 2 **d)** 1.60
9. **a) i)** $1500 **ii)** $1694.59 **iii)** $1914.42
   b) i) 14.2 years **ii)** 28.4 years
10. **a)** 2.613 **b)** 3.210 **c)** 0.732 **d)** -0.594
    e) -2.727 **f)** -6.530
11. **a)** $\log_4 9$ **b)** $\log_5 12$ **c)** $\log_{\frac{5}{7}} \frac{1}{3}$
    d) $\log_{(x-5)}(x+3)$
12. **a)** 4.292 **b)** 100 **c)** 1.250 **d)** 4.096
13. **a)** Initially, the investment is made
    at $t = 0$, so
    $$A(t) = 1200(1.06)^{2t}$$
    $$A(0) = 1200(1.06)^0$$
    $$= 1200$$
    Therefore, the initial investment is $1200
    b) To triple means that the investment
    needs to grow to $3600, so
    $$A(t) = 1200(1.06)^{2t}$$
    $$3600 = 1200(1.06)^0$$
    $$3 = (1.06)^{2t}$$
    $$\ell n\, 3 = 2\,t\,\ell n\,(1.06)$$
    $$\frac{\ell n\, 3}{2\,\ell n\,(1.06)} = t$$
    $$t = 9.4$$

Therefore, it will take approximately
9.4 years for the investment to grow
to $3600.
14. **a)** 21 **b)** 21 **c)** Answers may vary. For
    example: Power law of logarithms is easier.
15. **a)** $t = \log_{0.5}\left(\dfrac{d}{250}\right)$ becomes

    $$t = \log_{0.5}\left(\frac{1}{250}\right)$$
    $$= 7.97$$
    Therefore the docking procedures can begin
    approximately 8 hours after the controlled
    breaking starts.
    b) Due to the answer for a), we have
    a domain $\{d \in \mathbb{R}, 1 \leq x \leq 250\}$,
    range $\{t \in \mathbb{R}, 0 \leq t \leq 8\}$
16. **a)** $A(t) = I(1.04)^t$, where I is the initial
    investment
    b) i) 28 years **ii)** 35.3 years
    c) i) 26.5% **ii)** 60.1%
17. **a)** $\dfrac{\log_3 1024}{\log_3 4}$ **b)** $\dfrac{\log_3 37}{\log_3 10}$
18. **a)** $A(t) = I(1.0275)^{2t}$, where I is the initial
    investment
    b) i) 12.8 years **ii)** 20.2 years

6.5 Making Connections: Logarithmic Scales in the Physical Science

1. **a)** -2 **b)** 8.3 **c)** 0.001 mol/L
   d) tomato juice has 10 times higher
   concentration of hydronium ions than
   soft drinking water
2. approximately 4 times
3. approximately 8 times
4. **a)** maximum stereo output is 100 times as
   intense as a shout **b)** 100 dB
5. **a)** 15 849 times **b)** 4.7
6. **a)** 3 **b)** 3.1 **c)** 5 **d)** 7.4
7. **a)** 10^{-15} mol/L **b)** 10^{-4} mol/L
   c) 5.012×10^{-12} mol/L
   d) 6.31×10^{-7} mol/L
8. Substitute $I = 1.15 \times 10^{-10}$ in $L = 10 \log$
   $L = 10 \log$
   $= 10 \log 115$
   $= 20.6$ dB
9. 39.5 dB **10.** 100 times
11. **a)** 10^7 times **b)** 10^{15} times
12. 3981 times **13.** 6

14. a) 5 011 872 times **b)** 2.5×10^{-6} times
15. 3162 times
16. a) The factor of the increase is given by
$\log\left(\dfrac{L}{L_O}\right)$, so when the brightness
increased by 200 times, the factor can be
found by evaluating $\log(200)$ which is
2.301. Therefore, the magnitude increased
by a factor of 2.3
b) The factor of the increase is given by log
$\left(\dfrac{L}{L_O}\right)$, so when the brightness increased
by 1000 times, the factor can be found by
evaluating $\log(1000)$ which is 3 Therefore,
the magnitude increased by a factor of 3
17. a) 10^{-6} W/m^2 **b)** 0.5 W/m^2

Chapter 6 Challenge Questions
C1. 3.35 mg, 0.45 mg
C2. $N = P(1 - e^{-0.15d})$ becomes
$N = 1000(1 - e^{-0.15(3)})$
$= 1000(0.36237)$
$= 362.37$
Therefore, 362 students would have heard
the rumour after 3 days.
C3. a) 38.2 W **b)** 0.84 W **c)** -0.0827 W/day,
-0.0149 W/day **d)** -0.0856 W/day,
-0.0019 W/day
C4. 6.8 **C5. a)** 50 119 **b)** star B

C6. a) $h = \dfrac{-\ln\left(\dfrac{P}{760}\right)}{0.145}$

$= \dfrac{-\ln\left(\dfrac{271.5}{760}\right)}{0.145}$

$= \dfrac{1.029\ 356\ 294}{0.145}$

$= 7.099$ km

b) $8.85 = \dfrac{-\ln\left(\dfrac{P}{760}\right)}{0.145}$

$8.85 \times 0.145 = -\ln\left(\dfrac{P}{760}\right)$

$-1.283\ 25 = \ln\left(\dfrac{P}{760}\right)$

$e^{-1.283\ 25} = \dfrac{P}{760}$

$P = 760 \times e^{-1.283\ 25}$

$P = 210.6$ or approx 211 mm
of mercury

c) $2.1 = \dfrac{-\ln\left(\dfrac{P}{760}\right)}{0.145}$

$2.1 \times 0.145 = -\ln\left(\dfrac{P}{760}\right)$

$-0.3045 = \ln\left(\dfrac{P}{760}\right)$

$e^{-0.304\ 5} = \dfrac{P}{760}$

$P = 760 \times e^{-0304\ 5}$

$P = 560.49$ or approx
560.5 mm or mercury
The pressure difference can be found by
subtraction: $(760 - 560.5) = 199.5$ mm
of mercury
C7. a) 3541.5 m **b)** 83 mm or mercury
C8. a) 9.8 years **b)** 4.3 years
C9. a)

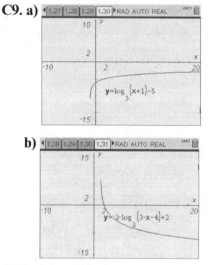

b)

C10. a) $0 < a < 1$
b) point of intersection (x, y) is always
in quadrant 1, where $0 < x < 1$ and
$0 < y < 1$
C11. a) $A(t) = I(1.002\ 307\ 692)^{52t}$
b) i) 9.2 years **ii)** 11.6 years
c) i) 604% **ii)** 1099%
C12. 4.04 years **C13.** approximately 10%
C14. 1 584 893 times **C15.** 4
C16. 7 **C17.** 6.31×10^{-5} mol/L
C18. 20 times **C19.** $x(t) = \dfrac{\left(ab2^{\frac{t}{c}} - 1\right)}{a2^{\frac{t}{c}} - b}$

Chapter 7
7.1 Equivalent Forms of Exponential Equations

1. a) 2^{16} **b)** 2^{14} **c)** 2^{-9} **d)** $2^{\log_2 11}$

2. a) 3^8 **b)** 3^{21} **c)** 3^{-6} **d)** $3^{\log_3 \frac{1}{5}}$

3. a) 4^9 **b)** 2^{-10} **c)** $4^{\frac{3\log 5}{\log 4}}$

4. a) $3^{\frac{4}{3}}$ **b)** 3^1

5. a) $x = -10$ **b)** $t = 28$ **c)** $x = \dfrac{17}{9}$

6. a) 27^3 **b)** $9^{\frac{9}{2}}$ **c)** $3^9 = 27^3 = 9^{\frac{9}{2}} = 19\,683$

7. a) 4^{10} **b)** $4^{\frac{3}{5}}$ **c)** $4^{\frac{49}{10}}$ **d)** 4^3

8. a) $x = \dfrac{13}{3}$ **b)** $w = 4$ **c)** $x = 12$ **d)** $w = \dfrac{5}{6}$

9. a) $x = -3$ **b)** $x = -\dfrac{23}{14}$ **c)** $y = -\dfrac{8}{7}$ **d)** $k = \dfrac{39}{8}$

10. a) $x = 7$ **b)** $x = 7$ **c)** Answers may vary.

11. a) $x = -\dfrac{7}{2}$ **b)** $k = -\dfrac{3}{2}$

12. a) $x = \dfrac{1}{\log 3}$ **b–c)** Answers may vary.

13. a) $x = -\dfrac{2}{5}$ **b)** $x = -\dfrac{2}{5}$

c)

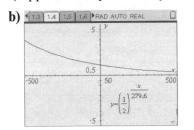

$x = -\dfrac{2}{5} = -0.4$ **d)** Answers may vary.

14. a) $x = -\dfrac{1}{3}$ **b)** $x = -\dfrac{1}{3}$

15. a) i) $x = \log 5$ **ii)** $x = \log 3$ **iii)** $x = \log 7$
b) $x = \log b$

16. a) $x = \dfrac{11}{15}$ **b)** $x = \dfrac{11}{15}$ **c)** $x = \dfrac{11}{15}$

d) Answers may vary.

17. a) i) no solution **ii)** $x < 5$ **b)** Answers may vary. For example: Graph both side of the inequality. Identify where the graphs intersect. Identify the interval(s) where the inequality is true.

7.2 Techniques for Solving Exponential Equations

1. Graph 1: $y = 200\left(\dfrac{1}{3}\right)^{\frac{x}{3}}$; Graph 4: $y = 70\left(\dfrac{1}{3}\right)^x$

Graph 3: $y = 70\left(\dfrac{1}{3}\right)^{\frac{x}{3}}$; Graph 2: $y = 200\left(\dfrac{1}{3}\right)^x$;

2. a) 6.19 **b)** 6.18 **c)** 2.71 **d)** 8.78 **e)** -4.10
f) -1.46 **g)** -12.01 **h)** -5

3. a) approximately 76.7 mg **b)** approximately 6.2 min **c)** no

4. a) $x = \dfrac{2\log 4}{\log 4 - \log 3}$ **b)** $x = \dfrac{3\log 7}{\log 5 - \log 7}$

c) $x = \dfrac{2\log 4 + 4\log 9}{\log 9 - \log 4}$

d) $x = \dfrac{2\log 5 - 5\log 8}{3\log 8 - \log 5}$

5. a) $x = 9.638$ **b)** $x = -17.350$
c) $x = 14.257$ **d)** $x = -1.551$

6. a) $z^2 + z - 12 = 0,\ a = 1,\ b = 1,\ c = -12$
b) $z = 3$ or $z = -4$ **c)** $z = -4$

7. a) $z^2 - 2z - 3 = 0,\ a = 1,\ b = -2,\ c = -3$
b) $z = 3$ or $z = -1$ **c)** $z = -1$ **8.** $\dfrac{3}{4}$ h

9. a) 10.7 min **b)** 35.5 min

10. a) approximately 279.6 days

b)

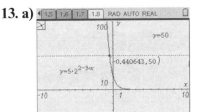

c) i) graph would decrease faster
ii) graph would decrease slower
d) i) graph would stretch vertically
ii) graph would compress vertically

11. $x = \log_3 6$

12. a) $x \cong -0.44$ **b)** $x \cong 0.28$ **c)** $x = 0.5$
d) $x \cong 0.56$ **e)** $x \cong -1.58$ **f)** $x = -1$

13. a)

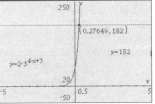

b)

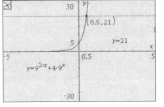

c)

d)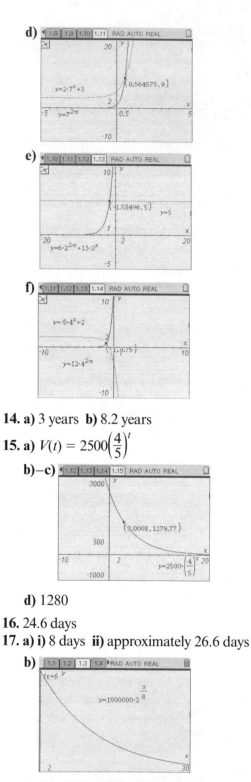

e)

f)

14. a) 3 years **b)** 8.2 years

15. a) $V(t) = 2500\left(\dfrac{4}{5}\right)^t$

b)–c)

d) 1280

16. 24.6 days

17. a) i) 8 days **ii)** approximately 26.6 days

b)

c) i) half life of 8 will be replaced by a larger number
ii) graph decreases slower

18. a) $P(t) = 5000(2)^t$ **b)** $P(t) = 3500(3)^t$
   c) $t \cong 1.9$ days; approximately 2 days after each of the movie trailers was posted, they reached the same number of people.

19. a) 65 h **b)** 49 h **20. a)** 1.18 m **b)** 29

21. $P(t) = 4(2)^{\frac{t \log 1.4}{24 \log 2}}$ **22. a)** 16.5% **b)** 360.5%

23. a) $A(t) = A_0\left(\dfrac{1}{2}\right)^{\frac{t}{15}}$ **b)** $\{t \in R, t \geq 0\}$,
   $\{A \in R, 0 < A \leq A_0\}$

7.3 Product and Quotient Laws of Logarithms

1. a) $\log 40$ **b)** $\log 8$ **c)** $\log_2 24$ **d)** 1
2. a) 1.602 **b)** 0.903 **c)** 4.585 **d)** 1
3. a) $\log(6xyz), x > 0, y > 0, z > 0$

   b) $\log_2\left(\dfrac{3xy}{z^5}\right), x > 0, y > 0, z > 0$

   c) $\log\left(\dfrac{a^3y^4}{z^2}\right), a > 0, y > 0, z > 0$

   d) $\log\left(\dfrac{9x^2y^3}{2\sqrt{w}}\right), x > 0, y > 0, w > 0$

4. a) 8 **b)** 3 **c)** 6.5 **d)** 3
5. a) 8 **b)** 4 **c)** 6 **d)** 2
6. a) 1 **b)** 2 **c)** 1 **d)** 4
7. a) 1 **b)** 2 **8.** $\log_3 5(x-2)^2$
9. $\log a + 4\log b - \dfrac{1}{4}\log c$
10. a) $\log\dfrac{x+2}{3}, x > 6$

   b) $\log(x^2 + 3x + 9), x > 3$
11. a) $\log_5 x + \log_5 y, x > 0, y > 0$
   b) $\log_8 a - \log_8 b, a > 0, b > 0$
   c) $3 + \log_2 5$
   d) $1 + \log_6 20$
12. a) $-\dfrac{3}{2}\log x, x > 0$ **b)** $\dfrac{38}{3}\log x, x > 0$

   c) $\dfrac{29}{6}\log x, x > 0$ **d)** $\dfrac{11}{2}\log x, x > 0$

13. a) $\log(x-3), x > 3$ **b)** $\log(x-4), x > 7$

   c) $\log\left(\dfrac{x+9}{3}\right), x > 4$ **d)** $\log\left(\dfrac{2x+3}{x-2}\right)$,
   $x < -2, x > 2$
14. a) $4\log m, m > 0$ **b)** $\log p, p > 0$
   c) $\log\dfrac{x^2 - 5x - 6}{x - 3}, x > 6$
   d) $\log(3x - 2), x > \dfrac{3}{2}$

15. a)

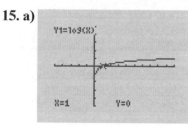

b)

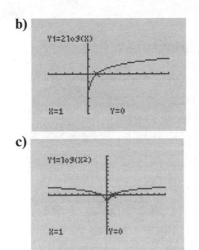

c)

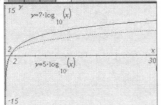

d) same for $x > 0$; power law

16. a) $y = \dfrac{(x - 3)^2}{x}$, $\{x \in \mathbb{R}, x > 3\}$

b) $y = \dfrac{x}{1000 - x}$, $\{x \in \mathbb{R}, x > 0, x \neq 1000\}$

c) $y = \dfrac{x^2}{(x + 5)^2}$, $\{x \in \mathbb{R}, x > 0\}$

17. Answers may vary.

18. a)

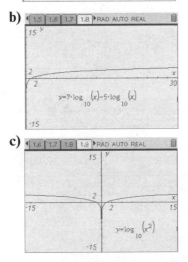

b)

c)

d) $r(x)$ and $s(x)$ are the same for $x > 0$.
This illustrates power law of logarithms.

19. a) approximately 8.7 years
b) i) Firm B **ii)** Firm B

c) Answers may vary. Sample answer:
Other issues such as promotions, health insurance, vacation, maternity, travel, commuting time, etc., may influence Ifra's decision.

20. a) i) approximately -0.42
ii) approximately -0.67
b) E is negative; the cell is expending energy.

21. a) $A_v = 20 \log\left(\dfrac{V_o}{V_i}\right)$ **b)** approximately 4.24

22. Answers may vary.

7.4 Techniques for Solving Logarithmic Equations

1. a) $x = 15$ **b)** $x = 135$ **c)** $x = 927$
d) $x = 6$ **e)** $x = 106$ **f)** $n = \dfrac{100}{3}$

2. a) $x = 7$ **b)** $x = \dfrac{76}{3}$ **c)** $x = 44$
d) $x = -25$ **e)** $t = 6$ **f)** $n = -3, n = 5$

3. a) $x = 5$ **b)** $x = \pm 3$ **c)** no solution
d) no solution **e)** $x = 5$ **f)** $x = 6$

4. $x = 13$

5. a) $x = 3 \pm 3\sqrt{2}$ **b)** $x = \dfrac{-21 \pm \sqrt{40\,441}}{2}$

6. a) $x = 2$ **b)** $x = \dfrac{6}{7}$ **c)** $x = \dfrac{7}{15}$

7. a) $x = 2$

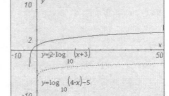

b) no solution

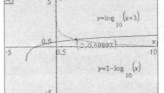

8. a) approximately 9139.6 m **b)** approximately 5539.0 m **c)** Answers may vary. For example: The difference in height will be calculated as follows:
$$h = 18\,400 \log \dfrac{P_0(original)}{P_0\,(new)}, \text{ where}$$
$P_0\,(original)$ is the original air pressure at ground level and $P_0\,(new)$ is the changed air pressure at ground level.

9. a) 3229.5 m **b)** 7.6 mm of mercury
c) 61.49 mm of mercury
10. $x = 16$ **11.** $x \cong 2.6$

7.5 Making Connections: Mathematical Modeling with Exponential and Logarithmic Functions

1. a)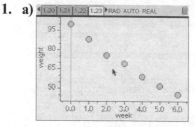

b) $A(t) = 100e^{-0.13t}$

c) approximately -3.1 weeks (3.1 weeks ago) **d)** approximately 0.15 gm

e) $A(t) = 100.326(0.876\ 865)^t$

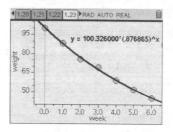

2. a)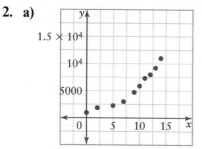

b) From the graphing calculator:
$A = 1035(1.185\ 23)^t$, with $t = 0$ at 1983.
To convert this to an exponential function in base e:
$$(1.18523)^t = e^{kt}$$
$$\ln(1.18523)^t = e^{kt}$$
$$t\ln(1.18523) = kt$$
$$k = \ln(1.18523)$$
$$k = 0.170$$
Therefore $A = 1035e^{0.170t}$

c)
$$A = 1035e^{0.170t}$$
$$15\ 000 = 1035e^{0.170t}$$
$$\frac{15\ 000}{1035} = e^{0.170t}$$
$$\ln\left(\frac{15\ 000}{1035}\right) = 0.170t$$
$$t = \frac{\ln\left(\dfrac{15\ 000}{1035}\right)}{0.170}$$
$$t = 15.7 \text{ or approx } 16$$
Therefore, the population of home-schooled students reached 15 000 in approximately 1999 (1983 + 16).

d) $A = 1035e^{0.170t}$
$A = 1035e^{0.170(37)}$
$\quad = 1035e^{6.29}$
$\quad = 1035(539.15)$
$\quad = 558\ 023.7$
Therefore, in 2020, there will be 558 024 home-schooled students in Canada.

e) verified using a graphing calculator

3. a) $A(t) = 2500(1.025)^{2t}$
b) approximately $\$ 3200.21$
c) approximately 14 years

4. a) $A(t) = 2500(1.025)^{2t} - 75$
b) translation 75 units down

5. a)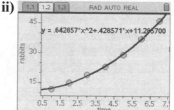

b) i)

ii)

iii)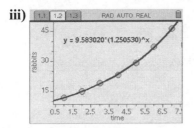

c) i) $y = 5.571\,43x + 3.571\,43$

ii) $y = 0.642\,857x^2 + 0.428\,571x + 11.285\,7$

iii) $y = 9.583\,02(1.250\,53)^x$

d) Exponential model is preferred because it best expresses steady growth for several months before the collection of data.

e) approximately 10.5 years

f) Answers may vary. For example: Population of predators, food supply, health issues, etc., may affect this trend of rabbit population.

6. a) $P = 200(1.122)^t$

b) $P = 200(1.122)^{t-20}$

c)

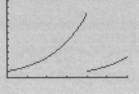

7. a) approximately 17.2 min

b) approximately 18.7 °C; approximately 20.8 °C

8. a) 10^9 **b)** 100 dB

Chapter 7 Challenge Questions

C1. a) 6^3 **b)** 6^{-2} **c)** $6^{\frac{7}{5}}$ **C2. a)** $x = 2$

b) $x = -23$

C3. a) approximately 297.3 mg

b) approximately 185.8 days

C4. a) $x = \dfrac{2 \log 4}{\log 4 - \log 7}$

b) $x = \dfrac{7 \log 3 + 3 \log 2}{\log 2 - \log 3}$

C5. a) $b \neq 0$ **b)** $b > 0$ **c)** $b < 0$

C6. a) no solution **b)** $x = 1$

c) no solution **d)** $x = \log_7 2$

C7. a) approximately 722.5

b) approximately 124.6

C8. a) 5 **b)** 3 **c)** 2 **d)** 2

C9. a) $\log_8 21$ **b)** $\log_a\left(\dfrac{bd^c}{s^r}\right)$, $a > 0$, $a \neq 1$, $b > 0$, $d > 0$, $s > 0$

C10. a) $2\log_4 a + \log_4 b - \dfrac{1}{2}\log_4 c$, $a > 0$, $b > 0$, $c > 0$

b) $\dfrac{1}{3}\log_9 y + \dfrac{1}{3}\log_9(y + 1)$, $y > 0$

C11. a) $\log\left(\dfrac{2}{x - 5}\right)$, $x > 5$

b) $\log\left(\dfrac{x + 2}{x - 5}\right)$, $x < -2$, $x > 5$

C12. a) $x = -22$ **b)** $x = \dfrac{9}{2}$ **C13.** $x = 3$

C14. a) 10 hours **b)** approximately 46.7%

C15. Answers may vary.

C16. Answers may vary.

C17. a) $x = 4096$

b) $x = 0$, $x = \dfrac{\log_5\left(\dfrac{3}{2}\right)}{2} \cong 0.13$

$x = \dfrac{\log_5 2}{2} \cong 0.22$

C18. a)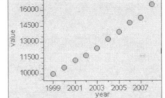

b) $A(t) = 10\,000e^{0.055\,9(t - 1999)}$

c) $A \cong \$\,32\,345.80$

d) $t \cong 2015.4$ (approximately first half of year 2015)

e)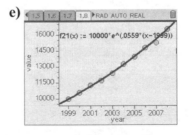

C19. a) $A(t) = 1500(1.044)^{2t}$

b) approximately \$ 4216.03

c) approximately 12.8 years

d) i) translation of 75 up

ii) vertical stretch by factor of 2

C20. a) approximately 8.5 days **b)** 45 items

Chapter 8
8.1 Sum and Difference of Functions

1. **a) i)** $y = 7x - 4$ **ii)** $y = 5x + 4$
   iii) $y = -5x - 4$
   b) i) $y = -5x + 10$ **ii)** $y = -x + 4$
   iii) $y = x - 4$
   c) i) $y = x^2 + 2$ **ii)** $y = x^2 - 6$
   iii) $y = -x^2 + 6$
   d) i) $y = 2x^2 + 8x - 9$ **ii)** $y = 2x^2 - 2x - 5$
   iii) $y = -2x^2 + 2x + 5$

2. **a)** $h(x) = 8x + 2, h(-2) = -14$
   b) $h(x) = 4x + 12, h(4) = 28$
   c) $h(x) = -4x - 12, h(-3) = 0$

3. **a)** $h(x) = 2x^2 + 5x - 4, h(0) = -4$
   b) $h(x) = 2x^2 - 5x + 10, h(-5) = 85$
   c) $h(x) = -2x^2 + 5x - 10, h(6) = -52$

4. **a)**

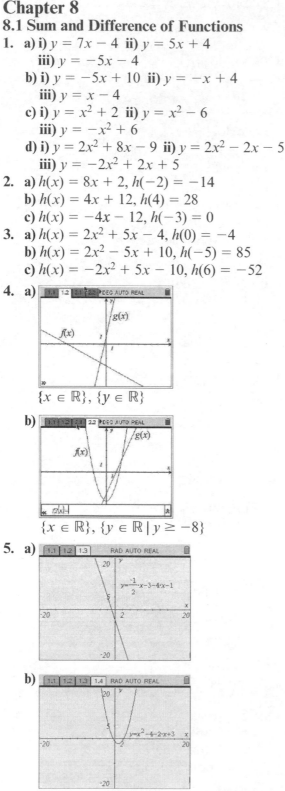

$\{x \in \mathbb{R}\}, \{y \in \mathbb{R}\}$

b)

$\{x \in \mathbb{R}\}, \{y \in \mathbb{R} \mid y \geq -8\}$

5. **a)**

b)

6. $f(x) = |x|, g(x) = 5$
   a) i) $y = f(x) + g(x) = |x| + 5$

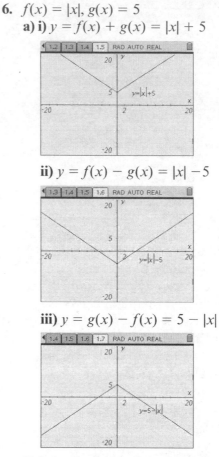

ii) $y = f(x) - g(x) = |x| - 5$

iii) $y = g(x) - f(x) = 5 - |x|$

b) i) Apply translation of 5 units up.
   ii) Apply translation of 5 units down.
   iii) Apply reflection in the x-axis first and then apply translation of 5 units up.
c) i) The domain is $\{x \in \mathbb{R}\}$ and the range is $\{y \in \mathbb{R} \mid y \geq 5\}$. **ii)** The domain is $\{x \in \mathbb{R}\}$ and the range is $\{y \in \mathbb{R} \mid y \geq -5\}$. **iii)** The domain is $\{x \in \mathbb{R}\}$ and the range is $\{y \in \mathbb{R} \mid y \leq -5\}$.

7. **a)**

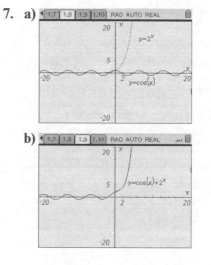

b)

c)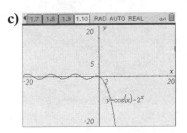

8. a) $C(p) = 12.50 + 0.25p$, $R(p) = 4.25p$

b)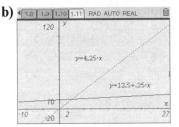

c) Break-even point (3.125, 13.281 25) is where the cost equals the revenue and the courier starts to make profit.

d) $P(p) = 4p - 12.50$

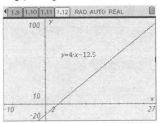

e) $C(p)$: $\{p \in \mathbb{R} \mid 0 \leq p \leq 27\}$, $\{C \in \mathbb{R} \mid 12.50 \leq C \leq 19.25\}$
$R(p)$: $\{p \in \mathbb{R} \mid 0 \leq p \leq 27\}$, $\{R \in \mathbb{R} \mid 0 \leq R \leq 114.75\}$
$P(p)$: $\{p \in \mathbb{R} \mid 0 \leq p \leq 27\}$, $\{P \in \mathbb{R} \mid -12.50 \leq P \leq 95.50\}$

f) $95.50

9. a) i) reduce fixed cost **ii)** reduce variable cost

b) Answers may vary. For example: If more than 23 (rounded up from 22.5) packages are delivered per day, then reducing variable cost is the better option because the daily profit is higher.

10. a) $T_c(x) = \dfrac{(x^2 + 4)^{\frac{1}{2}}}{3}$, $T_h(x) = \dfrac{12 - x}{5}$

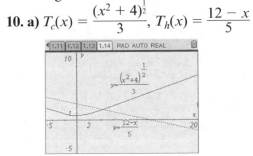

b) $T_c(x) + T_h(x) = \dfrac{(x^2 + 4)^{\frac{1}{2}}}{3} + \dfrac{12 - x}{5}$

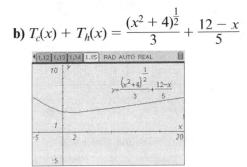

c) The domain is $\{x \in R \mid x \geq 0\}$ and the range is $\{T \in R \mid y > 2.9\}$.

11. a)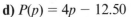

b)

c) $h(x) = 3^x$ **d)** As x increases, the rate of change of $f(x) = 3x + 1$ is positive and constant. As x increases, the rate of change of $g(x) = 2x^2$ is positive and increasing. As x increases, the rate of change of $h(x) = 3^x$ is positive and increasing faster than $g(x)$, which influences the rate of change of the combined function $T(x)$.

12. a) $-g(x) = -x - 7$

b)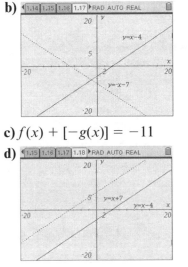

c) $f(x) + [-g(x)] = -11$

d)

e) $f(x) - g(x) = -11$, same as in part c)

13. a) Let x represent the number of units sold:
$C(x) = 175x + 750\,000$ **b)** $S(x) = 599x$
c) $P(x) = 424x - 750\,000$

14. $f(x) = 2x^2 + 7x + 8$ and
$g(x) = 3x^2 - 5x + 3$

15. Answers may vary. Sample answer: If the domains of the two functions are not the same, a value of either $f(x)$ or of $g(x)$ will not have a corresponding value from the other function to combine with in the addition or subtraction. As a result, the two functions could not be combined.

16. Answers may vary. Sample answer: The degree of the addition of the functions $f(x)$ and $g(x)$ will be determined by the highest degree of the two individual functions. This highest degree will determine the type of function for $(f + g)(x)$.

17. a)

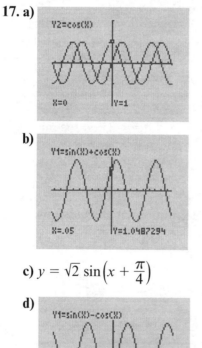

b)

c) $y = \sqrt{2} \sin\left(x + \dfrac{\pi}{4}\right)$

d)

e) $y = \sqrt{2} \sin\left(x - \dfrac{\pi}{4}\right)$

18. a)

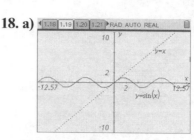

b) periodic (like the sine function), but follows the slope of the line $g(x) = x$

c)

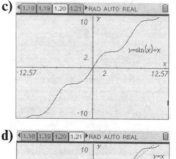

d)

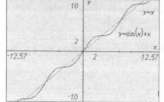

infinitely many intersection points

e) ..., -3π, -2π, $-\pi$, 0, π, 2π, 3π, ...;
$g(x)$ intersects $h(x)$ at the zeros of $f(x)$

f) The curvature is up because $g(x)$ has positive slope.

8.2 Products and Quotients of Functions

1. a) $y = x^3 + 3x^2 - 9x - 27$

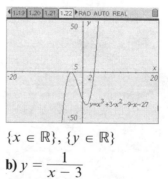

$\{x \in \mathbb{R}\}$, $\{y \in \mathbb{R}\}$

b) $y = \dfrac{1}{x - 3}$

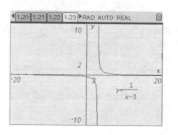

$\{x \in \mathbb{R} \mid x \neq 3, x \neq -3\},$

$\left\{y \mid y \in \mathbb{R} \mid y \neq -\dfrac{1}{6}\right\};$ hole at $\left(-3, -\dfrac{1}{6}\right);$

horizontal asymptote: $y = 0$ vertical

asymptote: $x = 3$

c) $y = x - 3$

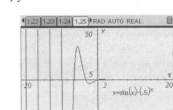

$\{x \in \mathbb{R} \mid x \neq -3\}, \{y \in \mathbb{R} \mid y \neq -6\};$
hole at $(-3, -6)$

2. a) $y = 0.5^x \sin x$

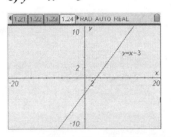

$\{x \in \mathbb{R}\}, \{y \in \mathbb{R}\}$

b) $y = \dfrac{\sin x}{0.5^x}$

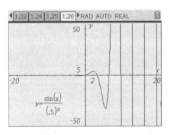

$\{x \in \mathbb{R}\}, \{y \in \mathbb{R}\};$

c) $y = \dfrac{0.5^x}{\sin x}$

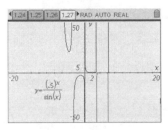

$\{x \in \mathbb{R} \mid x \neq k\pi, k = 0, \pm1, \pm2, ...\},$
$\{y \in \mathbb{R} \mid y \neq 0\};$ vertical asymptotes:
$x = k\pi, k = 0, \pm1, \pm2, ...$

3. a)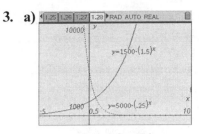

   exponential functions

   b) $P(t)$: $\{t \in \mathbb{R} \mid t \geq 0\}, \{P \in \mathbb{R} \mid P \geq 1500\};$ $F(t)$: $\{t \in \mathbb{R} \mid t \geq 0\}, \{F - \mathbb{R} \mid 0 \leq F \leq 5000\}$

   c) point of intersection: $(0.67, 1969.77);$ the crisis point is when the food supply from surrounding farms is not enough for the increasing population of the town.

   d)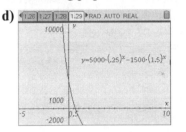

   It shows how much time the town has before the food supply from surrounding farms is not enough.

   e) The t-intercept is approximately 0.67 and it represents the crisis point. **f)** The model for $P(t)$ is not valid for t values greater than the crisis point, because the surrounding farms are not the only source of food; the town can bring food from other locations.

4. a)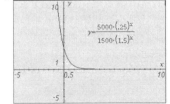

   This function represents food available from surrounding farms per person. The function is an exponential function.

   b) crisis point coordinates: $(0.67, 1);$
   at $t = 0.67$ years, the ratio of $\dfrac{F(t)}{P(t)}$ is 1, which means there is just enough food for each person in town from the surrounding farms.

c) Before the crisis point, the town had enough food supply from surrounding farms. After the crisis point, the food supply from surrounding farms is not enough, which means they would have to bring food from other locations.

5. $f(-x) = \sqrt{x^2 - 4}$, $g(x) = \cos x$

a)

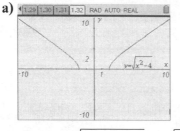

$f(-x) = \sqrt{(-x)^2 - 4} = \sqrt{x^2 - 4} = f(x)$
The function is even.

b)

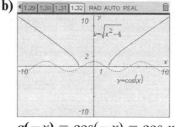

$g(-x) = \cos(-x) = \cos x$
The function is even.

c) The function is periodic (period 2π). As $x \to \pm\infty$, the amplitude increases. It is symmetric about the y-axis.

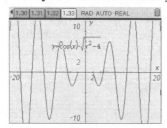

d) The domain is $\{x \in \mathbb{R} \mid x \geq 2, x \leq -2\}$ and the range is $\{y \in \mathbb{R}\}$.

6. a)

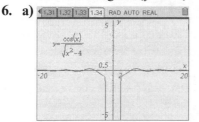

even $\{x \in \mathbb{R} \mid x > 2, x < -2\}$, $\{y \in \mathbb{R} \mid y < 0.170\,623\}$

b)

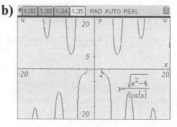

even $\{x \in \mathbb{R} \mid x > 2, x < -2, x \neq \dfrac{k\pi}{2}$, $k = \pm1, \pm3, \pm5, \pm7, ...\}$, $\{y \mid y \in \mathbb{R}, y \pm 5\}$

7. a)

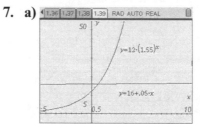

Both functions increase over time; $P(t)$ has a slope that is positive and increasing and $F(t)$ has a slope that is positive and constant. $P(t)$ is increasing at faster rate than $F(t)$.

b)

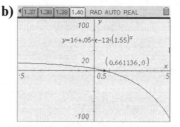

The function is decreasing. Between $t = 0$ and $t \cong 0.66$, there is a food surplus. After $t \cong 0.66$, there is food shortage.

c) $(0, 4)$; the maximum food surplus, 4, occurred at year $t = 0$

8. a)

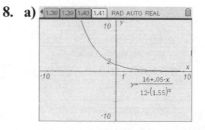

The function is decreasing.

b) $t = 0$; same result as in question 7. b) Analyzing the difference function (as in question 7. b) and analyzing the quotient function are two different methods that provide the same answers.

c) When $\frac{F(t)}{P(t)} > 1$, there is food surplus;

$\frac{F(t)}{P(t)} > 1$ occurs at the interval $(0, 0.67)$

When $\frac{F(t)}{P(t)} < 1$, there is food shortage;

$\frac{F(t)}{P(t)} < 1$ occurs at the interval $(0.67, \infty)$

9. $f(x) = 3^{-x}$, $g(x) = x^2$, $y = f(x)$
$g(x) = (3^{-x})x^2$

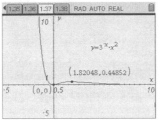

Domain: $\{x \in \mathbb{R}\}$; Range: $\{y \in \mathbb{R} \mid y \geq 0\}$;
x-intercept: 0; y-intercept: 0; Horizontal
asymptote: $y = 0$; End behaviour:
As $x \to +\infty$, $y \to 0$ from above; as
$x \to -\infty$, $y \to +\infty$; Minimum: $(0, 0)$;
Local maximum: $(1.82, 0.45)$

	$(-\infty, 0)$	$x = 0$	$(0, 1.85)$	$x = 1.85$	$(1.85, +\infty)$
Sign of Function	$+$	0	$+$	$+$	$+$
Sign of Slope	$-$	0	$+$	0	$-$

10. a) i) $y = x^3 - 7x^2 + 15x - 9$; **ii)** $y = \dfrac{1}{x - 1}$

b) $\{x \in \mathbb{R} \mid x \neq 1, x \neq 3\}$,
$\left\{y \in \mathbb{R} \mid y \neq 0, y \neq \dfrac{1}{2}\right\}$

11. a) 5 m
b) Original function:

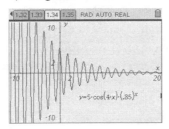

i) Air resistance reduced:

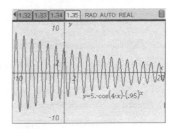

ii) Swing lengthened:

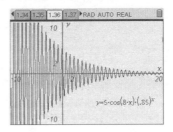

12. a)–c) Answers may vary. **d)** For functions,
odd $\times$ odd $=$ even, odd $\times$ even $=$ odd,
and even $\times$ even $=$ even. This is exactly the
same as the multiplication of numbers.

13. $f(x) = 3x^2 + 4x - 1$
$g(x) = 2x + 4$
or
$\{f(x) = 3x^2 + \dfrac{7}{2}x - 1$
$g(x) = \dfrac{1}{2}x^2 + 2x + 4$

8.3 Composite Functions

1. a) $0.6t^2 + 20t + 160$ **b)** 486.4
2. a) $y = x^2 - 2x - 1$ **b)** $y = x^2 - 6x + 9$
c) $y = x - 4$ **d)** $y = x^4 - 4x^3 + 4x^2$
e) $y = x$

3. a)

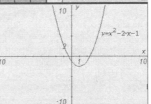

$\{x \in \mathbb{R}\}$, $\{y \in \mathbb{R} \mid y \geq -2\}$

b)

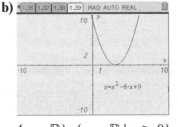

$\{x \in \mathbb{R}\}$, $\{y \in \mathbb{R} \mid y \geq 0\}$

c)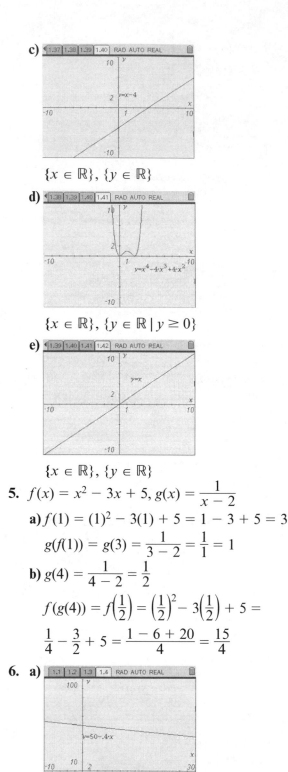

$\{x \in \mathbb{R}\}, \{y \in \mathbb{R}\}$

d)

$\{x \in \mathbb{R}\}, \{y \in \mathbb{R} \mid y \geq 0\}$

e)

$\{x \in \mathbb{R}\}, \{y \in \mathbb{R}\}$

5. $f(x) = x^2 - 3x + 5$, $g(x) = \dfrac{1}{x - 2}$

a) $f(1) = (1)^2 - 3(1) + 5 = 1 - 3 + 5 = 3$

$g(f(1)) = g(3) = \dfrac{1}{3 - 2} = \dfrac{1}{1} = 1$

b) $g(4) = \dfrac{1}{4 - 2} = \dfrac{1}{2}$

$f(g(4)) = f\left(\dfrac{1}{2}\right) = \left(\dfrac{1}{2}\right)^2 - 3\left(\dfrac{1}{2}\right) + 5 =$

$\dfrac{1}{4} - \dfrac{3}{2} + 5 = \dfrac{1 - 6 + 20}{4} = \dfrac{15}{4}$

6. a)

Popularity is decreasing
i) 50% **ii)** -0.4; popularity is decreasing at 0.4 % per day **iii)** There may be more than two candidates. At the beginning of the campaign Candidate A has 50% popularity; Candidate B has 40% popularity.

The rest 10% could be popularity of other candidate(s) or could be undecided voters.

b)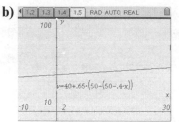

Popularity is increasing
i) 40% **ii)** 0.26; popularity is increasing at 0.26 % per day **iii)** The answer depends on how long the campaign is and how many undecided voters there are.

c) i)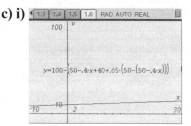

The graph represents the popularity of the rest of the candidate(s). Popularity is increasing **ii)** If the campaign lasts less than about 15 days, candidate A will win. If the campaign lasts more than about 15 days, candidate B will win. **iii)** The results will be the same as in part c). The last two candidates have no chance of winning.

7. a) $\pm\sqrt[4]{x}$ **b)** x **c)** $\pm\sqrt[4]{x}$ **d)** The answer in part c) is an inverse of the answer in part b) **e)** 2; 4; -2. Notice that $f(f^{-1}(x)) = x$ and $f^{-1}(f(x)) = x$.

8. a) periodic function with amplitude of 1 and the curve changes its concavity from up to down or down to up at the zeros of the function $h(x) = \cos x$

b)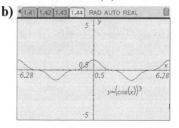

c) The function is periodic; the period is 2π, same as $h(x) = \cos x$ **d)** $\{x \in \mathbb{R}\}$, $\{y \in \mathbb{R} \mid -1 \leq y \leq 1\}$

9. a) periodic function with amplitude of 1; the curve changes its concavity from up to down or down to up at the zeros of the function $h(x) = \cos x$

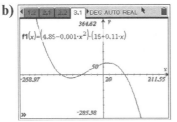

The function is periodic; the period is 2π, same as $h(x) = \cos x$; $\{x \in \mathbb{R}\}$, $\{y \in \mathbb{R} \mid -1 \leq y \leq 1\}$

b) same domain, range, period, amplitude, zeros; difference in the shape at the inflection points

10. a) $V(t) = -0.00011x^3 - 0.015t^2 + 0.5335x + 72.75$

b)

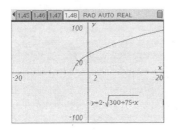

c) 15 s

11. $N(t) = 300 + 75t$, $W(N) = 2\sqrt{N}$

a) $W(t) = W(N(t)) = W(300 + 75t) = 2\sqrt{300 + 75t}$ **b)** t is the time in years since 2007. $t = 0$ represents the year 2007 and therefore the domain of the new function is $\{t \in \mathbb{R} \mid t \geq 0\}$. At $t = 0$, the size of the company's workforce is $W(0) = 2\sqrt{300 + 75(0)} = 2\sqrt{300} = 20\sqrt{3} = 34.6$, which is rounded to 35. Therefore the range of the new function is $\{W \in \mathbb{R} \mid W \geq 20\sqrt{3}\}$.

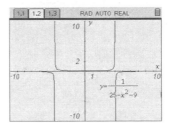

12. a) $C(h) = 2375 + 47.5h$
b) approximately 4.7 hours

13. a) i) $f(g(x)) = 2(4x - 7)^3$ **ii)** $h(g(x)) = \dfrac{-1}{4x - 7}$ **iii)** $g^{-1}(h(x)) = \dfrac{-1}{4x} + \dfrac{7}{4}$ **b)** 2

14. a) $\{x \in \mathbb{R}\}$ **b)** periodic function; looks like the sine function but every negative section of the sine function is reflected in the x-axis (scalloped shape)

c)

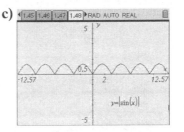

$\{x \in \mathbb{R}\}$, $\{y \in \mathbb{R} \mid 0 \leq y \leq 1\}$

d) "parabolic" shape

e)

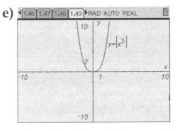

$\{x \in \mathbb{R}\}$, $\{y \in \mathbb{R} \mid y \geq 0\}$

15. a) $\{x \in \mathbb{R} \mid x \neq 9\}$, $\{y \in \mathbb{R} \mid y < 25\}$
b) $\{x \in \mathbb{R} \mid x \neq -4, x \neq 4\}$, $\{y \in \mathbb{R} \mid y \neq 0\}$

c)

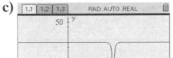

8.4 Inequalities of Combined Functions

1. a)

Points of intersection: $(1 + \sqrt{2}, 2 + 2\sqrt{2})$, $(1 - \sqrt{2}, 2 - 2\sqrt{2})$

b) i) $1 - \sqrt{2} < x < 1 + \sqrt{2}$
ii) $x < 1 - \sqrt{2}, x > 1 + \sqrt{2}$

2. $..., \left(-\dfrac{9\pi}{2}, -\dfrac{7\pi}{2}\right), \left(-\dfrac{5\pi}{2}, -\dfrac{3\pi}{2}\right), (-1.076\,9, 0)$

3. a)

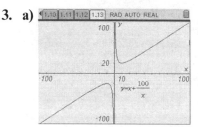

This function is a sum of a linear function and a reciprocal of linear function. It has two asymptotes $x = 0$ and $y = x$. The graph is made up of two branches with end behaviour as follows: As $x \to 0^+$, $y \to \infty$; As $x \to 0^-$, $y \to -\infty$; As $x \to \infty$, $y \to x$; As $x \to -\infty$, $y \to x$ Since n represents years, n cannot be negative, and also n cannot be zero. Therefore, the domain of interest for this problem is $\{n \in \mathbb{R} \mid n > 0\}$

b) $C(n) < 55$

$$n + \frac{100}{n} < 55$$

$$\frac{n^2 + 100}{n} < 55$$

$$n^2 + 100 < 55n$$

$$n^2 - 55n + 100 < 0$$

$$n = \frac{-b \pm \sqrt{b^2 - 4ac}}{2a}$$

$$n = \frac{55 \pm \sqrt{55^2 - 4(1)(100)}}{2(1)}$$

$$n = \frac{55 \pm \sqrt{2625}}{2}$$

$$n \cong 1.9 \text{ or } n \cong 53.1$$

$C(n) < 55$ in the interval $(1.9, 53.1)$ $C(n)$ is below 55 when inventory is between approximately 2 and 53 cell phones. Therefore, minimum number of cell phones that can be ordered is 2 and maximum is 53.

c) Use the graphing calculator to find local minimum.

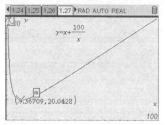

The optimum order size that will minimize storage costs is $n = 10$.

d) The best number to order is 10 cell phones because the storage costs are at minimum, $C = \$20$.

4. a) i) minimum number decreases, maximum number increases **ii)** maximum potential profit increases

b)

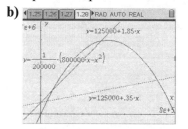

5. a) i) the restaurant chain could sell any number of hamburgers but at a loss
ii) profit turns to loss

b)

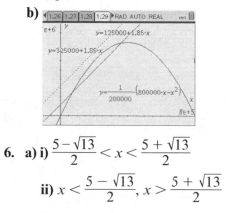

6. a) i) $\dfrac{5 - \sqrt{13}}{2} < x < \dfrac{5 + \sqrt{13}}{2}$

ii) $x < \dfrac{5 - \sqrt{13}}{2}, x > \dfrac{5 + \sqrt{13}}{2}$

b)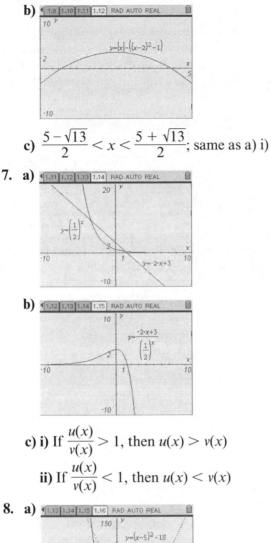

c) $\dfrac{5-\sqrt{13}}{2} < x < \dfrac{5+\sqrt{13}}{2}$; same as a) i)

7. a)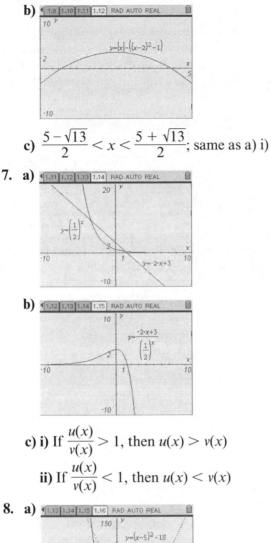

b)

c) i) If $\dfrac{u(x)}{v(x)} > 1$, then $u(x) > v(x)$

ii) If $\dfrac{u(x)}{v(x)} < 1$, then $u(x) < v(x)$

8. a)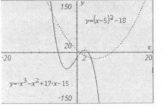

b) i) The graph of $f(x)$ is above the graph of $g(x)$ between $x \cong 0.9$ and $x \cong 3.7$, and also when x is less than approximately -6.6. Therefore, $f(x) > g(x)$ on the intervals $(-\infty, -6.6) \cup (0.9, 3.7)$

ii) The graph of $f(x)$ is below the graph of $g(x)$ between $x \cong -6.6$ and $x \cong 0.9$, and also when x is greater than approximately 3.7. Therefore, $f(x) < g(x)$ on the intervals $(-6.6, 0.9) \cup (3.7, \infty)$

9. Answers will be the same as question 8 when using the following methods:
Method 1: Analyzing the difference function $y = f(x) - g(x)$, and
Method 2: Analyzing the quotient function $y = \dfrac{f(x)}{g(x)}$

10. $-0.824 < x < 0.824$ **11.** $x > 0.718$

12. a)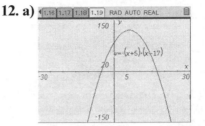

b) $-5 < x < 17$; therefore, given that minimum ticket price is \$12, maximum realistic ticket price is $12 < x < 17$.

c) $\{p \in \mathbb{R} \mid 12 \le p < 17\}$, $\{N \in \mathbb{R} \mid 0 < N \le 85\}$

13. a)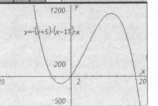

b) $0 < x < 17$; yes **c)** No, maxima of $N(p)$ occurs at $p = 6$ and maxima of $R(p)$ occurs at $p = 10.66$. In this case a combination of fewer visitors paying higher ticket price produces higher revenue than more people paying lower ticket price. **d)** \$10.66

14. a)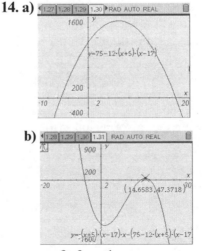

b)

profit function

c) $13.0524 < p < 16.1441$, profit **d)** no, because profit depends on both revenue and cost

e) Optimum ticket price is \$14.66; maximum profit per ticket is \$3.23

15. a)

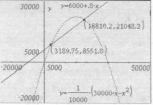

b) 2 points of intersection; when $C(x) = R(x)$ means 0 profit for the company **c)** (3190, 18 810); the company makes profit

d)

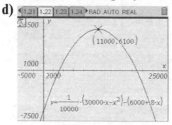

e) i) 11 000 units **ii)** 0.55 \$/unit **iii)** \$ 6100

f) $R(x)$ is a quadratic function; the graph is a parabola, facing down; after the maximum point the function decreases, and one reason for this is probably because demand for pens decreases

16. Let n be the number of necklaces made in a given week. **a)** $C(n) = $ fixed cost + variable cost $C(n) = 55 + 3.50n$

b) $R(n) = $ price per necklace $\times$ number of necklaces made per week
$R(n) = (25 - n)n$
$R(n) = 25n - n^2$

c) Stephanie will make profit if her revenue is greater than her cost,
$R(n) > C(n)$ or $R(n) - C(n) = 0$

d) Graph the functions $C(n) = 55 + 3.50n$ and $R(n) = 25n - n^2$ on the same graph. Compare the graph visually in order to find the interval(s) for which $R(n) > C(n)$.

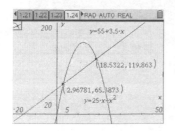

The graph of $R(n)$ is above the graph of $C(n)$ between $x \cong 3$ and $x \cong 19$. Therefore, $R(n) > C(n)$ on the interval (3, 19).
Stephanie should make between 3 and 19 necklaces each week in order to make profit.

e) $P(n) = R(n) - C(n)$
$P(n) = (25n - n^2) - (55 + 3.50n)$
$\quad = 25n - n^2 - 55 - 3.50n$
$\quad = -n^2 + 21.5n - 55$
$\quad = -(n^2 - 21.5n + 55)$ Complete the square

$= -\left[\left(n^2 - 21.5n + \left(\dfrac{21.5}{2}\right)^2\right) - \left(\dfrac{21.5}{2}\right)^2 + 55\right]$

$= -\left[(n - 10.75)^2 - \dfrac{462.25}{4} + 55\right]$

$= -[(n - 10.75)^2 - 115.5625 + 55]$
$= -[(n - 10.75)^2 - 60.5625]$
$= -(n - 10.75)^2 + 60.5625$

The maximum of the function $P(n) = R(n) - C(n)$ occurs at $n = 10.75$ and the value is approximately 60.56. Therefore, the optimum number of necklaces is approximately 11 and Stephanie will earn approximately \$60.56.

17. a) $N(t) - P(t) = 4200 + 45.2t - 1500(1.025)^t$

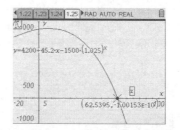

b) availability of local water supply for the town population **c)** In approximately 62.5 years there will be shortage of local water supply. **d)** $\dfrac{N(t)}{P(t)} = \dfrac{4200 + 45.2t}{1500(1.025)^t}$

e) availability of local water supply for the town population; If $\frac{N(t)}{P(t)} > 1$, there is enough local water supply; if $\frac{N(t)}{P(t)} < 1$, there is shortage of local water supply.

8.5 Making Connections: Modeling With Combined Functions

1. a)

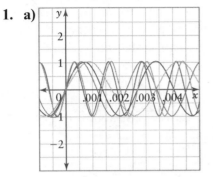

b) the D major triad of D, F# and A:

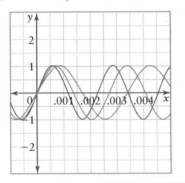

2. a) i)

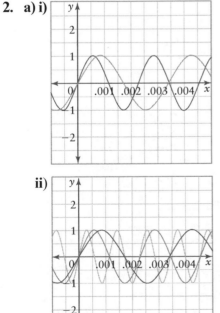

ii)

b) Compare to

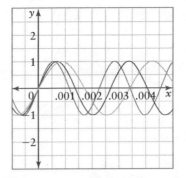

These notes will sound good together since the resultant curve of the combined function is similar to that formed from the individual notes

3. $y = 2x + 200 + 0.4 \sin\left(\frac{\pi}{3}x\right)$

4. Original graph:

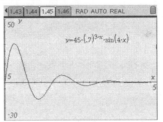

a) Greater height:

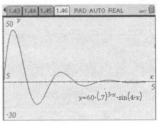

b) Lower height:

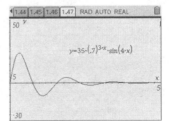

5. a) Longer cord:

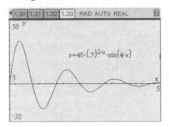

b) Shorter cord:

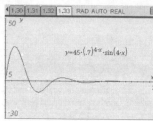

6. a) Springier cord:

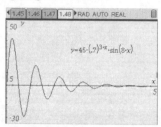

b) Stiffer cord:

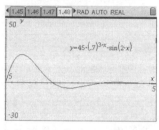

7. Original graph:

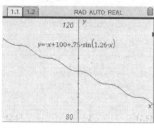

a) Shorter moguls:

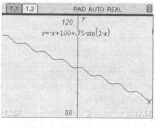

b) Farther apart moguls

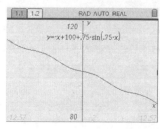

8. a)

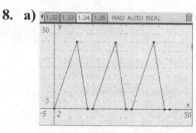

b) In the first region of each cycle, the skier travels up the chairlift. In the second region, assuming that the skier does not wait at the top, the skier skis down the hill. In the final region the skier waits in line for a chairlift.

c) Answers may vary. For example: Use a combination of straight lines with different slopes to represent the three different regions of a cycle.

9. a)

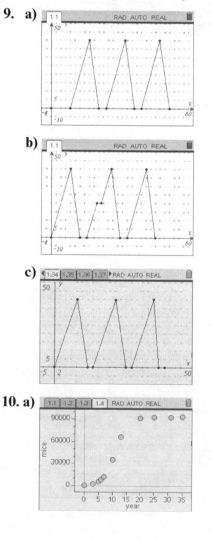

b)

c)

10. a)

b) Quartic function. When using technology, the regression curve for a quartic function fit best and had the r^2 value closest to 1. $y = 0.793\,812x^4 - 60.542\,x^3 + 1356.55\,x^2 - 4692.85\,x + 1524.55$

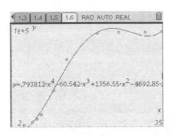

c) $N(t) = 0.793\,812\,t^4 - 60.542\,t^3 + 1356.55\,t^2 - 4692.85\,t + 1524.55$

d) Removing the data point caused a slight reduction in the coefficient of determination r^2. This implies that a quartic regression works better with that particular data point.

11. a) Use a graphing calculator to plot all the data points.

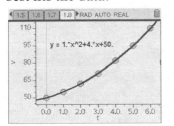

b) Use the regression function of the graphing calculator to find a curve that best fits the data points. In this case the quadratic function $y = x^2 + 4x + 50$ best fits the data.

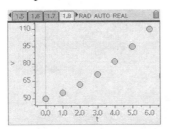

To check how close the curve fits the data points, display the value for the coefficient of determination, r^2.

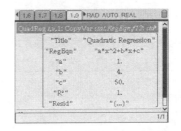

In this case $r^2 = 1$, which means the quadratic function $y = x^2 + 4x + 50$ is the best fit.

c) $v(t) = t^2 + 4t + 50$

d) $c(v) = \left(\dfrac{v(t)}{450} - 0.09\right)^2 + 0.18$

$c(v(t)) = \left(\dfrac{t^2 + 4t + 50}{450} - 0.09\right)^2 + 0.18$

12. a) i) Answers may vary. Sample answer: The motion of the runner would look like a cosine wave, but sketched along the line $y = t$, rather than along the time axis.

ii)

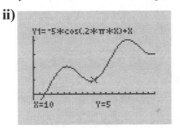

12. b) i) Answers may vary. Sample answer: The motion of the runner would look like a cosine wave, but sketched along the curve $y = t^2$, rather than along the time axis.

ii)

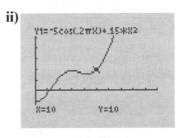

Chapter 8 Challenge Questions

C1.a)

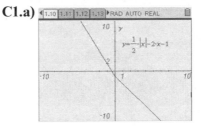

b)

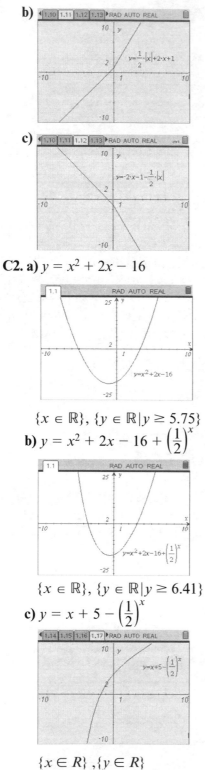

c)

C2. a) $y = x^2 + 2x - 16$

$\{x \in \mathbb{R}\}, \{y \in \mathbb{R} \mid y \geq 5.75\}$

b) $y = x^2 + 2x - 16 + \left(\dfrac{1}{2}\right)^x$

$\{x \in \mathbb{R}\}, \{y \in \mathbb{R} \mid y \geq 6.41\}$

c) $y = x + 5 - \left(\dfrac{1}{2}\right)^x$

$\{x \in R\}, \{y \in R\}$

C3. See answer for question C2

C4. a) $W(t) = 7.50t$ **b)** $T(t) = 12.25t$
  c) $E(t) = W(t) + T(t) = 19.75t$

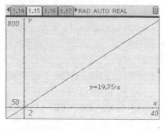

d) \$632

5. a) point symmetry, i.e., the graph is
  symmetrical about a point

b)

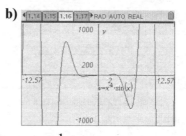

6. a) $y = \dfrac{1}{x - 4}, x \neq 5$

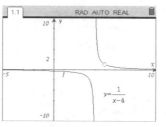

$\{x \in \mathbb{R} \mid x \neq 4, x \neq 5\}, \{y \in \mathbb{R} \mid y \neq 1\}$

b) $y = x - 4, x \neq 5$

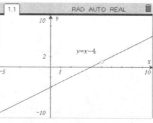

$\{x \in \mathbb{R} \mid x \neq 5\}, \{y \in \mathbb{R} \mid y \neq 0, y \neq 1\}$

7. a) $y = 49x^2 - 21x - 3$

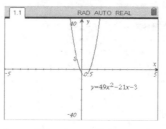

$\{x \in \mathbb{R}\}, \{y \in \mathbb{R} \mid y \geq 0.214\}$

b) $y = 7x^2 + 35x + 3$

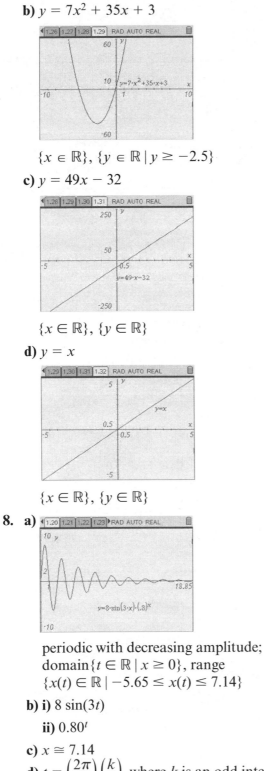

$\{x \in \mathbb{R}\}, \{y \in \mathbb{R} \mid y \geq -2.5\}$

c) $y = 49x - 32$

$\{x \in \mathbb{R}\}, \{y \in \mathbb{R}\}$

d) $y = x$

$\{x \in \mathbb{R}\}, \{y \in \mathbb{R}\}$

8. a)

periodic with decreasing amplitude; domain $\{t \in \mathbb{R} \mid x \geq 0\}$, range $\{x(t) \in \mathbb{R} \mid -5.65 \leq x(t) \leq 7.14\}$

b) i) $8 \sin(3t)$

ii) 0.80^t

c) $x \cong 7.14$

d) $t = \left(\dfrac{2\pi}{3}\right)\left(\dfrac{k}{4}\right)$, where k is an odd integer
When the pendulum changes direction

e) $t \cong 5.7$ s

9. a) i) $\ldots \cup (-8\pi, -6\pi) \cup (-4\pi, -2\pi) \cup (0.37, 2.78)$

ii) $\ldots \cup (-6\pi, -4\pi) \cup (-2\pi, 0.37) \cup (2.78, +\infty)$

b)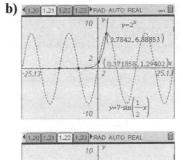

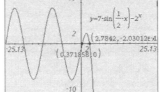

10. a)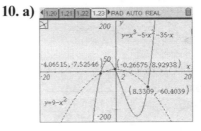

b) $(-4.07, -0.27) \cup (8.33, +\infty)$

c) Using algebraic method, find the points of intersection and then find the intervals for which $f(x) > g(x)$.

11. a) i) $(0, 4) \cup (5.5, \infty)$ **ii)** $(4, 5.5)$

b) running at a loss **c)** decrease costs

12. a)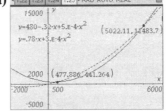

b) Two points of intersection: (477.89, 441.26) and (5022.11, 11 483.7)
This is when revenue equals cost.

c) $p(x) - 0.000\,2x^2 + 1.1x - 480$

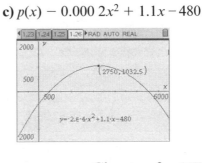

d) $1032.50

13. $f(t) = -3t + 350 + 1.5\sin(\pi x)$

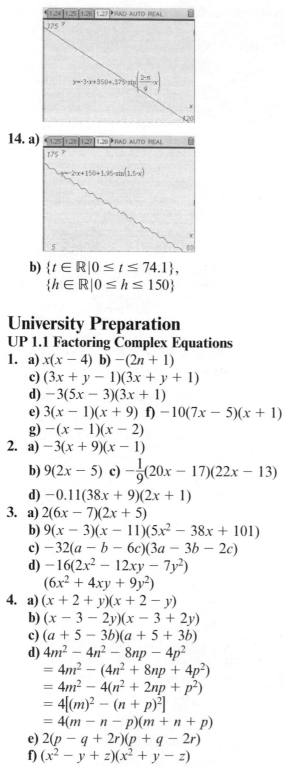

14. a)

b) $\{t \in \mathbb{R} \mid 0 \le t \le 74.1\}$,
$\{h \in \mathbb{R} \mid 0 \le h \le 150\}$

University Preparation
UP 1.1 Factoring Complex Equations

1. a) $x(x - 4)$ **b)** $-(2n + 1)$
c) $(3x + y - 1)(3x + y + 1)$
d) $-3(5x - 3)(3x + 1)$
e) $3(x - 1)(x + 9)$ **f)** $-10(7x - 5)(x + 1)$
g) $-(x - 1)(x - 2)$

2. a) $-3(x + 9)(x - 1)$

b) $9(2x - 5)$ **c)** $-\dfrac{1}{9}(20x - 17)(22x - 13)$

d) $-0.11(38x + 9)(2x + 1)$

3. a) $2(6x - 7)(2x + 5)$
b) $9(x - 3)(x - 11)(5x^2 - 38x + 101)$
c) $-32(a - b - 6c)(3a - 3b - 2c)$
d) $-16(2x^2 - 12xy - 7y^2)$
$(6x^2 + 4xy + 9y^2)$

4. a) $(x + 2 + y)(x + 2 - y)$
b) $(x - 3 - 2y)(x - 3 + 2y)$
c) $(a + 5 - 3b)(a + 5 + 3b)$
d) $4m^2 - 4n^2 - 8np - 4p^2$
$= 4m^2 - (4n^2 + 8np + 4p^2)$
$= 4m^2 - 4(n^2 + 2np + p^2)$
$= 4[(m)^2 - (n + p)^2]$
$= 4(m - n - p)(m + n + p)$
e) $2(p - q + 2r)(p + q - 2r)$
f) $(x^2 - y + z)(x^2 + y - z)$
g) $(x - y - 3a)(x - y + 3a)$

5. a) $(3a + 3b - 2x + 2y)(3a + 3b + 2x - 2y)$

b) $(4s - 4t - p - 2q)(4s - 4t + p + 2q)$
c) $(5r - 6s - 3q + 2h)(5r - 6s + 3q - 2h)$
d) $s^2 - 14st + 49t^2 - a^2 - 18ab - 81b^2$
$= s^2 - 14st + 49t^2 - (a^2 + 18ab + 81b^2)$
$= (s - 7t)^2 + (a + 9b)^2$
$= (s - 7t - a - 9b)(s - 7t + a + 9b)$

6. a) $(x + 5)(x + 8)$ **b)** $4(x + 1)(x + 6)$
c) $6(x^2 - 1)^2 + 23(x^2 - 1) + 7$
Let $n = x^2 - 1$
$6n^2 + 23n + 7$
$= (3n + 1)(2n + 7)$
$= (3(x^2 - 1) + 1)(2(x^2 - 1) + 7)$
$= (3x^2 - 3 + 1)(2x^2 - 2 + 7)$
$= (3x^2 - 2)(2x^2 + 5)$
d) $3(13x + 3)(8x - 15)$

7. a) $(x^{2n} - y^{3n})(x^{2n} + y^{3n})$
b) $(3x^{3n} - 2y^{2n})^2$ **c)** $(4x^{2n+1} + 3y^{4n})^2$

UP 1.2 Techniques for Solving
Complex Equations

1. a) $m^2 - 17m + 16 = 0$
b) $x = \pm 4$ or $x = \pm 1$

2. $x = \pm 5$ or $x = \pm 1$

3. a) $n^2 - 6n + 8 = 0$ **b)** $x = 2$ or $x = 1$

4. a) i) $n = x^2$ **ii)** $x = \pm 2$ or $x = \pm 1$
b) i) $n = x^2$ **ii)** $x = \pm 2$
c) i) $n = x^2$ **ii)** $x = \pm\sqrt{10}$ or $x = \pm\sqrt{6}$
d) i) $n = x^2$ **ii)** $x = \pm\sqrt{35}$ or $x = \pm 1$
e) i) $n = x^2$ **ii)** $x = \pm 2$ or $x = \pm 4$
f) i) $n = x^2$ **ii)** $x = \pm 2$ or $x = \pm 5$
g) i) $n = x^2$ **ii)** $x = \pm\sqrt{2}$ or $x = \pm\sqrt{3}$
h) i) $n = x^2$ **ii)** $x = \pm\sqrt{5}$

5. a) i) $n = 5^x$ **ii)** $x = 0$ or $x = 1$
b) i) $n = 3^x$ **ii)** $x = 1$ or $x = 3$
c) i) $n = 2^x$ **ii)** $x = 2$ or $x = 3$
d) i) $n = 2^x$ **ii)** $x = 1$ or $x = 4$
e) i) $n = 2^x$ **ii)** $x = 1$ or $x = 3$
f) i) $n = 3^x$ **ii)** $x = 1$ or $x = 2$
g) $5^{2x} - 30(5^x) + 125 = 0$
Let $n = 5^x$.
$n^2 - 30n + 125 = 0$
$(n - 25)(n - 5) = 0$
$n - 25 = 0 \qquad n - 5 = 0$
$n = 25 \qquad\quad n = 5$
$5^x = 25 \qquad 5^x = 5$
$x = 2 \qquad\quad x = 1$

6. a) $x = 1$ or $x = 0$ **b)** $x = 1$ or $x = -1$
c) $x = \pm 1$ or $x = \pm 3$

7. a) $x = 3$ or $x = 0$ **b)** $x = 1$ or $x = -\dfrac{2}{3}$

c) $x = -3$, $x = 1$, $x = -4$ or $x = 2$

d) $x = 4$, $x = -1$, $x = 1$ or $x = 2$

e)
$$(x^2 - 2x)^2 - 4 = 2(x^2 - 2x) - 1$$
$$(x^2 - 2x)^2 - 2(x^2 - 2x) - 3 = 0$$
Let $n = x^2 - 2x$.
$$n^2 - 2n - 3 = 0$$
$$(n - 3)(n + 1) = 0$$
$$(x^2 - 2x - 3)(x^2 - 2x + 1) = 0$$
$$(x - 3)(x + 1)(x - 1)^2 = 0$$
$$x - 3 = 0 \quad x + 1 = 0 \quad x - 1 = 0$$
$$x = 3 \quad\quad x = -1 \quad\quad x = 1$$

8. a) $x = \pm 2$ or $x = \pm 3$ **b)** $x = -\dfrac{1}{2}$ or $x = -3$

c) $x = \dfrac{1}{3}$ or $x = -\dfrac{1}{4}$ **d)** $x = \pm\dfrac{1}{2}$ or $x = \pm\dfrac{\sqrt{5}}{5}$

e) $x = \pm\dfrac{\sqrt{2}}{4}$ or $x = \pm 1$

9. a) $x = \dfrac{15}{7}$ or $x = \dfrac{11}{5}$ **b)** $x = -\dfrac{13}{3}$ or $x = -6$

c) $x = -2$, $x = 1$, $x = -4$ or $x = 3$

10. a) $x = 6$, $x = 1$, $x = -2$ or $x = -3$

b) $x = 2$, $x = 1$ or $x = 4$

c) $x = 2 \pm \sqrt{5}$ or $x = \dfrac{3 \pm \sqrt{13}}{2}$

11. a) $n = x + \dfrac{1}{x}$

b) $x = -2 \pm \sqrt{3}$ or $x = \dfrac{3 \pm \sqrt{5}}{2}$

UP 2.1 Solving Equations Involving Absolute Value

1. a) 6 **b)** 8 **c)** 7 **d)** 11 **e)** 4

2. a) $x = \pm 2$ **b)** $x = \pm 9$ **c)** $x = \pm 9$

d) $x = \pm 33$ **e)** $x = \pm 12.5$ **f)** $x = \pm 39$

g) $x = \pm 35$ **h)** $x = \pm 8$ **i)** no solution

3. a) $x = -1$ or $x = -7$ **b)** $x = 9$ or $x = -3$

c) $x = 9$ or $x = -5$ **d)** $x = 4$ or $x = -6$

e) no solution **f)** $x = 9$ or $x = -7$

4. a) $x = 5$ or $x = -4$ **b)** $x = 1$ or $x = -\dfrac{1}{2}$

c) $x = 0$ or $x = -6$ **d)** $x = -3$ or $x = \dfrac{13}{3}$

e) no solution **f)** $x = \dfrac{1}{4}$ or $x = -\dfrac{5}{4}$

g) no solution

5. a) $x = \dfrac{2}{3}$ **b)** $x = -\dfrac{5}{3}$ **c)** $x = \dfrac{1}{2}$ **d)** $x = 1$

e) $x = \dfrac{1}{4}$ **f)** $x = -\dfrac{3}{2}$ or $x = \dfrac{9}{2}$

6. a) $x = \dfrac{2}{3}$ **b)** no solution **c)** $x = 4$ **d)** $x = 3$

e) $16x - 3|2x - 1| = |10x - 5|$

Both $2x - 1$ and $10x - 5$ are equal to zero at $x = \dfrac{1}{2}$, which sets up two cases:

Case 1
$$x < \dfrac{1}{2}$$
$$16x - 3[-(2x - 1)] = -(10x - 5)$$
$$16x - 3(-2x + 1) = -10x + 5$$
$$16x + 6x - 3 = -10x + 5$$
$$16x + 6x + 10x = 5 + 3$$
$$32x = 8$$
$$x = \dfrac{1}{4}$$

Case 2
$$x > \dfrac{1}{2}$$
$$16x - 3(2x - 1) = (10x - 5)$$
$$16x - 6x + 3 = 10x - 5$$
$$16x - 6x - 10x = -5 - 3$$
$$0x = -8 \quad \textit{no solution}$$

Therefore, the only solution is $x = \dfrac{1}{4}$.

f) $x = -\dfrac{6}{11}$

7. a) $x = 0$ or $x = -2$ **b)** $x = 1$ or $x = -5$

c) $x = 5$ or $x = -\dfrac{5}{3}$ **d)** $x = 2$ or $x = \dfrac{2}{5}$

e) $x = 9$ or $x = -11$

8. a) $x = 1$ or $x = \dfrac{1}{3}$ **b)** $x = 2$ or $x = 4$

c) $x = -\dfrac{3}{4}$ or $x = \dfrac{7}{2}$ **d)** $x = \dfrac{4}{3}$ or $x = 2$

e) $|3x - 7| = |2 - x|$

For intervals:
$$3x - 7 = 0 \text{ } and \text{ } 2 - x = 0$$
$$3x = 7 \quad\quad\quad 2 = x$$
$$x = \dfrac{7}{3}$$

Case 1
$$x < 2$$
$$-(3x - 7) = (2 - x)$$
$$-3x + 7 = 2 - x$$
$$-3x + x = 2 - 7$$
$$-2x = -5$$
$$x = \dfrac{5}{2}$$

Since this solution is not in the interval of $x < 2$, it is not a valid solution.

Case 2
$$2 < x < \frac{7}{3}$$
$$-(3x - 7) = -(2 - x)$$
$$-3x + 7 = -2 + x$$
$$-3x - x = -2 - 7$$
$$-4x = -9$$
$$x = \frac{9}{4}$$

This solution is in the interval, so it is a solution.

Case 3
$$x > \frac{7}{3}$$
$$(3x - 7) = -(2 - x)$$
$$3x - 7 = -2 + x$$
$$3x - x = -2 + 7$$
$$2x = 5$$
$$x = \frac{5}{2}$$

This solution is in the interval, so it is a solution.

9. **a)** $x = \pm 4$ **b)** no solution

UP 2.2 Solving Inequalities Involving Absolute Value

1. **a)** $x < -3$ or $x > 3$ **b)** $-2 < x < 2$
   c) $-5 \le x \le 5$ **d)** all values of x
   e) $-\frac{7}{4} \le x \le \frac{7}{4}$ **f)** $x < -4$ or $x > 4$
   g) $-\frac{14}{5} < x < \frac{14}{5}$
   h) $-7 < x < 7$ **i)** $-4 \le x \le 4$

2. **a)** $x < -\frac{19}{2}$ or $x > \frac{19}{2}$

   b) no solution
   c) $-\frac{27}{2} < x < \frac{27}{2}$

   d) $-10 \le x \le 10$

   e) $-7 \le x \le 7$

f) $x \in \mathbb{R}$

g) $-7 < x < 7$

3. **a)** $x < 0$ or $x > 6$

   b) $-5 \le x \le -3$

   c) $-6 < x < 8$

   d) $x \in \mathbb{R}$

   e) $x < -13$ or $x > 7$

   f) $-7 \le x \le 23$

   g) $x < -15$ or $x > 3$

   h) $x \le 0$ or $x \ge 4$

   i) $-16 < x < -4$

4. **a)** $x < -2$ or $x > 1$ **b)** $x \le -1$ or $x \ge \frac{11}{5}$
   c) $\frac{1}{7} < x < \frac{3}{7}$ **d)** $1 \le x \le 4$
   e) $-\frac{10}{3} < x < \frac{8}{3}$ **f)** $x \le -\frac{3}{2}$ or $x \ge 5$
   g) $x < -7$ or $x > 4$ **h)** $x \le \frac{1}{6}$ or $x \ge \frac{7}{6}$
   i) $x < -\frac{67}{3}$ or $x > \frac{65}{3}$
   j) $x \le -\frac{22}{5}$ or $x \ge -\frac{18}{5}$

5. a) $x > \dfrac{1}{2}$ **b)** $x > 1$ **c)** $x = 2$

d) $2 - 3x = 0$

$2 = 3x$

$x = \dfrac{2}{3}$

Two cases:

Case 1

$x < \dfrac{2}{3}$

$2 - 3x > 3x - 6$

$-3x - 3x > -6 - 2$

$-6x > -8$

$x < \dfrac{-8}{-6}$

$x < \dfrac{4}{3}$

This is in the interval for the case, so all values of x are solutions in this interval.

Case 2

$x > \dfrac{2}{3}$

$-(2 - 3x) > 3x - 6$

$3x - 2 > 3x - 6$

$3x - 3x > -6 + 2$

$0x > -4$

This is always true, so all values of x are solutions in this interval.

As a result of the two cases, the solution is $x \in \mathbb{R}$.

e) $x \in \mathbb{R}$

f) $x < -\dfrac{1}{4}$ **g)** $x \geq \dfrac{3}{7}$

6. a) $-\dfrac{17}{5} \leq x \leq 19$ **b)** $-1 < x < 1$

c) $|x + 2| > 4 + |x|$

$x + 2 = 0 \qquad x = 0$

$x = -2$

The solutions to the expressions equal to zero set up the intervals for the cases of the solution.

Case 1

$x < -2$

$-(x + 2) > 4 - (x)$

$-x - 2 > 4 - x$

$-x + x > 4 + 2$

$0x > 6 \quad$ *no solution*

Case 2

$-2 < x < 0$

$(x + 2) > 4 - (x)$

$x + 2 > 4 - x$

$x + x > 4 - 2$

$2x > 2$

$x > 1$

This is not in the interval of the case, so there is no solution in this interval.

Case 3

$x > 0$

$(x + 2) > 4 + (x)$

$x + 2 > 4 + x$

$x - x > 4 - 2$

$0x > 2 \quad$ *no solution*

Since there is no solution in any interval, there is no solution to the original inequality.

7. a) $-2 < x < 3$

b) $x \leq -\dfrac{1}{2}$

c) $x < -\dfrac{13}{4}$ or $x > -\dfrac{3}{4}$

8. a) $x > -1$ **b)** $-\dfrac{5}{6} \leq x \leq \dfrac{1}{10}, x \neq -\dfrac{1}{4}$

c) $-12 \leq x \leq -\dfrac{8}{3}$

UP 3.1 Introduction to Matrices

1. a) 2×3 **b)** $3; -2$

c) $\begin{bmatrix} 4 & -3 & -8 \\ -5 & -1 & 2 \end{bmatrix}$ **d)** $\begin{bmatrix} -24 & 18 & 48 \\ 30 & 6 & -12 \end{bmatrix}$

e) $\begin{bmatrix} -12 & 9 & 24 \\ 15 & 3 & -6 \end{bmatrix}$

2. a) BC; B is a 2×3 matrix and C is a 2×2 matrix. Since the number of columns of B does not match the number of rows of C, this product does not exist.

b) CB; C is a 2×2 matrix and B is a 2×3 matrix. Since the number of columns of C equals the number of rows of B, this product exists. The new matrix will have dimensions 2×3.

c) B^2; B is not a matrix with an equal number of rows and columns, and so cannot be multiplied by itself.

d) C^2; C is a matrix with an equal number of rows and columns, and so can be multiplied by itself. The new matrix will have dimensions 2×2.

3. b) $\begin{bmatrix} -28 & 20 & -23 \\ -4 & 8 & 28 \end{bmatrix}$ d) $\begin{bmatrix} 9 & 1 \\ 0 & 16 \end{bmatrix}$

4. a) $\begin{bmatrix} -7 & 5 & -1 \\ -3 & -2 & 5 \\ 3 & 4 & 5 \end{bmatrix}$ b) $\begin{bmatrix} -21 & 15 & -3 \\ -9 & -6 & 15 \\ 9 & 12 & 15 \end{bmatrix}$

c) does not exist because R and Q have different dimensions

d) $\begin{bmatrix} -8 & -2 \\ 0 & \frac{2}{3} \\ 2 & -\frac{14}{3} \end{bmatrix}$

5. a) $\begin{bmatrix} -66 & 24 & 30 \\ -2 & -4 & 2 \\ 32 & 25 & -23 \end{bmatrix}$ b) $\begin{bmatrix} -58 & 22 & 30 \\ 3 & -11 & 1 \\ 29 & 26 & -34 \end{bmatrix}$

c) does not exist because number of columns of Q is not equal to number of rows of P

d) $\begin{bmatrix} 15 & -7 \\ 12 & 43 \\ 18 & -47 \end{bmatrix}$ e) $\begin{bmatrix} -104 & -13 & 59 \\ 14 & 184 & -50 \\ -202 & -170 & 148 \end{bmatrix}$

f) $\begin{bmatrix} 7 & -29 & 17 \\ -6 & 107 & -62 \\ 10 & -75 & 56 \end{bmatrix}$

g) does not exist because RS and P^2 have different dimensions

h) $\begin{bmatrix} -33 & 53 & -25 \\ 47 & -170 & 97 \\ -53 & 116 & -117 \end{bmatrix}$ i) $\begin{bmatrix} 20 & -48 & 16 \\ 24 & -94 & 24 \\ -8 & 76 & -106 \end{bmatrix}$

6. a) false
Example:
$AB = \begin{bmatrix} 1 & 2 \\ 3 & 4 \end{bmatrix}\begin{bmatrix} 1 & 2 \\ 2 & 1 \end{bmatrix} = \begin{bmatrix} 5 & 4 \\ 11 & 10 \end{bmatrix}$
$BA = \begin{bmatrix} 1 & 2 \\ 2 & 1 \end{bmatrix}\begin{bmatrix} 1 & 2 \\ 3 & 4 \end{bmatrix} = \begin{bmatrix} 7 & 10 \\ 5 & 8 \end{bmatrix}$

b) true
Example:
$(AB)C = \left(\begin{bmatrix} 1 & 2 \\ 3 & 4 \end{bmatrix}\begin{bmatrix} 1 & 2 \\ 2 & 1 \end{bmatrix}\right)\begin{bmatrix} 1 & 1 \\ 3 & 3 \end{bmatrix}$
$= \begin{bmatrix} 17 & 17 \\ 41 & 41 \end{bmatrix}$
$A(BC) = \begin{bmatrix} 1 & 2 \\ 3 & 4 \end{bmatrix}\left(\begin{bmatrix} 1 & 2 \\ 2 & 1 \end{bmatrix}\begin{bmatrix} 1 & 1 \\ 3 & 3 \end{bmatrix}\right)$
$= \begin{bmatrix} 17 & 17 \\ 41 & 41 \end{bmatrix}$

c) true
Example:
$k(AB) = 2\left(\begin{bmatrix} 1 & 2 \\ 3 & 4 \end{bmatrix}\begin{bmatrix} 1 & 2 \\ 2 & 1 \end{bmatrix}\right) = \begin{bmatrix} 10 & 8 \\ 22 & 20 \end{bmatrix}$
$(kA)B = \left(2\begin{bmatrix} 1 & 2 \\ 3 & 4 \end{bmatrix}\right)\begin{bmatrix} 1 & 2 \\ 2 & 1 \end{bmatrix} = \begin{bmatrix} 10 & 8 \\ 22 & 20 \end{bmatrix}$
$A(kB) = \begin{bmatrix} 1 & 2 \\ 3 & 4 \end{bmatrix}\left(2\begin{bmatrix} 1 & 2 \\ 2 & 1 \end{bmatrix}\right) = \begin{bmatrix} 10 & 8 \\ 22 & 20 \end{bmatrix}$

7. $a = 5, b = 2, c = 2, d = -1$

8. a) $\begin{bmatrix} -186 & 264 \\ -10 & 2 \end{bmatrix}$

b) $[3 \quad -4]\begin{bmatrix} -1 & 1 & 2 \\ 8 & 3 & -5 \end{bmatrix}$
$+ 4[2 \quad -1 \quad -2]$
$\begin{bmatrix} 3 & 2 & 4 \\ -1 & 0 & 1 \\ 5 & 6 & -2 \end{bmatrix}$
$[3 \times -1 - 4 \times 8 \quad 3 \times 1 - 4 \times 3 \quad 3 \times 2$
$- 4 \times -5] + 4[2 \times 3 - 1 \times -1 - 2 \times 5$
$2 \times 2 - 1 \times 0 - 2 \times 6 \quad 2 \times 4 - 1 \times 1$
$-2 \times -2]$
$= [-3 - 32 \quad 3 - 12 \quad 6 + 20] +$
$4[6 + 1 - 10 \quad 4 - 12 \quad 8 - 1 + 4]$
$= [-35 \quad -9 \quad 26] + 4[-3 \quad -8 \quad 11]$
$= [-35 \quad -9 \quad 26] + [-12 \quad -32 \quad 44]$
$= [-35 - 12 \quad -9 - 32 \quad 26 + 44]$
$= [-47 \quad -41 \quad 70]$

9. $I = \begin{bmatrix} 1 & 0 \\ 0 & 1 \end{bmatrix}$

10. a) $x = \frac{19}{13}, y = \frac{43}{13}$ b) $x = -11, y = -26, z = 3$

11. $M^2 = \begin{bmatrix} 2 & -1 \\ -6 & 3 \end{bmatrix}\begin{bmatrix} 2 & -1 \\ -6 & 3 \end{bmatrix} = \begin{bmatrix} 10 & -5 \\ -30 & 15 \end{bmatrix}$
$5M = 5\begin{bmatrix} 2 & -1 \\ -6 & 3 \end{bmatrix} = \begin{bmatrix} 10 & -5 \\ -30 & 15 \end{bmatrix}$

12. No.
Counterexample:
$A = \begin{bmatrix} 1 & 2 \\ 3 & 4 \end{bmatrix}, B = \begin{bmatrix} 2 & 3 \\ 4 & 4 \end{bmatrix}$
$(A + B)(A - B) = \begin{bmatrix} -8 & -3 \\ -15 & -7 \end{bmatrix}$
$A^2 - B^2 = \begin{bmatrix} -9 & -8 \\ -9 & -6 \end{bmatrix}$

UP 3.2 Determinants

1. a) unique solution: $\left(\frac{9}{4}, -\frac{17}{4}\right)$ b) no unique solution c) unique solution: $\left(-\frac{22}{9}, -4\right)$

2. Determinant is a real number. Matrix is a rectangular array of number(s) arranged in rows and columns.

3. a) 48 **b)** 22 **c)** -263 **d)** 58

e) $5\begin{vmatrix} 9 & 10 \\ -7 & 4 \end{vmatrix} - \dfrac{2}{3}\begin{vmatrix} 6 & 27 \\ 18 & -15 \end{vmatrix}$

$= 5[9 \times 4 - (-7) \times 10]$
$\quad - \dfrac{2}{3}[6 \times (-15) - 27 \times 18]$

$= 5(106) - \dfrac{2}{3}(-576)$

$= 530 + 384$

$= 914$

4. a) unique solution: $\left(\dfrac{25}{23}, \dfrac{28}{23}\right)$ **b)** no unique

solution **c)** unique solution: $\left(-\dfrac{11}{7}, -\dfrac{12}{7}\right)$

d) no unique solution **e)** unique solution:

$\left(\dfrac{10}{33}, -\dfrac{31}{11}\right)$

5. $\begin{vmatrix} 1 & 1-x \\ x-4 & 2 \end{vmatrix} = 0$

$1(2) - (x-4)(1-x) = 0$
$2 - (x - x^2 - 4 + 4x) = 0$
$2 - (-x^2 + 5x - 4) = 0$
$2 + x^2 - 5x + 4 = 0$
$x^2 - 5x + 6 = 0$
$(x-3)(x-2) = 0$
$x - 3 = 0$ or $x - 2 = 0$
$x = 3 \qquad x = 2$

6. $a = 1, b = 7$

7. a) $x = -\dfrac{37}{58}, y = -\dfrac{20}{29}, z = \dfrac{141}{58}$ **b)** no

unique solution **c)** $x = 1, y = -2, z = -4$

8. $f(x) = 2x^2 - 5x + 8$

UP 4.2 The Ellipse

1. a) $\dfrac{x^2}{49} + \dfrac{y^2}{25} = 1$ **b)** $\dfrac{x^2}{9} + \dfrac{y^2}{64} = 1$

c) $\dfrac{x^2}{100} + \dfrac{y^2}{36} = 1$

2. a)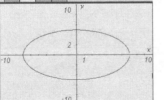

b)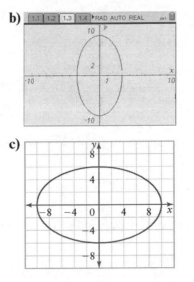

c)

	$\dfrac{x^2}{49} + \dfrac{y^2}{25} = 1$	$\dfrac{x^2}{9} + \dfrac{y^2}{64} = 1$	$\dfrac{x^2}{100} + \dfrac{y^2}{36} = 1$
Centre	$(0, 0)$	$(0, 0)$	$(0, 0)$
Vertices	$(\pm 7, 0)$	$(0, \pm 8)$	$(\pm 10, 0)$
Intercepts	$y = \pm 5$	$x = \pm 3$	$y = \pm 6$
Major axis and length	x-axis, 14	y-axis, 16	x-axis, 20
Minor axis and length	y-axis, 10	x-axis, 6	y-axis, 12
Foci	$(\pm 2\sqrt{6}, 0)$	$(0, \pm\sqrt{55})$	$(\pm 8, 0)$
Distance between foci	$4\sqrt{6}$	$2\sqrt{55}$	16

3. a) i) $(0, \pm 4\sqrt{3})$ **ii)** Major axis: y-axis; Minor axis: x-axis

b) i) $(\pm\sqrt{19}, 0)$ **ii)** Major axis: x-axis; Minor axis: y-axis

c) i) $(0, \pm 3\sqrt{5})$ **ii)** Major axis: y-axis; Minor axis: x-axis

d) i) $(0, \pm\sqrt{11})$ **ii)** Major axis: y-axis; Minor axis: x-axis

e) i) $(\pm\sqrt{21}, 0)$ **ii)** Major axis: x-axis; Minor axis: y-axis

f) i) $(0, \pm\sqrt{18.75})$ **ii)** Major axis: y-axis; Minor axis: x-axis

4.

	$\dfrac{x^2}{121} + \dfrac{y^2}{64} = 1$	$\dfrac{x^2}{16} + \dfrac{y^2}{81} = 1$	$\dfrac{x^2}{144} + \dfrac{y^2}{169} = 1$	$\dfrac{x^2}{18} + \dfrac{y^2}{44} = 1$
Vertices	$(\pm 11, 0)$	$(0, \pm 9)$	$(0, \pm 13)$	$(0, \pm 2\sqrt{11})$
Intercepts	$y = \pm 8$	$x = \pm 4$	$x = \pm 12$	$x = \pm 3\sqrt{2}$
Major axis and length	x-axis, 22	y-axis, 18	y-axis, 26	y-axis, $4\sqrt{11}$
Minor axis and length	y-axis, 16	x-axis, 8	x-axis, 24	x-axis, $6\sqrt{2}$
Foci	$(\pm\sqrt{57}, 0)$	$(0, \pm\sqrt{65})$	$(0, \pm 5)$	$(0, \pm\sqrt{26})$
Distance between foci	$2\sqrt{57}$	$2\sqrt{65}$	10	$2\sqrt{26}$

5. a) i) $\dfrac{x^2}{25} + \dfrac{y^2}{16} = 1$ **ii)** $\dfrac{x^2}{25} + \dfrac{y^2}{9} = 1$

iii) $\dfrac{x^2}{25} + \dfrac{y^2}{49} = 1$

b) i) Yes, if the y-axis is the major axis.
ii) No, the y-axis has to be the minor axis because the one vertex is on the x-axis.
iii) No, the x-axis has to be minor axis and the y-axis has to be major axis in order to satisfy the given intercept and vertex.

6. a) Let $P(x, y)$ be any point on the ellipse, such that $PF_1 + PF_2 = 20$

$\sqrt{(x + 8)^2 + y^2} + \sqrt{(x - 8)^2 + y^2} = 20$

$\sqrt{(x + 8)^2 + y^2} = 20 - \sqrt{(x - 8)^2 + y^2}$

Square both sides.

$(x + 8)^2 + y^2 =$
$\left(20 - \sqrt{(x - 8)^2 + y^2}\right)^2$

$x^2 + 16x + 64 + y^2 =$
$400 - 40\sqrt{(x - 8)^2 + y^2} + (x - 8)^2 + y^2$

$x^2 + 16x + 64 + y^2 =$
$400 - 40\sqrt{(x - 8)^2 + y^2} +$
$x^2 - 16x + 64 + y^2$

$16x + 64 = 464 - 40\sqrt{(x - 8)^2 + y^2} - 16x$

$32x - 400 = -40\sqrt{(x - 8)^2 + y^2}$

$4x - 50 = -5\sqrt{(x - 8)^2 + y^2}$

Square both sides.

$(4x - 50)^2 = \left(-5\sqrt{(x - 8)^2 + y^2}\right)^2$

$16x^2 - 400x + 2500 =$
$25(x^2 - 16x + 64 + y^2)$

$16x^2 - 400x + 2500 =$
$25x^2 - 400x + 1600 + 25y^2$

$9x^2 + 25y^2 = 900$

$\dfrac{x^2}{100} + \dfrac{y^2}{36} = 1$

b) In $\dfrac{x^2}{100} + \dfrac{y^2}{36} = 1$, $a^2 = 100$ and $b^2 = 36$, so $a = 10$ and $b = 6$. As well, $c^2 = a^2 - b^2$, so $c^2 = 100 - 36$ or $c^2 = 64$. This gives $c = \pm 8$.

	$\dfrac{x^2}{100} + \dfrac{y^2}{36} = 1$
centre	$(0, 0)$
vertices	$(-10, 0)$ and $(10, 0)$
intercepts	$y = -6$ and $y = 6$
major axis length	$2a = 2(10)$ or 20
minor axis length	$2b = 2(6)$ or 12
foci	$c = \pm 8$
distance between foci	$2(8) = 16$

c)

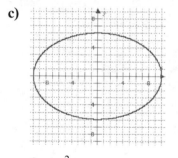

7. a) $\dfrac{x^2}{32} + \dfrac{y^2}{81} = 1$

b)

	$\dfrac{x^2}{32} + \dfrac{y^2}{81} = 1$
Vertices	$(0, \pm 9)$
Intercepts	$x = \pm 4\sqrt{2}$
Major axis and length	y-axis, 18
Minor axis and length	x-axis, $8\sqrt{2}$
Foci	$(0, \pm 7)$
Distance between foci	14

c)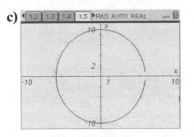

8. a) Assume that the major axis is on the x-axis, therefore, $a = 5$ and $b = 4$. This gives $a^2 = 25$ and $b^2 = 16$.

$\dfrac{x^2}{a^2} + \dfrac{y^2}{b^2} = 1$ *becomes*

$\dfrac{x^2}{25} + \dfrac{y^2}{16} = 1$ *or* $16x^2 + 25y^2 = 400$

b) To find the width of the pool at a point on the major axis that is 2 m from the centre, we substitute $x = 2$ into the equation of the ellipse and solve for y. We will then multiply this value by 2 to find the width.

$$16x^2 + 25y^2 = 400$$
$$16(2)^2 + 25y^2 = 400$$
$$16(4) + 25y^2 = 400$$
$$64 + 25y^2 = 400$$
$$25y^2 = 400 - 64$$
$$25y^2 = 336$$
$$y^2 = \frac{336}{25}$$
$$y = \sqrt{\frac{336}{25}}$$
$$y \doteq 3.7$$

9. a) $e \doteq 0.69$ **b)** $e \doteq 0.90$ **c)** $e \doteq 0.38$
d) $e \doteq 0.77$

10. $\dfrac{x^2}{36} + \dfrac{y^2}{20} = 1$

11. a)

	$\dfrac{(x-2)^2}{4} + \dfrac{(y+3)^2}{9} = 1$
Centre	$(2, -3)$
Vertices	$(2, -3 \pm 3)$
Intercepts	$x = 2 \pm 2$
Major axis and length	y-axis, 6
Minor axis and length	x-axis, 4
Foci	$(2, -3 \pm \sqrt{5})$
Distance between foci	$2\sqrt{5}$

b)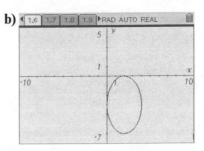

4.3 The Hyperbola

1. a) Transverse axis and length: y-axis, 16; Conjugate axis and length: x-axis, 8
b) Transverse axis and length: x-axis, 20; Conjugate axis and length: y-axis, 18
c) Transverse axis and length: x-axis, 4; Conjugate axis and length: y-axis, 14
d) Transverse axis and length: y-axis, 12; Conjugate axis and length: x-axis, 10
e) Transverse axis and length: y-axis, 4; Conjugate axis and length: x-axis, 10
f) Transverse axis and length: x-axis, 5; Conjugate axis and length: y-axis, 10

2. a)

b)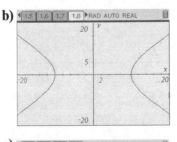

c)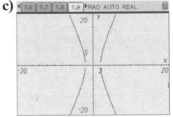

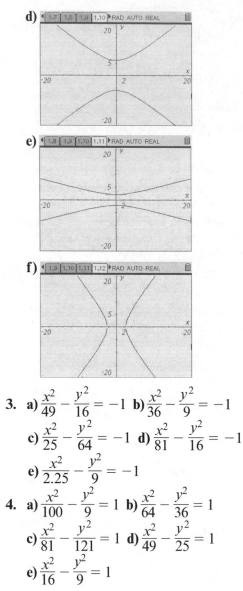

d) 1.7 1.8 1.9 1.10 ▸RAD AUTO REAL

e) 1.8 1.9 1.10 1.11 ▸RAD AUTO REAL

f) 1.9 1.10 1.11 1.12 ▸RAD AUTO REAL

3. a) $\dfrac{x^2}{49} - \dfrac{y^2}{16} = -1$ **b)** $\dfrac{x^2}{36} - \dfrac{y^2}{9} = -1$

c) $\dfrac{x^2}{25} - \dfrac{y^2}{64} = -1$ **d)** $\dfrac{x^2}{81} - \dfrac{y^2}{16} = -1$

e) $\dfrac{x^2}{2.25} - \dfrac{y^2}{9} = -1$

4. a) $\dfrac{x^2}{100} - \dfrac{y^2}{9} = 1$ **b)** $\dfrac{x^2}{64} - \dfrac{y^2}{36} = 1$

c) $\dfrac{x^2}{81} - \dfrac{y^2}{121} = 1$ **d)** $\dfrac{x^2}{49} - \dfrac{y^2}{25} = 1$

e) $\dfrac{x^2}{16} - \dfrac{y^2}{9} = 1$

5.

	a) $\dfrac{x^2}{16} - \dfrac{y^2}{64} = -1$	**b)** $\dfrac{x^2}{100} - \dfrac{y^2}{81} = 1$	**c)** $\dfrac{x^2}{4} - \dfrac{y^2}{49} = 1$
Centre	$(0, 0)$	$(0, 0)$	$(0, 0)$
Vertices	$(0, \pm 8)$	$(\pm 10, 0)$	$(\pm 2, 0)$
Transverse axis and length	y-axis, 16	x-axis, 20	x-axis, 4
Conjugate axis and length	x-axis, 8	y-axis, 18	y-axis, 14
Foci	$\left(0, \pm 4\sqrt{5}\right)$	$\left(\pm\sqrt{181}, 0\right)$	$\left(\pm\sqrt{53}, 0\right)$
Distance between foci	$8\sqrt{5}$	$2\sqrt{181}$	$2\sqrt{53}$
Asymptotes	$y = \pm 2x$	$y = \pm\dfrac{9}{10}x$	$y = \pm\dfrac{7}{2}x$

	d) $\dfrac{x^2}{25} - \dfrac{y^2}{36} = -1$	**e)** $\dfrac{x^2}{25} - \dfrac{y^2}{4} = -1$	**f)** $\dfrac{x^2}{6.25} - \dfrac{y^2}{25} = 1$
Centre	$(0, 0)$	$(0, 0)$	$(0, 0)$
Vertices	$(0, \pm 6)$	$(0, \pm 2)$	$(\pm 2.5, 0)$
Transverse axis and length	y-axis, 12	y-axis, 4	x-axis, 5
Conjugate axis and length	x-axis, 10	x-axis, 10	y-axis, 10
Foci	$\left(0, \pm\sqrt{61}\right)$	$\left(0, \pm\sqrt{29}\right)$	$\left(\pm\sqrt{31.25}, 0\right)$
Distance between foci	$2\sqrt{61}$	$2\sqrt{29}$	$2\sqrt{31.25}$
Asymptotes	$y = \pm\dfrac{6}{5}x$	$y = \pm\dfrac{2}{5}x$	$y = \pm 2x$

6.

	$\dfrac{x^2}{81} - \dfrac{y^2}{64} = 1$	$\dfrac{x^2}{4} - \dfrac{y^2}{36} = -1$	$\dfrac{x^2}{144} - \dfrac{y^2}{121} = 1$	$\dfrac{x^2}{9} - \dfrac{y^2}{25} = -1$
Vertices	$(\pm 9, 0)$	$(0, \pm 6)$	$(\pm 12, 0)$	$(0, \pm 5)$
Transverse axis and length	x-axis, 18	y-axis, 12	x-axis, 24	y-axis, 10
Conjugate axis and length	y-axis, 16	x-axis, 4	y-axis, 22	x-axis, 6
Foci	$\left(\pm\sqrt{145}, 0\right)$	$\left(0, \pm 2\sqrt{10}\right)$	$\left(\pm\sqrt{265}, 0\right)$	$\left(0, \pm\sqrt{34}\right)$
Distance between foci	$2\sqrt{145}$	$4\sqrt{10}$	$2\sqrt{265}$	$2\sqrt{34}$
Asymptotes	$y = \pm\dfrac{8}{9}x$	$y = \pm 3x$	$y = \pm\dfrac{11}{12}x$	$y = \pm\dfrac{5}{3}x$

7. a) Let $P(x, y)$ be any point on the hyperbola, such that $|PF_1 - PF_2| = 10$

$\sqrt{(x + 6)^2 + y^2} - \sqrt{(x - 6)^2 + y^2} = 10$

$-\sqrt{(x - 6)^2 + y^2} = 10 - \sqrt{(x + 6)^2 + y^2}$

Square both sides.

$(x - 6)^2 + y^2 = \left(10 - \sqrt{(x + 6)^2 + y^2}\right)^2$

$x^2 - 12x + 36 + y^2$

$= 100 - 20\sqrt{(x + 6)^2 + y^2}$

$+ (x + 6)^2 + y^2$

$x^2 - 12x + 36 + y^2$

$= 100 - 20\sqrt{(x + 6)^2 + y^2}$

$+ x^2 + 12x + 36 + y^2$

$-12x = 100 - 20\sqrt{(x + 6)^2 + y^2} + 12x$

$20\sqrt{(x + 6)^2 + y^2} = 24x + 100$

$5\sqrt{(x + 6)^2 + y^2} = 6x + 25$

Square both sides.

$25[(x + 6)^2 + y^2] = (6x + 25)^2$

$25(x^2 + 12x + 36 + y^2)$
$= 36x^2 + 300x + 625$

$25x^2 + 300x + 900 + 25y^2$
$= 36x^2 + 300x + 625$

$9x^2 - 25y^2 = 275$

$\dfrac{9x^2}{275} - \dfrac{25y^2}{275} = 1$

$\dfrac{9x^2}{275} - \dfrac{y^2}{11} = 1$

Here $a^2 = \dfrac{275}{9}$ so $a = \pm\dfrac{5\sqrt{11}}{3}$ and $b^2 = 11$

so $b = \pm\sqrt{11}$. As well,

$c^2 = \dfrac{275}{9} + 11$

$= \dfrac{275}{9} + \dfrac{99}{9} = \dfrac{374}{9}$

$c = \pm\dfrac{\sqrt{374}}{3}$

b) $\dfrac{9x^2}{275} - \dfrac{y^2}{11} = 1$

	$\dfrac{9x^2}{275} - \dfrac{y^2}{11} = 1$
Centre	$(0, 0)$
Vertices	$\left(-\dfrac{5\sqrt{11}}{3}, 0\right)$ and $\left(\dfrac{5\sqrt{11}}{3}, 0\right)$
Transverse axis and length	x-axis, $\dfrac{10\sqrt{11}}{3}$
Conjugate axis and length	y-axis, $2\sqrt{11}$
Foci	$\left(-\dfrac{\sqrt{374}}{3}, 0\right), \left(\dfrac{\sqrt{374}}{3}, 0\right)$
Distance between foci	$\dfrac{2\sqrt{374}}{3}$
Asymptotes	$y = \pm\dfrac{b}{a}x$ so $y = \pm\left(\sqrt{11} \div \dfrac{5\sqrt{11}}{3}\right)x$ or $y = \pm\dfrac{3}{5}x$

c)
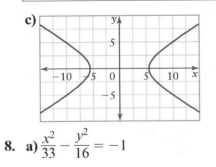

8. a) $\dfrac{x^2}{33} - \dfrac{y^2}{16} = -1$

b)

	$\dfrac{x^2}{33} - \dfrac{y^2}{16} = -1$
Centre	$(0, 0)$
Vertices	$(0, \pm 4)$
Transverse axis and length	y-axis, 8
Conjugate axis and length	x-axis, $2\sqrt{33}$
Foci	$(0, \pm 7)$
Distance between foci	14
Asymptotes	$y = \pm\dfrac{4}{\sqrt{33}}x$

c)
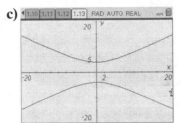

9. Since the vertex is $(\sqrt{6}, 0)$, then $a = \sqrt{6}$. As well, if the curve passes through the point $(9, 5)$, substitute all of this into the equation.

$\dfrac{x^2}{a^2} - \dfrac{y^2}{b^2} = 1$

$\dfrac{(9)^2}{(\sqrt{6})^2} - \dfrac{(5)^2}{b^2} = 1$

$\dfrac{81}{6} - \dfrac{25}{b^2} = 1$ Multiply by $6b^2$.

$\dfrac{81(6b^2)}{6} - \dfrac{25(6b^2)}{b^2} = 1(6b^2)$

$81b^2 - 150 = 6b^2$

$75b^2 = 150$

$b^2 = 2$

Therefore, the equation is $\dfrac{x^2}{6} - \dfrac{y^2}{2} = 1$.

10. a) $e \doteq 1.34$ **b)** $e \doteq 1.05$ **c)** $e \doteq 1.36$

d) $e \doteq 1.17$

11. $\dfrac{x^2}{16} - \dfrac{y^2}{20} = 1$

12.

	$\dfrac{(x-2)^2}{4} - \dfrac{(y+3)^2}{9} = 1$
Centre	$(2, -3)$
Vertices	$(2 \pm 2, -3)$
Transverse axis and length	x-axis, 4
Conjugate axis and length	y-axis, 6
Foci	$(2 \pm \sqrt{13}, -3)$
Distance between foci	$2\sqrt{13}$
Asymptotes	$y = \pm\dfrac{3}{2}(x-2) - 3$

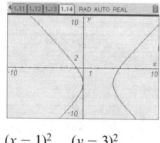

13. $\dfrac{(x-1)^2}{\frac{90}{7}} - \dfrac{(y-3)^2}{45} = 1$

Practice Exam

1. i) a) 6 **b)** extends from quadrant 2 to 1
c) -1 (order 1), 1 (order 1), -0.867 (order 1), 1.867 (order 1)
ii) a) 8 **b)** extends from quadrant 2 to 1
c) 4 (order 3), 2 (order 2), -11 (order 2), -2 (order 1)

2. Answers may vary. Sample answer:
$f(x) = -5(x+1)^2(x-1)$

3. a) $f(x) = \dfrac{1}{20}(x+5)^2(x+3)(x-2)$
shape suggests a polynomial function; extends from quadrant 2 to quadrant 1, therefore polynomial of even degree with positive coefficient; zeros: -5 (order 2), -3 (order 1); 2 (order 1); y-intercept: -7.5

b) $f(x) = \dfrac{3}{(2x-1)^2}$; shape suggests a reciprocal of a quadratic function; vertical asymptote: $x = \dfrac{1}{2}$; horizontal asymptote: $y = 0$; y-intercept: 3

c) $f(x) = \dfrac{x-5}{(2x-1)(x-3)}$; shape suggests a reciprocal of a quadratic function; vertical asymptotes: $x = \dfrac{1}{2}$, $x = 3$; horizontal asymptote: $y = 0$; y-intercept: $-\dfrac{5}{3}$; minimum of the parabolic part (middle branch) is at point $(2, 1)$

4. $-\sqrt{2} \le x \le \sqrt{2}$ or $x \le -3$ or $x \ge 3$

5. a)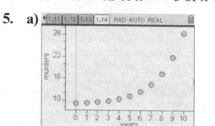

b) quartic **c) i)** fourth (degree is 4) **ii)** 0.07 (fourth difference is a constant) **iii)** 0.003 (4th difference = leading coefficient $\times 4 \times 3 \times 2 \times 1$) **d)** $f(x) = 0.003x^4 - 0.023x^3 + 0.114x^2 + 0.013x + 9.11$

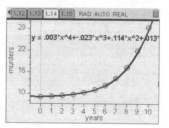

e) find the zeros **f)** never

6. a) \$468.20 **b)** 1087.27 **c)** 1076.87; total value of investments, T, at the point when the interest rate, x, reaches the average annual rate (6.25%) plus one

7. 37.8 cm $\times$ 52.8 cm

8. a) $x = 4$, $x = \dfrac{-4 \pm 2\sqrt{7}}{3}$
b) $x = 2$, $x = -1.582$, $x = 0.277$, $x = 1.306$

9. i) a) no x-intercept, y-intercept: $\dfrac{1}{2}$
b) vertical asymptote: $x = 2$, horizontal asymptote: $y = 0$, no oblique asymptote
c) domain: $\{x \in \mathbb{R}, x \ne 2\}$, range: $\{y \in \mathbb{R}, y \ne 0\}$

d)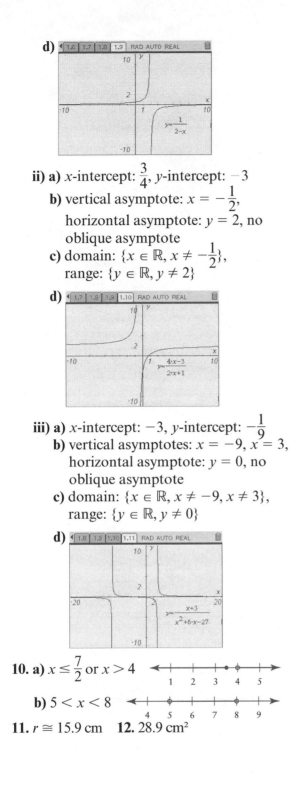

ii) a) x-intercept: $\frac{3}{4}$, y-intercept: -3

  b) vertical asymptote: $x = -\frac{1}{2}$, horizontal asymptote: $y = 2$, no oblique asymptote

  c) domain: $\{x \in \mathbb{R}, x \neq -\frac{1}{2}\}$, range: $\{y \in \mathbb{R}, y \neq 2\}$

  d)

iii) a) x-intercept: -3, y-intercept: $-\frac{1}{9}$

  b) vertical asymptotes: $x = -9$, $x = 3$, horizontal asymptote: $y = 0$, no oblique asymptote

  c) domain: $\{x \in \mathbb{R}, x \neq -9, x \neq 3\}$, range: $\{y \in \mathbb{R}, y \neq 0\}$

  d)

10. a) $x \leq \frac{7}{2}$ or $x > 4$

b) $5 < x < 8$

11. $r \cong 15.9$ cm   **12.** 28.9 cm²

13.

θ	$\sin \theta$	$\cos \theta$	$\tan \theta$	$\csc \theta$	$\sec \theta$	$\cot \theta$
a) $\frac{11\pi}{6}$	$-\frac{1}{2}$	$\frac{\sqrt{3}}{2}$	$-\frac{1}{\sqrt{3}}$	-2	$\frac{2}{\sqrt{3}}$	$-\sqrt{3}$
b) $\frac{2\pi}{3}$	$\frac{\sqrt{3}}{2}$	$-\frac{1}{2}$	$-\sqrt{3}$	$\frac{2}{\sqrt{3}}$	-2	$-\frac{1}{\sqrt{3}}$
c) $\frac{5\pi}{4}$	$-\frac{1}{\sqrt{2}}$	$-\frac{1}{\sqrt{2}}$	1	$-\sqrt{2}$	$-\sqrt{2}$	1
d) π	0	-1	0	Undefined	-1	Undefined

14. a) $0.959\,4$ (apply addition formula for cosine)

  b) $0.989\,8$ (apply cofunction identity)

15. $f(x) = 3 \sin\left[\frac{1}{2}\left(x - \frac{\pi}{3}\right)\right]$

16. Answers may vary.

17. a) $-\frac{\sqrt{3}}{2}$ **b)** $\frac{1}{2}$ **c)** 0 **d)** $-\frac{1}{2}$

18. $f(x) = -\frac{1}{2} \cos\left[4\left(x + \frac{\pi}{6}\right)\right] + 3$

19. a)

b) i) amplitude changes to 4

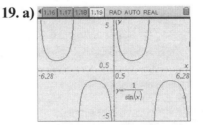

ii) period changes to $\frac{2\pi}{3}$

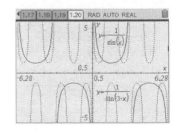

iii) vertical translation of 5 units up

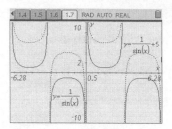

iv) phase shift of 2 units to the right

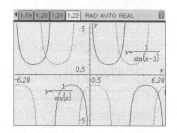

20. a) 2 **b)** $\frac{\pi}{2}$ **c)** $\frac{\pi}{6}$ to the right **d)** 1 unit up

e)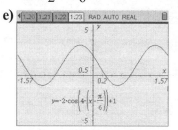

21. a) $\frac{3\pi}{2}$ **b)** $0, \frac{\pi}{3}, \frac{5\pi}{3}, 2\pi$ **c)** 0.564, 5.075

22. a)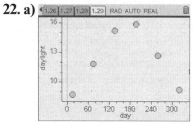

b) Answers may vary. For example:
$y = 3.555 \sin[0.017(x - 105.75)] + 12.275$

c)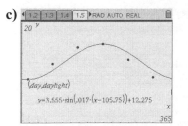

The model does not fit well. It is shifted too much to the right; therefore the phase shift needs to be adjusted.

d) $y = 3.867 \sin[0.017(x - 81.070)] + 12.169$

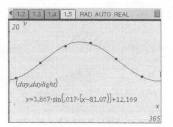

The regression equation is a much better fit than the model from part b)

e) 30%

23. a)

x	$y = 3^x$
-2	$\frac{1}{9}$
-1	$\frac{1}{3}$
0	1
$\frac{1}{2}$	$\sqrt{3}$
1	3
2	9
3	27

b)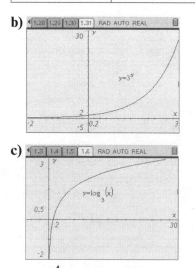

c)

24. a) 3 **b)** $\frac{4}{5}$ **c)** 2 **d)** 2 **e)** 1
25. a) 2.77 **b)** 3
26. a) \$35 000 **b)** approximately 3.1 years
27. a) 88.4 dB **b)** 3.98×10^{10} W/m²

28. a) $\frac{19}{4}$ **b)** 1 **c)** −1

29. a) 1.40 **b)** 3.57 **c)** 2.72 **d)** 3.83 **e)** −3.58
f) 0.45

30. a) 191 h **b)** 2.7 h

31. a) $\log(x - 4)$, $x > 4$ **b)** $\log(64x^6)$, $x > 0$

c) $\log\left(\dfrac{2x^2 + 3xy + 4y^2}{x^4}\right)$, $x > 0$,
$2x^2 + 3xy + 4y^2 > 0$

32. a) 4 **b)** 21 **c)** 3

33. a) $P(t) = 48\,000(1.09)^t$ **b)** 12.7 years
c) approximately 3.9 years

34. a) $y = 3^x + 1 + 3x^2 + 9x$

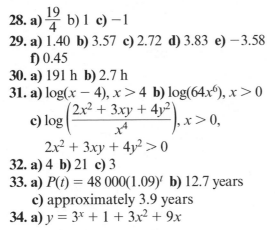

domain: $\{x \in \mathbb{R}\}$,
range: $\{y \in \mathbb{R}, y \geq -5.561\}$

b) $y = 3^x + 1 + 3x^2 + 6x$

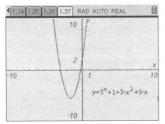

domain: $\{x \in \mathbb{R}\}$,
range: $\{y \in \mathbb{R}, y \geq -1.677\}$

c) $y = 9x^3 + 27x^2$

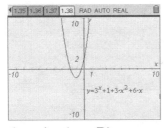

domain: $\{x \in \mathbb{R}\}$, range: $\{y \in \mathbb{R}\}$

d) $y = x + 3$

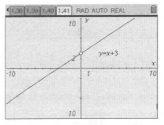

domain: $\{x \in \mathbb{R}, x \neq 0\}$,
range: $\{y \in \mathbb{R}, y \neq 3\}$

35. a) $2.295t^2 + 66.6t + 153$
b) 1668 connections / week

36. a) straight line with slope 2, x-intercept $\frac{1}{2}$,
and y-intercept -1; neither **b)** continuous
wave with constant frequency and
amplitude; odd **c)** continuous wave with
constant frequency and variable amplitude

d)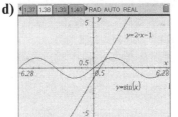

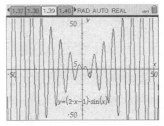

e) domain: $\{x \in \mathbb{R}\}$, range: $\{y \in \mathbb{R}\}$

37. a)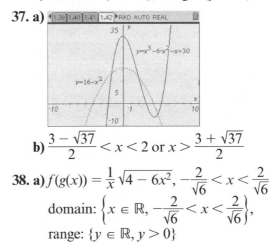

b) $\dfrac{3 - \sqrt{37}}{2} < x < 2$ or $x > \dfrac{3 + \sqrt{37}}{2}$

38. a) $f(g(x)) = \frac{1}{x}\sqrt{4 - 6x^2}$, $-\dfrac{2}{\sqrt{6}} < x < \dfrac{2}{\sqrt{6}}$

domain: $\left\{x \in \mathbb{R}, -\dfrac{2}{\sqrt{6}} < x < \dfrac{2}{\sqrt{6}}\right\}$,
range: $\{y \in \mathbb{R}, y > 0\}$

b) $g(f(x)) = \dfrac{1}{x-3}, x > 3$
domain: $\{x \in \mathbb{R}, x > 3\}$,
range: $\{y \in \mathbb{R}, y > 0\}$

39. a) 19 600

b)

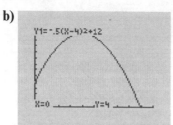

Initially a poor team, winning only 4 of the 14 games in the first season, then becomes a good team after 4 years, then becomes poor again.

c) $0 \leq t < 9$ starts in 2009, number of wins cannot be less than 0 **d)** No. $N(W(4)) = 48\ 400$ **e)** It will make team better right away, so would move vertex to the left. **f)** It will make team better in 4 years, so would move vertex up.